BIOLOGICAL SCIENCE

APPLICATIONS IN AGRICULTURE

BIOLOGICAL

Edward W. Osborne, Ph.D.

Associate Professor
Agricultural Education
University of Illinois

SCIENCE

Applications in Agriculture

AgriScience and Technology Series

Series Editor
Jasper S. Lee, Ph.D.

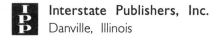 Interstate Publishers, Inc.
Danville, Illinois

Cover Photos Credit:
Agricultural Research Service, USDA

Line Art Credits:
Computer Generated Graphics by
M. E. Carter, Interstate Publishers, Inc.

Order from
Interstate Publishers, Inc.
510 North Vermilion Street
P.O. Box 50
Danville, IL 61834-0050
Phone: (800) 843-4774
FAX: (217) 446-9706

Library of Congress Catalog Card No. 93-78225

ISBN 0-8134-2957-9

1　2　3
4　5　6
7　8　9

Dedicated to

Susie, Whitney, and Karley,
who continue to fill my life
with love, anticipation, and joy.

Preface

Like music and musicians, agriculture and science are inseparable. The 1980s and 1990s have seen science applications in agriculture streak to the forefront of science and technology. For some students this has been an intriguing turnaround, bolstering their interest in both agriculture and science. But for many other students, the shift to a more science-based high school agriculture curriculum has not been such a great thing. National studies continue to suggest that many students dislike science and are performing poorly in science courses. These trends point to even higher science course requirements in the future.

Biological Science Applications in Agriculture is not just another text-book for a science course. A dramatically different approach is taken in this text and in the newly developed courses for which this text was designed. High school agriculture courses have historically been liked by students because of their hands-on nature. This text strongly promotes a hands-on approach to teaching and learning in agriculture and serves as a motivator and technical reference for students.

Hands-on activities will continue to comprise a large part of agriscience, but the nature of these activities will be different. Rather than learning only *how* to raise animals and grow crops and plants, laboratory activities in this text will give equal emphasis to *why* producers raise animals and grow plants and crops as they do—that is, why specific agricultural practices are used in farm, home, and agribusiness settings. For example, if you understand *how and why* a plant responds to growth regulators, then you will be able to make the right decisions about the use of growth regulators in your own situation. On the other hand, if you only attempt to memorize the practices, isolated from the relevant science, then the eventual result is incomplete or incorrect practice. The hands-on activities promoted in this text consist mostly of experiments. These experiments are designed to bring to life the science concepts that you have studied in science textbooks but may have already begun to forget.

The goal of this text is to help you begin to see science as an interesting field that has strong connections to agriculture (if you have not already come to this conclusion). A large part of agriculture is applied science. Rather than learning science as a set of terms and concepts to recall for a test, this text and the complementary course activities provided by your teacher will help you realize that science is relevant and important to you, and it affects nearly all areas of the vast food and agricultural system. As you read and study this text, try to make the agriculture/science connections. If you can do this, your involvement in agriculture, however limited or extensive it may be, will then be more than merely doing what you are told to do or doing things the way they have always been done. Your actions will reflect a working knowledge of science that is guaranteed to bring success and enjoyment to your work and study in agriculture.

Acknowledgments

The author is extremely grateful to numerous colleagues for their unknowing inspiration of ideas that led to the writing of this book. In particular, Jeff Moss and Phil Buriak, both faculty at the University of Illinois, teamed up with the author to develop innovative instructional materials for secondary agriculture curricula. *Biological Science Applications in Agriculture* closely parallels these materials and can serve as a primary student textbook when these laboratory-oriented courses are taught.

In 1990 the author was invited by the Chicago Board of Education to present a series of teacher inservice workshops designed to enhance integration of science concepts into agriculture curricula. This cutting edge experience was instrumental in shaping the author's ideas about how science and agriculture could be more explicitly connected in high school agriculture programs. Following this teacher inservice program, the author was able to secure several state-funded projects that provided the opportunity to develop new, experiment-based agriculture courses that were well grounded in science. These recent opportunities have been instrumental in developing the author's views on how science and agriculture can best be merged in a secondary instructional setting.

The author extends special appreciation to the agriculture teachers in Illinois who have used the newly developed course materials, expressed the need for a student text, and offered suggestions for text design. Their feedback has been invaluable in the progressive development of the new agriscience courses, as well as in the preparation of this student text.

Contents

Chapter 1

CONDUCTING EXPERIMENTS

AGRICULTURAL APPLICATIONS
Experimental Research in Agriculture

The *scientific method* was first applied to agricultural problems in the nineteenth century. As research programs gradually became established, dramatic increases in food production and standard of living were realized. Today, the U.S. agricultural research system consists of 72 educational institutions, 58 state agricultural experiment stations, and 200 federal laboratories. Over 15,000 scientists comprise this nationwide network for conducting research in agriculture.

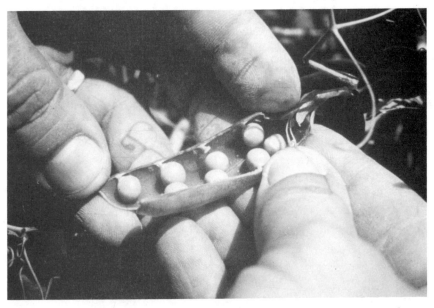

Figure 1-1. Scientists are working to improve the storage and nutritional value of plant products. (Courtesy, Illinois Dept. of Agriculture)

1

Agricultural scientists conduct research through the use of laboratory and field experiments. Recent plant science research has focused on identifying the genes that control various plant functions. Scientists are seeking to develop plants that are insect and drought resistant. They are also attempting to enhance the storage and nutritional characteristics of food products. New insect resistant cotton varieties are currently being tested, as are new tomato varieties that have slower rates of fruit spoilage. Animal research is focused on mapping the genetic makeup of animals, with hopes of increasing rate of gain, feed efficiency, and disease resistance. New vaccines are being tested that are the direct result of ongoing research programs in agricultural laboratories.

In addition to the direct benefits of an increased food supply, agricultural scientists have discovered many new commercial uses for agricultural products. For example, oils, starches, and cellulose obtained from plants are used today in paints, lipstick, jet engine lubricants, explosives, adhesives, plastics, soap, textiles, photographic film, and many other products. A major thrust in today's agricultural research programs is to develop new uses for agricultural products to reduce dependence on nonrenewable resources in industrial and manufacturing processes.

OBJECTIVES—QUESTIONS FOR INVESTIGATION

After studying this chapter and completing the supporting laboratory exercises provided by your teacher, you should be able to answer the following questions:

1. What are the steps in conducting experimental research in plant and animal agriculture?

TERMS

control	hypothesis	replication
dependent variable	independent variable	scientific method
experimental method	manipulation	treatment

Figure 1-2. Plant products are used in manufacturing many items commonly used in homes and businesses. (Courtesy, Illinois Dept. of Agriculture)

Figure 1-2b. Corn is an excellent example of how plant products are transformed into various food products. (Courtesy, OACE, University of Illinois)

Figure 1-3. Improved crop varieties have been introduced as a result of plant breeding research. (Courtesy, Agricultural Research Service, USDA)

Figure 1-3b. Productive agricultural research programs have allowed the U.S. to be among the best fed populations in the world. (Courtesy, OACE, University of Illinois)

2. What do the terms *dependent variable, independent variable, control, manipulation, hypothesis,* and *replication* mean?

3. How is the research process applied to a laboratory or field experiment?

4. What general safety precautions should be followed in conducting research in plant and animal agriculture?

THE RESEARCH PROCESS

The process of scientific inquiry, or the scientific method, is a carefully controlled, systematic process for discovering the unknown. There are several major types of research, but in your study and investigations in this course you will be using the *experimental method* of research.

When conducting experimental research, all factors except the factor (variable) under investigation are controlled, or held constant. As a result, you can then be confident that any observed results are in fact due to the single variable being examined. This is what is meant by a *cause and effect* relationship. For example, suppose you wanted to compare the quality of a number of sound systems for your car. In such an experiment all factors except the sound system itself must be the same. Let's assume that you have visited several retailers, talked to your friends to determine the models they like, and done some independent reading on

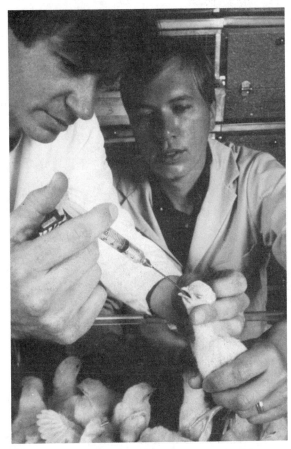

Figure 1-4. **Good research requires controlled experimentation and systematic research procedures. These researchers are inoculating chicks. (Courtesy, Agricultural Research Service, USDA)**

your own. This preliminary work has led you to select four models that you feel fit your needs and budget. How do you determine which of the four sound systems to buy? The best strategy would be to compare the sound quality of the four systems—a good, practical experiment.

Figure 1-5. Increases in rate of gain and feed efficiency may be realized through genetic mapping. (Courtesy, Agricultural Research Service, USDA)

One immediate problem is where to conduct your experiment. A single local retailer may have all four models on display so you can compare their performance. But will they sound the same in your car as they do in the showroom? You may want to investigate further. You may be lucky enough to find friends who have each of the models to be tested in their cars. If so, it should be easy to test the systems and make a choice. Right? But wait, since your friends each drive different cars, would that affect the performance of the sound systems during your experiment? Probably. What other *variables* might affect the performance of the four sound systems to be tested? In this experiment each sound system should ideally be evaluated under the *exact* same conditions; only the system being tested itself should vary from one test to the next. Thus, a carefully controlled experiment would involve testing the four models in the same setting (ensuring similar acoustical effects and background noise) using the same musical piece, and following the same steps in tuning and volume adjustment.

Not many people are this thorough when buying a sound system for their car. But, if they were, they would probably be more pleased with their purchase in the long run. Instead, most people find an affordable price range, get a general idea of the system's performance, and go for it. A scientific approach involves making this decision based more on knowledge and less on intuition. Fortunately, research in plant and animal agriculture is not so sloppy. If it were, we would have machines that don't work, crops that don't produce, animals that don't grow, or foods that spoil or taste bad.

THE PROCESS OF SCIENTIFIC INQUIRY

All experimentation is generally the same. Every experiment has variables to be controlled and one or more variables to be carefully measured. The process of scientific inquiry, or the research method, consists of five major steps:

1. Identify the problem

2. Gather data

3. Formulate possible solutions

4. Implement the preferred solution(s)

5. Evaluate the results

These five steps translate into the four major stages of experimentation: planning and design, conducting the experiment, data summary and interpretation, and follow-up.

Steps in Conducting Research

1. Identify the problem or question to be answered.

2. Gather data related to the problem or research question.

3. Formulate possible solutions.

4. Implement one or a combination of several solutions.

5. Evaluate the results and pursue further research as needed.

Planning and Design

Just as with any laboratory project, proceeding without a good plan for the experiment kills any chance of success. The first step in the planning phase of experimentation is *identifying the problem* to be investigated. This is most easily stated in the form of a question, such as, "What are the effects of soil pH on plant growth?" This research problem should grow out of your areas of interest and personal experience in agriculture. The study and reading you do in school and on your own will suggest good topics for experimental investigation. Of course, you will be limited by the availability of materials and equipment needed for some experiments. Don't let that stop you from tackling an experiment that really interests you. Instead, be creative in identifying alternative ways of conducting the experiment, yet recognize that your control and measurement procedures may not be as precise as you would like. Without the expensive, scientific equipment needed to conduct some experiments, you can still perform a modified version of the design as an exploratory investigation.

Sample Research Problems in Agriculture

The effects of . . .

> growth hormones on plant growth
>
> planting depth on seed germination
>
> rate of herbicide application on plant injury
>
> temperature on plant growth
>
> wind on transpiration
>
> temperature on evapotranspiration
>
> soil fertility on plant growth
>
> light on flowering
>
> food preservatives on food quality
>
> type of feed on animal growth
>
> growth hormones on animal growth
>
> feed additives on animal growth and health
>
> type of feed on digestibility
>
> type of feed on milk production

vitamin supplements on animal growth

temperature on milk quality

enzymes on meat tenderness

immunization schedules on animal health

The next step in planning and designing the experiment is to predict the results of your experiment—that is, develop one or more hypotheses. A *hypothesis* is a tentatively accepted theory that explains the relationship between two variables—in this case, soil pH and plant growth. Generally, hypotheses should indicate the *nature* of the relationship between variables. For example, one hypothesis for this experiment would be that *as soil pH increases, plant growth decreases*. Background knowledge and experience in this area should lead to the formulation of several hypotheses, since most plants have a pH range which best supports plant growth. Thus, when planning the experiment, all hypotheses to be tested should be stated. This ensures that the design of the experiment will allow the necessary data to be collected so that each hypothesis can be accepted or rejected. Normally no more than two or three hypotheses will be tested in a single experiment.

Step three in planning the experiment is the *design* step. This is a critical step in conducting experimental research. Factors to consider in the design of the experiment include observation and measurement procedures, control measures, and selection of variables. In our example, soil pH is the *independent variable*. A *variable* is a characteristic by which an object or phenomenon may be described. Variables change from time to time and must have more than one value. Thus, pH is a variable that describes a key characteristic of soil and has values that range from 0 to 14. An independent variable is the characteristic that you believe will affect another variable (plant growth). Researchers *manipulate* an independent variable by managing its presence in the experiment. The manipulation of the independent variable is known as the *treatment*. For example, in this experiment you could manipulate the independent variable, soil pH, by adjusting soil pH levels in the soil/growing media to desired levels, such as 5.0, 6.0, and 7.0. Thus, plant growth is being "treated with" various levels of the independent variable, soil pH. Of course, as the researcher, you must use the best means available to ensure that the specified levels of the independent variable are, in fact, used throughout the experiment. The *dependent variable* is the characteristic that will be observed; it is expected to change as a result of the independent variable. You expect plant growth (the dependent variable) to change as a result of changes in soil pH. Researchers observe and measure (collect data on) the dependent variable. A single experiment can involve more than one independent variable and more than one dependent variable. For example, in our experiment we could manipulate soil pH and temperature, while measuring their effects on plant height and total leaf surface area. However, the experimental design must allow for the effects of each independent variable to be separately determined. Likewise, each independent variable must be individually measured. The possible effects of all other variables must be eliminated by holding these characteristics constant. In our experiment you would manipulate soil pH and measure plant growth. Other possible effects, such as soil type, soil fertility, plant species, and soil moisture must be the same for all three pH levels tested. This ensures proper *control* of other factors that might influence the dependent variable.

Measurement of the dependent variable is critical to the success of the experiment. In our example, we could measure the dependent variable, plant growth, in a number of ways. During this design phase of the experiment, we must determine the most precise and appropriate way to measure plant growth. Our measurement strategy must also fit the tools and time we have to conduct the experiment. Visual comparison would be too imprecise. An excellent strategy in this experiment would be to start the experiment with plants of equal size and condition. An alternative strategy would be to record the height of each plant at the beginning of the experiment and define the dependent variable as any growth that occurs beyond that point. Any species of field or horticultural crops could be used, with the samples potted and grown in a greenhouse to provide for maximum control in the experiment. Of course, the soil pH in each of the pots would need to be adjusted to match the specified levels of the independent variable (e.g., 5.0, 6.0, 7.0). The pH of the soil/growing media must be monitored and maintained at the desired levels throughout the experiment. Plant growth could then be defined as the height of the plant (in centimeters), with measurements taken on all plants at predetermined times (e.g., day 7, 14, 21, 28). The method for locating the highest growth point of the plant must be exactly the same as each plant is measured.

The final step in planning the experiment is deciding upon the detailed procedures for conducting the experiment and measuring the dependent variable. The *design* of the experiment must match stated hypotheses. Precise strategies for measuring the dependent variable must be identified. You could measure plant growth in a number of ways—height after 20 days, appearance, leaf surface area, and so on. Select a measurement strategy that

Figure 1-6. Replications of an experiment increases confidence in the results.

Figure 1-6b. Agricultural research often involves a combination of laboratory and field research. (Courtesy, Kenneth Rhodes)

best matches the research question and hypotheses and which will be as precise as possible. The research design should also provide for *replication—* exact duplication of the experiment. For example, rather than having only a single plant in a soil pH of 5.0, you should grow a number of such plants. In addition, other students in your class can provide further replication by conducting the same experiment. Replication allows the results to be verified across numerous trials, resulting in greater confidence in the results. Finally, in planning and designing the experiment, all materials and equipment needed to set up and carry out the experiment should be prepared.

Exercise 1.1 Identifying Elements of the Research Design

Your research team is conducting an experiment on the effects of light and temperature on seed germination. You have decided to use a variety of vegetable crop seeds, such as sweet corn, lettuce, peas, and squash. The amount of light available will vary from none to eight hours per day. You may also compare the effects of artificial versus natural light, or light of different colors. Temperature conditions will include 41°F and 64°F. Seed germination will be determined by the number of seeds germinated after 3, 6, 9, and 12 days.

Questions:

Is this an acceptable research design?
What is the independent variable(s)?
What is the dependent variable(s)?
What variables in this experiment will be manipulated?
What hypotheses are being tested in this experiment?
What is the research problem?
What variables are being controlled?
Does this experiment allow for replication?

Conducting the Experiment

This is the "doing" stage of the experiment. In this stage the previously determined process for conducting the experiment is carefully carried out

Figure 1-7. Precise measurement of experimental effects is essential. (Courtesy, Agricultural Research Service, USDA)

Figure 1-7b. Experiments must be continuously monitored. (Courtesy, National FFA Organization)

in a systematic way, that is, the exact same way for each variable under study. Both the procedures for conducting the experiment and the procedures for measuring the outcomes (dependent variable) must be systematically completed. *Precision is critical in scientific investigation.* Your experiment should be designed to allow you to be as precise as possible, within the limitations of your equipment and laboratory facilities. Thus, in our experiment we should *consistently and precisely* follow our previously determined method of measuring plant growth. If we use height as the indicator of plant growth, then height must be measured consistently and accurately in all samples used in the experiment.

Exercise 1.2 Measuring Dependent Variables

Precise measurement of dependent variables is crucial in research. How could each of the following dependent variables be accurately measured using instruments available to you in your agriscience laboratory?

plant growth	soil moisture loss
germination	transpiration
animal growth	plant injury
animal health	meat tenderness
flowering	milk quality
plant nutrients	product taste

The second major task in conducting the experiment is recording the results. A pattern or format for collecting and recording data should have been developed during the planning stages of the experiment. Data summary charts are usually used to record experimental data. These charts should be as simple as possible, yet provide for all data to be completely and consistently recorded. Sometimes as an experiment is conducted, the researcher discovers that procedures for conducting the experiment or recording data need to be modified. Such midstream adjustments are acceptable, as long as they are consistently applied to all cases or trials in the study and still allow for the original purposes of the investigation to be addressed. However, in some cases scientists find that they must restart the experiment from the beginning, using the revised procedures.

Agricultural scientists usually work in teams as they design and conduct their research. Thus, the ability to work cooperatively with others is essen-

Figure 1-8. Agricultural scientists usually work in teams and collaborate with other researchers. (Courtesy, OACE, University of Illinois)

Figure 1-8b. Careful attention must be paid to the procedures of the experiment. (Courtesy, OACE, University of Illinois)

tial. Members of a research team must be team players who are receptive to other scientists' ideas and are willing to work together. Each member of the team must contribute throughout the planning and execution of the experiment.

A clean and safe environment for conducting the research must be provided and maintained. This means properly storing any equipment or materials after each use. This also means properly using research instruments, from measuring devices to microscopes. Safe laboratory practices must always be followed while conducting scientific investigations in agriculture.

Data Summary and Interpretation

This can be a very exciting stage of the research process because results of the experiment become evident. Were your original hypotheses confirmed? Sometimes the data obtained during the course of the experiment must be organized into another format or transformed by one or more calculations. In our experiment on soil pH and plant growth, we could record our data into a summary table as shown in Figure 1-10. Data should be totaled and averaged in each replication by treatment group. After the experiment is completed, we may want to calculate rate of growth or similar indicators. Sometimes data graphs are used to help in summarizing and interpreting data from an experiment (see Figure 1-11).

Figure 1-9. The research area must be kept clean and well organized. These researchers are checking the germination of rice varieties. (Courtesy, Agricultural Research Service, USDA)

	pH		
	5.0	6.0	7.0
Day 7	10.2 cm	9.2 cm	9.6 cm
Day 14	10.4 cm	10.1 cm	10.2 cm
Day 21	10.7 cm	11.5 cm	10.8 cm
Day 28	10.8 cm	13.8 cm	11.9 cm

Plant Height

Effects of soil pH on plant growth

Figure 1-10. Sample data summary chart.

After the data are summarized you are ready to draw conclusions from the experiment. This is done by looking for patterns in the data or by interpreting calculations that were performed on the data. For example, the data in Figure 1-10 would suggest conclusions such as those listed below. Can you identify a fourth conclusion from the data presented?

1. The rate of plant growth was different among the three soil pH levels.

2. Plant growth occurred in all three treatments (soil pH levels).

3. Plants growing in the soil with a pH of 6.0 exhibited the greatest growth during the 28 day trial.

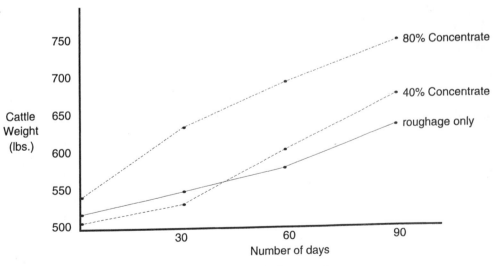

Figure 1-11. Sample data graph.

During the process of drawing conclusions from the data, the researcher must also determine if there is any evidence to suggest that the data might be inaccurate or in any way misrepresent what actually happened in the experiment. At this point any limitations of the experiment must be noted. For example, perhaps data were collected on the ninth day rather than the seventh day for some of the trials; or perhaps the procedures for measuring plant growth were not consistently followed by each member of the research team; or perhaps difficulties were encountered in monitoring and maintaining the pH levels of the soils in the experiment. This insight has an effect on the nature of conclusions drawn and the confidence the researcher has in the results of the experiment.

Depending upon the nature of the experiment, the researcher then formulates recommendations for practice based upon the results of the completed investigation. Findings should be explained in detail through conclusions, written discussion, and recommendations. Results of this experiment should be compared to results obtained from similar experiments, including research conducted by other research teams and research published in research reports. Finally, based upon the results of the completed experiment, the research team should identify new research questions to explore through further experimentation. Through this continuing cycle of questioning, experimentation, further questioning, and further experimentation, agricultural research is done, answers are provided, and new technologies for agriculture are discovered.

Follow-up

Discoveries in science and technology are the result of sustained research over a period of years that is focused on specific questions or problems. This programmatic approach to the research process means that one experiment leads to another, which leads to another, and so on until the problem is solved or the question answered. After each investigation the scientist predicts relationships or effects based upon the newly acquired information. For example, after conducting our initial experiment on soil pH and plant growth, we might predict that the effects of pH vary the most at the mid-point of the pH scale (4.0 to 8.0); or we might predict that the effects of pH vary, depending upon the soil type or plant species.

From these predictions additional hypotheses are formulated, new follow-up experiments are designed and conducted, and perhaps additional discoveries are made or confirmed. In addition, the scientist makes adjust-

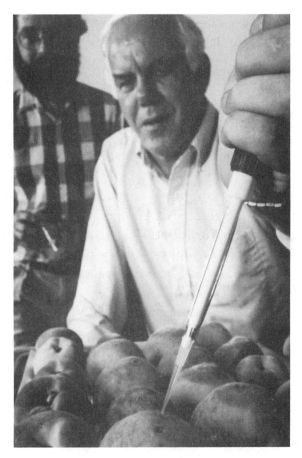

Figure 1-12. Each experiment raises new questions for subsequent investigation. These scientists are injecting peaches with a fungicide. (Courtesy, Agricultural Research Service, USDA)

ments in the process of science by altering the procedures used in subsequent experiments.

Steps in Conducting an Experiment

Stage One—Planning and Design

1. State problem in the form of a research question.

2. Identify hypotheses to be tested.

3. Design procedures for conducting the experiment and measuring the dependent variable(s).

    a. Identify the independent variable(s).

    b. Identify the dependent variable(s).

    c. Design measurement procedures.

    d. Design control measures.

    e. Provide for replication.

    f. Plan data summary procedures.

Stage Two—Conducting the Experiment

1. Follow the procedures as identified in stage one.

2. Make observations and measurements.

3. Use systematic procedures for collecting and recording data.

4. Revise procedures, if needed.

5. Work with other members of the research team.

6. Follow safe procedures.

Stage Three—Data Summary and Interpretation

1. Record data onto summary tables or charts.

2. Note inaccuracies or gaps in the data.

3. Identify conclusions.

4. Explain findings, noting any limitations of the research.

5. Identify further research questions based upon the results and conclusions of this experiment.

Stage Four—Follow-up

1. Redefine the research problem based upon this new information.

2. Formulate new hypotheses.

3. Conduct additional experiments in response to remaining questions.

CONDUCTING EXPERIMENTS SAFELY

Working in an agriscience research laboratory is much like working in other agricultural laboratories—a number of general safety procedures must be followed to prevent personal injury. Agriscience research often involves the use of expensive instruments or equipment, as well as everyday tools that can be dangerous if not properly used.

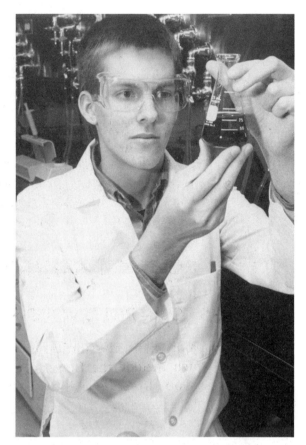

Figure 1-13. Safety is always important when conducting agricultural research. (Courtesy, National FFA Organization)

The following practices should be followed when conducting experiments in the agriscience laboratory.

1. Wear protective clothing, including an apron, gloves, and approved safety goggles.

2. Handle and dispose of all chemicals according to manufacturers' directions. Since many concentrated chemicals do not have handling, storage, and disposal directions on the containers, check with your teacher before proceeding with the experiment.

3. Be careful with scalpels, knives, dissecting needles, and other sharp instruments, especially when working around other students.

4. Locate adequate work space for your experiment. Place all equipment away from the edges of tables and lab counters.

5. Be aware of your surroundings (flammables, electricity, obstructions, etc.) as you conduct your experiment.

6. Place all materials and instruments in their designated storage areas at the end of the laboratory period.

7. Keep your work area clean and free from clutter.

8. Work carefully with glass instruments and lab supplies. Use holding racks and containers designed to be used with breakable items.

9. Keep flammable materials away from fire or sparks.

10. Never leave hot liquid or glassware unattended.

11. If you spill a chemical, notify your teacher immediately.

12. Follow recommended techniques for handling live animals.

13. Inform your teacher of any allergies you have before beginning your research activities.

14. Report any unlabelled or mislabelled chemicals to your teacher, as well as instruments that are not functioning properly.

15. Because of the chemicals, glassware, and other materials used to conduct agriscience experiments, student researchers need to work cooperatively and professionally in the laboratory.

Exercise 1.3 Applying the Research Process

Believe it or not, the seeds you buy each spring for planting in your field or garden are alive! Seeds remain in a dormant state until conditions for growth are present. One of these necessary conditions for all seeds is adequate soil moisture, which helps activate biological processes within the seed for germination. As we have all seen, seeds swell when they come in contact with water. How much water do seeds absorb during the early phases of germination?

Design an experiment to test the water absorption rates of various seeds. Determine the procedures for conducting the experiment. Identify the variables involved, and specify how they will be measured. Develop a format for recording data. Conduct the experiment, and summarize the data you collect into a table, chart, or graph. Draw conclusions from the data. What additional research questions or procedures are suggested by the results you obtained from your experiment?

SUMMARY

Agricultural research has made unbelievable contributions to the standard of living we enjoy today. Through sophisticated, specialized research programs that are carried out over a period of several years, scientists in agriculture have discovered solutions to many agricultural problems and developed many new technologies for agriculture and society. These discoveries have been the result of thorough and careful experimental research. While the problems are much more complex, the research process is the same, whether it's carried out at a USDA research center or in a high school agriscience laboratory.

Experimental research is conducted to find answers to identified questions. This scientific process involves defining the problem, gathering data, formulating possible solutions, testing preferred solutions, and evaluating the results. When conducting an experiment in the agriscience laboratory, research is carried out in a four stage process: planning and design, conducting the experiment, analyzing and interpreting data, and following up with further experimentation.

When conducting experiments, researchers control all variables except the ones that they want to manipulate and observe in the experiment. In general, scientists investigate the effects of independent variables (e.g., temperature) on dependent variables (e.g., plant growth). Accurate control of independent variables and precise measurement of dependent variables is essential. Carefully designed procedures for conducting the experiment must be consistently followed throughout. Replication provides confidence in the results obtained.

Agricultural research is an ongoing cycle of asking and answering, posing and investigating, finding and searching for more. Agriscience research programs across the country in industry and government will continue to make new discoveries that affect the way we live today and in the future.

FOR FURTHER STUDY AND DISCUSSION

1. Select a research problem in agriculture and design an experiment that will allow you to solve the problem to some degree. Follow the steps for conducting experi-

ments as outlined in this chapter. Label the independent and dependent variables.

2. Examine the data in Figure 1-11 and prepare a set of conclusions that are supported by the data.

3. Prepare a chart or table that could be used to record and/or summarize data from a selected experiment.

4. Define the following terms: manipulation, replication, variable, measurement, control, dependent variable, independent variable, and hypothesis.

5. What can you do to ensure a safe environment for you and your fellow student researchers as you conduct your experiments in agriscience?

Chapter 2

SUMMARIZING AND REPORTING RESEARCH

AGRICULTURAL APPLICATIONS

Literally thousands of agricultural research studies are completed each year. Some of this research is published, but scientists often complete many experiments before reaching the stage of formally publishing their findings. Written publication outlets include trade journals, newspapers and popular magazines, research journals, and technical reports. In addition, agricultural scientists report the findings of their research at professional meetings and news conferences.

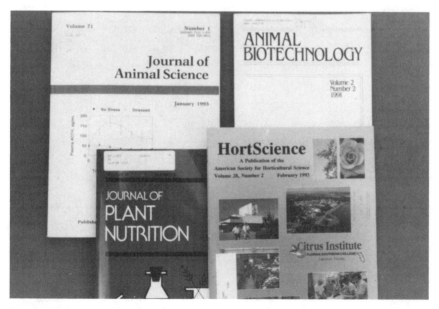

Figure 2-1. Publishing results is an important last stage in conducting research.

Figure 2-2. **Many scientists present their research at meetings and conferences.** (Courtesy, Agricultural Research Service, USDA)

As scientists conduct experiments in their field or research laboratories, they usually record their activities and findings in a log or journal. In agricultural research aimed at new product development many individual experiments may be conducted before a satisfactory product has been discovered. These researchers use the scientific method as a problem-solving process, continually searching and researching until they are able to "solve the problem" and develop a desirable new product.

Agricultural scientists at state universities, agricultural experiment stations, and federal laboratories share the results of their research with all groups, including both public and private agencies. The driving force behind their research programs is to solve agricultural problems for the betterment of society. Thus, research conducted by these scientists is widely and freely distributed. On the other hand, the vast amount of research conducted in

TERMS

conclusions	recommendations	research problem
findings	related studies	

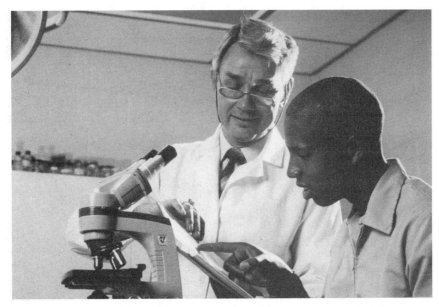

Figure 2-2b. Consulting with experienced scientists is always helpful. (Courtesy, National FFA Organization)

Figure 2-3. Keeping accurate field notes during an experiment is very important. (Courtesy, Agricultural Research Service, USDA)

Figure 2-4. Many important products and improvements have been developed by scientists in agribusiness and industry. (Courtesy, Agricultural Research Service, USDA)

agribusiness is driven by profit. Companies, rather then the public, "own" the research. For example, research conducted by a food processing company that may lead to a new product or food processing procedure will be kept "in-house" as much as possible to enhance that company's profit advantage.

Agricultural researchers must keep concise, yet thorough records of research activities. Otherwise, experiments may be repeated, and future experimentation will not be based on new knowledge generated through previous research. The same is true for your research in the agriscience laboratory.

Peach Trees That Fight Back

In 1987 scientists from the Agricultural Research Service and North Carolina State University planted more than 150 peach trees in an outdoor test for resistance to bacterial spot. Some of the trees were conventional Sunhigh and Redhaven grafts on standard rootstock. Others were propagated in tissue culture from axillary buds. This latter technique, called micropropagation, yields large numbers of plants that are clones, or genetic twins, of a parent plant.

About 100 of the test trees began as immature embryos that the scientists removed from seeds. The embryos were nurtured to form cell cultures, then small plants. Identical trees were cloned from each plant.

Several of the embryo-derived trees were more resistant to bacterial spot in 1990 and 1991 field tests. The most resistant trees were grown from cells derived from a Redhaven embryo. Bacterial spot damaged only 13% of these peaches, compared with nearly half the peaches from Redhavens that had not undergone tissue culture. Another set of trees came from toxin-resistant cells of a Sunhigh embryo. Fruit damage was considerable, but about one-third less than on standard Sunhighs.

Next, the scientists will evaluate the offspring of these top-performing plants. The scientists have concluded that several genes apparently help the plant resist the disease. Their goal is to isolate those genes so they can improve disease resistance even more. (Source: *Agricultural Research*, January 1993)

Figure 2-5. Computers are an important analytical and record keeping tool for researchers. (Courtesy, Agricultural Research Service, USDA)

OBJECTIVES—QUESTIONS FOR INVESTIGATION

After studying this chapter and completing the supporting laboratory exercises provided by your teacher, you should be able to answer the following questions:

1. What are the major parts of a research report?

2. How should I prepare my research report?

3. What is the difference between *findings*, *conclusions*, and *recommendations*?

4. How do I use the results of my completed experiment to identify additional experiments which should be conducted?

ELEMENTS OF A RESEARCH REPORT

Your research report should be concise, yet complete. One of your main objectives in preparing the report is provide enough information so that others can read your report and fully understand what you did and how you did it. Your report should contain the following sections:

1. Title Page

2. Introduction

3. Research Problem

4. Research Hypotheses

5. Findings From Related Studies

6. Procedures

7. Findings

8. Conclusions and Recommendations

9. Recommendations for Further Research

10. References

Exercise 2.1 Research Report Review

Clip from a recent newspaper or trade magazine an article that presents the results of agricultural research. Share an oral summary of the article with your agriscience class. In addition, locate a published research report from an agribusiness, the Cooperative Extension Service, USDA, a university, or some other agency. Note which of the 10 elements of a research report are contained in each of the two reports you located.

THE TITLE PAGE

Several important pieces of information should be included on the title page. Of course, your name, class, and the title of the experiment must be included. Also include the date that the report is written (versus the date that the experiment was conducted). Also, be sure to begin the first full page of the report with your name and the title of the experiment. The report should be stapled together with the pages numbered consecutively, beginning with the first page after the title page. Prepare the report on a computer or typewriter, if possible. In preparing reports for your agriscience class, feel free to use some creativity in "dressing up" the title page.

Figure 2-6. Your research report helps you and others better understand your research. (Courtesy, Agricultural Research Service, USDA)

INTRODUCTION

This beginning section of your research report should be a full paragraph that explains why the experiment was conducted. Use several sentences to describe the need for the research and the logic for the experiment. The introduction should make it clear to the reader *why* the research was conducted. See the sample introduction from a study on the hatchability of chicken eggs.

Elements of a Research Report

1. **Title Page**—Name, title of research, date, class

2. **Introduction**—Need and justification for the study, background information

3. **Research Problem**—Specific question under investigation, specify variables

4. **Research Hypotheses**—One or more predictions about the relationships between two or more variables

5. **Findings from Related Studies**—Summary of similar, previous research findings from printed or informal sources

6. **Procedures**—Design, treatments, measurement techniques

7. **Findings**—Data tables and/or graphs with brief descriptive statements

8. **Conclusions**—Specific statements about the relationships between variables as shown in your experiment

9. **Recommendations**—Suggestions on how your results should be used; suggestions for further experimentation on this problem

10. **References**—Complete listing of all sources used in designing the experiment and preparing the research report

---

RESEARCH PROBLEM

As explained in Chapter 1, the research problem is a precise statement of what the research addresses. For your purposes in agriscience class research problems are most easily and clearly stated in the form of a question. Usually a single problem (question) drives a particular experiment, but sometimes one or more secondary problems are also under investigated. All research problems to be addressed in your experiment should be stated in your research report.

HYPOTHESES

Hypotheses are predictions about the relationships of variables in the experiment. In agricultural research we usually look for differences

Figure 2-7. Experimentation must be guided by one or more research questions or problems. (Courtesy, Kenneth Rhodes)

between groups of subjects in the experiment (e.g., difference between eggs that are rotated during incubation and eggs that are not). Hypotheses can be stated to indicate that no difference between two or more groups is expected in your experiment, if that is your prediction. On the other hand, if you anticipate that one group will differ from the other, then state your hypothesis to reflect the difference that you expect.

RELATED STUDIES

This is a very important phase of the research process and an important part of your research report as well. If scientists went about their research without finding out what other scientists are doing (and discovering) in the same area, then much time, effort, and money would be wasted. While you may not have access to most of the agricultural research literature, your teacher can provide some key publications that will contain summaries of research conducted in federal, state, and agribusiness laboratories. When referring to published research, be sure to provide complete information about the printed source so others may read more about it, if desired. Use

Figure 2-8. Your research should be compared to the work of other researchers. (Courtesy, Agricultural Research Service, USDA)

Figure 2-9. Students should work together and discuss the results of their experiments. (Courtesy, Greg Beard)

more informal sources, like your fellow students, to add to these published research reports. In some cases you may be unable to locate other research that has been conducted on your specific topic.

PROCEDURES

This section of your written research report should include a detailed and complete description of *how* you conducted your experiment. A good procedures section in a research report makes it possible for other researchers to replicate your experiment by following the same procedures. As a scientist,

Figure 2-9b. Reading newsletters, magazines, and reports helps in formulating research ideas. (Courtesy, National FFA Organization)

clearly written procedures that produce the same results time after time will lend credibility to your research. Independent and dependent variables should be identified. Levels of the independent variable and how they were established and maintained during the experiment should be described. A critical part of the procedures section is careful description of the procedures you used for measuring the dependent variable. This includes when and how measurements or observations were taken. Methods used for summarizing and/or analyzing the data should also be described.

Sample Research Report
(excluding title page)

Introduction

Egg hatcheries have adopted a variety of techniques for handling eggs during the incubation period. In addition to controlling incubation temperature and relative humidity, eggs are incubated in an upright position and tilted back and forth several times daily. Trials have indicated that hatchability is greatest under these conditions.

The Research Problem

The research problem investigated in this experiment was, " *What effect does egg rotation during hatching have on hatching rate?*" The effects of egg position on hatchability were also investigated.

Hypotheses

1. Eggs that are tilted several times each day during the incubation period will have greater hatchability.

2. Egg position in the incubator (flat or on end) will have no effect on hatchability.

Related Studies

In a Cooperative Extension Service research bulletin (CES, 1993) Craddock and Thomas reported that tilting of eggs during the incubation period had a positive effect on hatchability. They cited several other studies which found similar results. However, the practice of tilting eggs during incubation had no effect on hatchability for smaller eggs, such as those from quail. Scientists at the Wilkes Research Center reported that egg position during incubation has no effect on hatchability (Cone, 1992). Experiments conducted by other students in this agriscience class have shown mixed findings for the effects of egg position and rotation on hatchability.

Procedures

Two incubators of the same brand and model were obtained for use in this experiment. Thermostats were calibrated so the same temperature was maintained in each incubator. Thermometers were used to verify incubation temperature. Each incubator was filled with 24 fertilized chicken eggs. In one incubator all 24 eggs were placed on their sides. Twelve of the eggs were gently rolled back and forth four times (9 am, 11 am, 1 pm,

3 pm) during each day of the incubation period. The other 12 eggs were not disturbed during the 21 day period. A similar procedure was followed in the second incubator, except that all 24 eggs were positioned with the large end up. In this treatment 12 of the eggs were tilted back and forth at a 90° angle four times daily. Hatchability was defined as the percentage of eggs that hatched for each group of 24 eggs.

Findings

In the incubator with the eggs positioned on their sides, a total of 20 of the 24 eggs hatched (83.3%). This included 11 in the rotated group (91.7%) and 9 in the undisturbed group (75%). For the eggs positioned with the large end up, 22 (91.7%) of the eggs hatched, including all 12 (100%) of those that were tilted several times each day. The hatching percentage for the undisturbed, upright eggs was 83.3%.

Conclusions

1. Tilting eggs several times per day during the incubation period significantly improves hatching percentage.

2. Hatchability is also increased by positioning eggs with the large end up throughout the incubation period.

Recommendations for Further Research

1. Vary the number of times eggs are titled per day from none to four.

2. Compare the effects on hatchability of different techniques for adjusting egg position during incubation.

References

Craddock, T. & Thomas, P. (1993). *The Effects of Egg Position on Hatchability*. Cooperative Extension Service Technical Report 2148, Prairie State University, Goodman, IL.

Cone, B. (1992). Increasing Egg Hatchability. *AgriResearch*, Vol. 53, (6), p. 22.

FINDINGS

The findings section of your report should contain actual data generated from the experiment. These data are usually presented in tables, graphs, or similar summary formats. Be sure to include the units of measure for the

Figure 2-10. Developing conclusions based upon your findings can be a difficult but important step. (Courtesy, National FFA Organization)

data presented. Each data table or graph should be accompanied by several statements that highlight patterns that the data seem to follow. However, at this point, limit these comments to describing *what the data look like versus what they mean*. Data should be presented by hypothesis. That is, restate hypothesis one, and then present the data from the experiment that pertain to this hypothesis. Follow with the remaining hypotheses, using the same approach.

CONCLUSIONS

Separating findings from conclusions is sometimes difficult, even for experienced researchers. Remember that findings indicate *what* you found, and conclusions suggest *what these findings mean*. As you look at each data table, ask yourself, "So what?" Or stated another way, "So what do I conclude from these findings?" For your experiments in agriscience classes you will rarely have more than three or four conclusions.

Conclusions should closely parallel the hypotheses initially stated for the study. In fact, conclusions should specifically indicate whether or not each hypothesis in your experiment was confirmed.

Exercise 2.2 Describing Results and Drawing Conclusions

Carefully examine the data in the table below. Write a short paragraph which *describes* the data contained in Table 2-1. Be careful not to offer interpretations of the data, that is, why these results were obtained. Next, develop at least four conclusions from the data contained in the table. Be sure that your conclusions are directly supported by the summary data. Have your teacher review your conclusions for accuracy.

Table 2-1
Transpiration in Plants

	Day 1		Day 2		Day 3		Day 4	
	Volume (ml)	Net Change	Volume (ml)	Net Change	Volume (ml)	Net Change	Volume (ml)	Net Change
One leaf, no fan	48	–2	45	–3	44	–1	42	–2
Three leaves, no fan	46	–4	43	–3	39	–4	37	–2
One leaf, fan	47	–3	44	–3	43	–1	41	–2
Three leaves, fan	45	–5	41	–4	37	–4	33	–4

Note: The beginning water volume for each treatment was 50 ml.

RECOMMENDATIONS

Many research reports will contain two types of recommendations: recommendations for practice and recommendations for further research. In developing your recommendations for practice, go back to the introduction section of your report and think about why you did the experiment. This reflection usually suggests ways your research findings should be implemented. Of course, if your findings are inconclusive or contradictory, then you may choose not to identify recommendations for practice, and instead suggest areas of further research that are needed to resolve the problem.

Even if your experiment provided valuable data and insight into the research problem, scientific investigations usually raise as many questions as they answer. These new questions represent topics for further experimentation. If you were a scientist pursuing a research program in a specific area, then each subsequent study would be driven by findings from your previous studies. In reality, you may choose not to research any of these new questions further, but by sharing them in written form others are made aware of your discoveries and can conduct their own research in that area.

There are several ways that a completed experiment can suggest areas where further research is needed. One common circumstance is where one scientist's findings contradict findings from previous research on that problem. This occurs in all agriscience research laboratories from time to time, and it is likely to occur among your student colleagues in the school agriscience lab. In this case more evidence is needed before researchers can be confident in their results and conclusions. Sometimes researchers are puzzled by unexpected findings. When this occurs, experiments should be replicated to determine if those same findings consistently occur. Unexpected results can be due to several factors: inaccurate measurement, procedures not properly followed, influence of external factors, or simply an unexpected, but true, discovery.

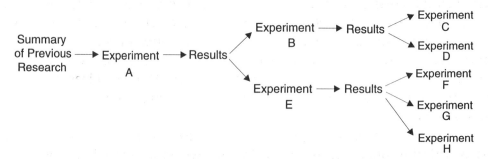

Figure 2-11. Identifying additional experiments to conduct.

REFERENCES

This section of your report includes complete bibliographic information for any piece that you cited in the introduction section or other parts of your report. The list of references serves to make other scientists in the field aware of the research to date, as well as the research that you used to guide your study. The following information should be included for each study cited: author, date published, title, source (including issue and page number), and publisher. Sometimes researchers use index cards to record bibliographic and technical information from a reference as they read it. These cards later become a major source of ideas when designing the experiment and preparing the written research report.

Exercise 2.3 Preparing a Research Report

Conduct a mini-experiment on the germination of lettuce seeds under light and dark conditions. Prepare a written research report to describe your experiment and results.

SUMMARY

Designing and conducting agricultural research is only part of the job of the scientist; summarizing and reporting the research is equally important. Who knows how many discoveries have been unknowingly made because the research findings were never shared with others! Fortunately, the U.S. agricultural research system has a well established network for disseminating research findings to the public, as well as to other scientists. As an agriscience student, preparing a research report helps you better understand what you have accomplished with your experiment. Reports underscore both the procedures and findings of the research and help stimulate ideas for further investigation. Research reports allow others to learn from your experiments and vice versa.

A complete research report should be concise and include 10 major parts: title, introduction, problem, hypotheses, related studies, procedures, findings, conclusions, recommendations, and references. Professional scientists do not consider their research complete until they have prepared a written research report and shared it with interested audiences. Class and school activities, science fairs, local media, and other avenues are available to help you share your agriscience research with friends, parents, teachers, and other groups. While scientists' research reports are very thorough and mathematically complex, they contain the same basic elements as your research reports. Preparing a good research report puts the finishing touches on your agriscience laboratory experiments.

FOR FURTHER STUDY AND DISCUSSION

1. Distinguish between findings, conclusions, and recommendations.

2. List several hypotheses for each of the following research problems: (a) What is the effect of vitamin supplements on health and weight gain in young horses? (b) How does a woody plant respond to pruning? (c) How does light affect flowering in plants?

3. What sources of information on agricultural research are available in your classroom, school, or community? (Develop a list of sources and the types of research they report.)

4. What is the purpose of the *Introduction* and *Related Studies* sections of your research report?

5. After you have completed an experiment, how do you decide what further experiments are needed in that area of investigation?

Chapter 3

HEREDITY AND REPRODUCTION

The Mamas and the Papas

AGRICULTURAL APPLICATIONS

Scientists are continuously searching for improved crop varieties by selectively mating plants, a practice known as plant breeding. The first major breakthrough in plant breeding occurred in the 1930s with the development of hybrid seed. Hybrids produce 25% to 50% greater yields than traditional corn varieties and are fairly tolerant of varying soil and climatic conditions. However, hybrids do not pass all of their desirable traits to their offspring, so parent lines must be crossed each year to produce new hybrid seed. Virtually all corn grown in the United States today is from hybrid seed.

Plant breeders use their knowledge of genetics and heredity to design plant breeding programs. Usually a combination of traditional and molecular techniques is used in today's plant breeding programs. Some question the need for ongoing research aimed at development of new crop varieties. Using traditional plant breeding methods, up to 10 years may be required to get a new variety ready for commercial release. Biotechnology can dramatically reduce this development time. Still, new varieties often lose their resistance to disease and other targeted enemies within three to ten years, and new plant enemies are continuously evolving. For example, the first Russian wheat aphid was found in U.S. fields in 1986, costing growers over $200 million to date. Scientists estimate that another five years will be needed before varieties that are highly resistant to the Russian wheat aphid are available.

Agricultural scientists have applied principles of plant *genetics* to develop a new iceberg mini-lettuce that makes just enough salad for a single serving. Other new cultivars include a thornless blackberry and new strawberry

Figure 3-1. New varieties of plants are continuously being developed through breeding programs. (Courtesy, Agricultural Research Service, USDA)

cultivars that are bigger, better tasting, longer fruiting, and resistant to anthracnose. A new hybrid orange, Ambersweet, was developed by USDA researchers and released for commercial use in 1989. Ambersweet is a cold hardy citrus variety whose parentage is one-half orange, three-eighths tan-

TERMS

allele	genetic engineering	petal
backcrossing	genetics	phenotype
biotechnology	genotype	pistil
carpel	heterozygous	plant breeding
cell culture	homozygous	Punnett Square
chromosome	hybridization	recombinant DNA
crossbreeding	inbreeding	self-fertile
cultivar	meiosis	self-pollination
dihybrid cross	microinjection	sepal
fertilization	micropropagation	stamen
gene	monohybrid cross	

gerine, and one-eighth grapefruit. Researchers have developed new bean varieties that are resistant to all 55 strains of the fungus that causes rust. In a bad year rust can cause up to $250 million in losses to green snap bean, wax bean, and dry bean crops. In corn, plant breeding programs are underway to reduce stalk lodging and increase resistance to insects, disease, and pests. A major goal in plant breeding programs today is to build in natural resistance to plant enemies so that inputs can be reduced. Biotechnology, including cell culture and gene splicing, will add an important new dimension to plant breeding efforts in the years ahead.

Scientists believe that there are about 50 controllable traits in plants that can be successfully produced through plant breeding tech-

Figure 3-1b. Geneticists examining wheat samples. (Courtesy, Agricultural Research Service, USDA)

niques. These include cold hardiness; palatability; heat and drought tolerance; shape and color; oil, starch, sugar, protein, and fiber content; height; salt tolerance; flavor; texture; and time to maturity.

OBJECTIVES—QUESTIONS FOR INVESTIGATION

After studying this chapter and completing the supporting laboratory exercises, you should be able to answer the following questions:

1. How is inheritance of traits in plants regulated?

Figure 3-2. Scientists have developed new bean varieties (right) that are
resistant to all 55 strains of the fungus that causes rust.
(Courtesy, Agricultural Research Service, USDA)

Figure 3-3. The Ambersweet orange, developed by crossing an orange,
grapefruit, and tangerine, is a new cold-resistant variety.
(Courtesy, Agricultural Research Service, USDA)

2. How do dominant and recessive genes affect plant characteristics?

3. How does pollination in plants occur?

4. Why are some plants unable to self-pollinate?

5. How do scientists use principles of plant genetics to guide their plant breeding programs?

6. How is biotechnology being used to supplement traditional plant breeding programs?

LABORATORY INVESTIGATIONS

EXERCISE I.
GENOTYPIC AND PHENOTYPIC RATIOS

Purpose

The purpose of this exercise is to apply the principles of simple Mendelian genetics to predict the phenotypes of offspring from a genetic cross. In addition, you will determine the parent genotypes in a monohybrid cross by counting the number of seedlings that display each phenotype.

Materials and Equipment

- normal:hairless F_2 tomato seed
- green:albino F_2 sorghum seed
- monohybrid segregating ear of genetic corn
- dihybrid segregating ear of genetic corn
- germination mix
- plant flats
- plastic covering or bag for flats

Procedures

Punnett Square Exercises. You are replicating Gregor Mendel's famous experiments with sweet peas. The genotype for the dominant smooth-seeded parent is designated as *AA*, while the genotype for the wrinkled-seeded parent is *aa*. In the Punnett square below fill in the margins and interior for this F_1 (first generation) cross. What are the genotypic and phenotypic ratios for this cross?

Following in Mendel's footsteps, you cross the F_1 plants by allowing them to self-pollinate. Thus, each parent in this F_2 cross has a genetic makeup on this trait of *Aa*. Using the Punnett square that follows, indicate all possible combinations for seed smoothness in this F_2 cross. What are the genotypic and phenotypic ratios for this cross?

Consider now a dihybrid corn cross involving kernel color (purple or yellow) and endosperm type (starchy or sweet). The dominant purple color is represented by the genotype *RR*, while the dominant starchy genotype is designated by *Su*. Complete the Punnett square for an F_2 cross in which each F_1 hybrid has the genotype *R/r x Su/su*. What are the genotypic and phenotypic ratios for this F_2 cross?

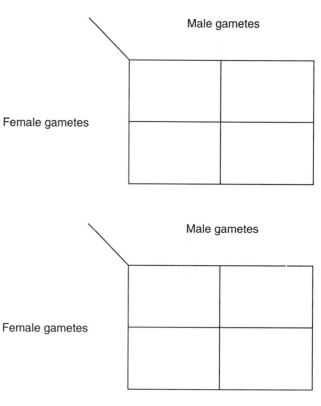

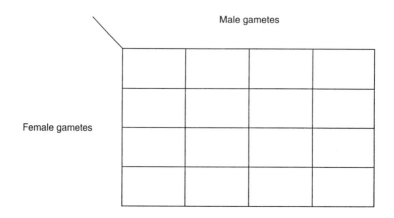

Genotypic Ratios in Corn. Examine samples of monohybrid and dihybrid segregating ears of genetic corn. Count and record the number of kernels on each ear that display the segregating traits. Calculate the ratio of expression for each trait under consideration. What would you theorize as the genotype for the sample ear? For the parents of the sample ear?

Genetic Seed Trials. Add the germination mix to the plant flats to within an inch of the top. Use one flat for each type of genetic seed to be germinated. Plant seeds at recommended depth evenly over the flat. (Seeds may be planted in lots of 25, 50, or 100 seeds.) Water thoroughly. Label each flat with your name, class, seed type, and planting date. Cover the flat with plastic, or enclose in a plastic bag. Place at room temperature. When seeds start to germinate (usually about one week), remove plastic and place in a sunny location. Add water as needed to keep soil moist.

Observations of phenotypes should be recorded at 10 to 14 days, depending upon the type of seed and the trait under consideration. Count the number of tomato plants that are normal and the number that are hairless. What is the phenotypic ratio? Count the number of green and albino sorghum plants. What is the phenotypic ratio? What would you theorize as the genotype of the parents used to produce your seed?

EXPERIMENT I.
FLOWER DISSECTION AND POLLEN GERMINATION

Purpose

This experiment will allow you to closely examine the reproductive parts of a flower and test the effects of temperature on the rate of pollen germination.

Materials

- flower samples (lily, snapdragon, sweet pea, vegetable crops)
- hand lens
- glass slides
- razor blade
- tweezers
- dissecting needles

- thionin stain

- petri dishes

- filter paper

- culture medium—10% sucrose

Procedures

Flower Dissection. Obtain several flower specimens and see if you can locate their primary structures: sepals, petals, stamens, and carpels. A complete flower has all four of these structures. Are your specimens complete flowers? If not, which structures are missing? (Not all flowers contain all four structures.)

Identify the male reproductive organ, or stamen, of your flower specimens. The stamen includes the anther and the filament. How many stamens does each of your specimens have? Carefully remove the stamens. Using a hand lens, look for pollen on the anthers. Use a dissecting needle to puncture one of the anthers and remove some grains of pollen.

Identify and closely examine the female reproductive organ, or pistil, on each of your specimens. Remove the pistil from its base. Cut the ovary in half and examine the inside. How do the pistils from each of your specimens differ?

Pollen Germination. Collect pollen on the tip of a dissecting needle. Place pollen grains in a clean petri dish containing the desired culture medium. Prepare several petri dishes in this manner. Include replications, as well as pollen from several plant species.

Place the prepared pollen samples in controlled temperatures: 82°F (room temperature), 50°F, and 91°F. Observe the rate of pollen germination in each of the samples after 30 minutes, one hour, two hours, and three hours. (Thionin stain may be added to make pollen tubes more visible.) What temperature resulted in the best rate of pollen germination?

EXPERIMENT 2.
CROSS-POLLINATION

Purpose

In this experiment you will hand pollinate two varieties of the same plant species.

Materials

- small paper bags, string
- flower labels made from poster board
- tweezers
- single-edged razor blade
- dissecting needle
- pollination record sheet
- plants grown to a preflowering (bud) stage
- small paintbrush, cotton swab, or toothpick

Procedures

Select several crop species and grow to the bud stage. Recommended species are bean, cucumber, squash, tomato, and pea. Rapid cycling *Brassica* can also be used. Cross-pollination experiments with corn grown at home or at your school's land laboratory can also be undertaken. Two varieties of each species selected will be needed. Plant enough seeds to provide for replication in this pollination experiment.

Select a "male" parent and a "female" parent of the same species, but different varieties. The female plant will be the one that produces the hybrid seed. Pollen will be collected from the male plant. Label each parent plant.

For species having complete flowers, remove the stamens from the flowers on the female plant. This is done by using a razor to cut off the stamens and petals just before the flower bud opens. Sterilize the tools that you will use by dipping them in alcohol for a few seconds and letting the alcohol evaporate. After the stamens have been removed, cover each female flower with a paper bag to prevent pollination by other plants.

As soon as the buds on the male plant open, collect pollen from the anthers. This can be done by gently tapping the flower on the male plant and allowing the pollen to shed onto a piece of paper. A paintbrush, cotton swab, or toothpick can also be used to collect pollen from the anther. In addition, the entire stamen can be removed from the male plant and used to pollinate the flowers on the female plant. Remove the paper bags covering the female flowers and transfer the pollen quickly. Replace the paper bags on each of the flowers after pollination. Be sure to label each pollinated flower. Remove the bags from the pollinated flowers three to five days after pollination.

Continue growing parent plants until fruit develops and matures. Note the success rate of your cross pollination experiment. What percent of the female flowers developed fruit? (Don't be surprised if fruit does not develop on some of the flowers. Practice makes perfect!) Remove the hybrid seeds from the mature fruit, dry if necessary, and plant. Observe the differences in the hybrid plants as compared to the parent plants.

SCIENCE CONNECTIONS

FLOWERING AND POLLINATION

The two major plant classifications are the gymnosperms and the angiosperms, which include the flowering plants, grasses, and cereals. All angiosperms develop flowers which contain one or more ovules that are enclosed in an ovary or carpel. The flower is the reproductive structure for the angiosperms. A flower is said to be complete if it has all four of the following structures: *sepals, petals, stamens,* and a *carpel* (also called the *pistil*). An incomplete flower lacks one or more of the structures. A flower that has both stamens (male reproductive tissues) and a carpel (female reproductive tissues) is said to be a perfect flower. Imperfect flowers have either stamens or a carpel, but not both.

The sepals and petals help to attract insects to the plant by producing a sugary solution called nectar. An incomplete flower is one which has no sepals or petals. Most cereal and grass plants have incomplete flowers, thus making the flowers less visible. Flowering is initiated by (1) the length of uninterrupted darkness (photoperiodism), (2) exposure to low temperatures (vernalization), or (3) morphological maturity. The majority of food-producing plants induce flowering without external stimulation. As long as they are

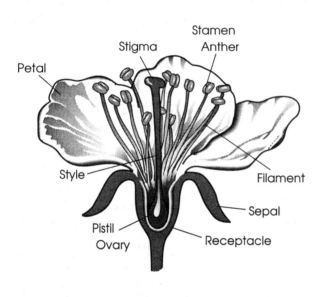

Figure 3-4. **Parts of a complete flower.**

actively growing, they initiate flowers at almost any temperature or day length.

The *stamen* consists of the anthers and their supporting filament. The development of pollen grains (microspores) occurs in the anthers. As the anthers mature they break open and pollen grains are spread by the wind and insects. The *carpel* includes the stigma, style, and ovary. The stigma is the swollen end of the style and is usually colorful and always sticky. Pollen grain must land on the stigma in order for pollination to occur. *Self-pollination* occurs when the anther and the stigma are from the same flower, from different flowers on the same plant, or from different flowers on different plants of the same cultivar or variety. *Cross-pollination* involves different flowers on plants of different cultivars.

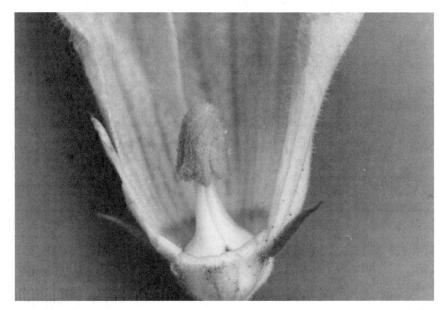

Figure 3-4b. This cutaway of a squash flower shows its incomplete structure.

Some plants are *self-fertile* and produce fruit and seed without the transfer of pollen from another *cultivar*. This is true of most monocot plants. A plant is considered self-sterile if it requires pollen from another plant in order to set fruit. Scientists believe sterility is due to the protein composition of the cell wall of pollen grains. This protein makeup sends a signal to the stigma indicating whether the pollen is from its own species or even from the same plant.

Each *pollen grain* contains a tube cell and a generative cell. When the

Figure 3-4c. The lily is a good example of a perfect flower, with the major structures easily seen.

pollen grain lands on the stigma, the sugary solution promotes "germination" of the pollen. The tube cell forms a pollen tube that grows through the stigma and style. Eventually, the pollen tube enters the nucleus of the ovule by passing through the micropyle. The generative cell has produced two male gametes through the process of mitosis. One gamete unites with the egg cell to form the zygote, which develops into the embryo. The other male gamete unites with the polar nucleus in the ovule to form the endosperm. The endosperm is where the seed's food reserves are stored for germination. The time between pollination and fertilization in most angiosperms is 24 to 48 hours. Once *fertilization* has occurred, the ovule becomes the seed and the ovary becomes the fruit.

GENETICS AND HEREDITY

The nucleus of a living cell contains *chromosomes*, which contain information about the genetic makeup of that plant and transmit that information to offspring. Each plant species has the same number of chromosomes in all vegetative cells. Sex cells have half the number of chromosomes as vegetative cells. Chromosomes are long, thread-like structures consisting of *DNA* (deoxyribonucleic acid), *RNA* (ribonucleic acid), and various proteins.

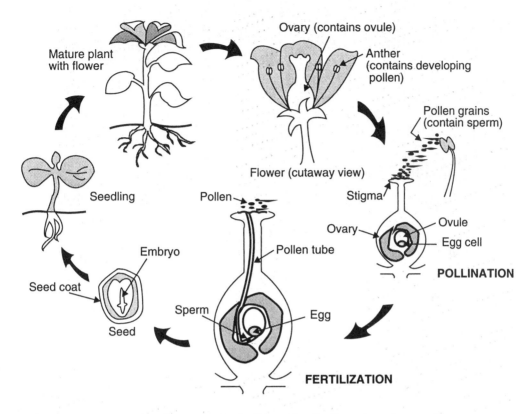

Figure 3-5. **Stages in the life cycle of a flowering plant.**

Genes are organic bases located along DNA molecules. The gene is the ultimate heredity unit of a plant.

Chromosomes are usually found in pairs in each vegetative cell. These are called *homologous chromosomes* if they have the same genes affecting the same traits and located at the same position along the chromosome. Matching genes on homologous chromosomes are called *alleles*. Gene alleles always occur on the same *locus* (location) along the pair of chromosomes. Allelic genes can be *dominant* or *recessive*. A dominant gene causes a certain characteristic to be expressed (present in offspring), while a recessive gene causes the character to be expressed only if the alleles from both parents are recessive. Dominant genes are represented by capital letters and recessive genes are indicated by using small letters. For example, the dominant allele that results in a starchy endosperm is represented by *Su*, while the recessive allele is shown as *su*. Similarly, a recessive allele that results in yellow corn kernels can be depicted as *r*. *Homozygous* plants have both alleles the same (*Su/Su*), and a *heterozygous* plant has different alleles for that trait (*R/r*).

Figure 3-5b. The ear on the right is the result of crossing the other two ears. Can you guess the genotype of these corn ears?

Meiosis controls the formation of egg and sperm cells (gametes). As gametes are formed, the two alleles for a particular trait separate (segregate) randomly so that each gamete receives one allele or the other.

The allele composition of a plant is referred to as its *genotype.* For example, the three possible height genotypes of a plant could be T/T, T/t, or t/t (T=tall, t=short). The physical appearance of the plant is known as the *phenotype.* In the case of plant height, the phenotype of both T/T and T/t alleles would be a tall plant, since T represents the dominant allele. Researchers have discovered that a single gene controls some physical traits, while many genes work together to control other traits, such as crop yield.

A common method of predicting the genotypes and phenotypes of offspring is the use of a matrix called a *Punnett Square.* A sample Punnett Square for plant height is shown below. In this example, both parents are heterozygous.

	Male gametes	
	T	t
T	T T	T t
t	T t	t t

Female gametes

The above example represents a *monohybrid cross*, since only one pair of alleles (one gene) is involved. A *dihybrid cross* involves two pairs of alleles (e.g., height and leaf color). The following example depicts a dihybrid cross, with plant height and leaf color (G=green, g= yellow) as the genetic traits under consideration. Again, both parents are heterozygous.

		Male gametes			
		T G	T g	t G	t g
	T G	TTGG	TTGg	TtGG	TtGg
	T g	TTGg	TTgg	TtGg	Ttgg
Female gametes	t G	TtGG	TtGg	ttGG	ttGg
	t g	TtGg	Ttgg	ttGg	ttgg

Genotypic ratio refers to the proportion of allele types for each genetic trait. In the examples above the genotypic ratio is 1:2:1 for the monohybrid cross and 1:2:2:4:1:2:1:2:1 for the dihybrid cross. For the dihybrid cross the number of blocks in the Punnett Square containing each unique genotype is as follows:

TTGG = 1   Ttgg = 2
TTGg = 2   ttGG = 1
TtGG = 2   ttGg = 2
TtGg = 4   ttgg = 1
TTgg = 1

The phenotypic ratio would be 3:1 (¾ tall, ¼ short) for the monohybrid cross. For the dihybrid cross the phenotypic ratio would be 9:3:3:1 (tall, green—9; tall, yellow—3; short, green—3; short, yellow—1).

PLANT BREEDING

Plant breeding is the process of selectively mating plants. Plant breeders try to change plants in numerous ways to make them more productive and

Figure 3-6. New sorghum varieties for tropical climates are being developed in this plant breeding program. Bags prevent unwanted cross-pollination. (Courtesy, Agricultural Research Service, USDA)

useful and to make their cultivation more economical. A basic type of plant breeding is *selection*, in which plants with desirable traits are chosen from a population and then reproduced.

Hybridization is the crossing of two plants that have different genotypes. This usually involves different varieties or cultivars of the same species, but different species have also been successfully crossed. *Crossbreeding*, or hybridization, usually produces a plant that is more vigorous in growth than either of its two parents. For example, hybrid corn produces 25% to 50% greater yields than traditional corn varieties. This hybrid vigor process is not well understood. Hybrids that result from crossing two different species are usually sterile, due to the uneven number of chromosomes in the parent plants. Hybrids from the same species are often sterile, and even those that can reproduce generate widely varying offspring. Hybrids do not pass many of their desirable traits to their offspring, so parent stocks must be crossed each year to produce new seed.

The production of hybrid seed is managed by production organizations who contract with farmers to grow the parent lines and make the hybrids. Seed production fields must be isolated from other fields to prevent unwanted cross-pollination. In corn, when the tassels begin to emerge, the female plants are detasseled to prevent self-pollination. Producers then rely on the wind to cross-pollinate the male parent with the female parent to produce the hybrid seed.

Inbreeding is the process of crossing two similar parents. By continuously self-pollinating or inbreeding (five to seven generations), a plant breeder can develop seed that will consistently express certain phenotypes. These inbred lines or varieties are then used as parent seed to generate hybrid seed for planting. Nearly all hybrid seed corn is produced by a single cross of two inbred parent lines.

Backcrossing is another plant

─── Single Cross ───
Inbred parent A X Inbred parent B
↓
Single cross A x B

─── Three-way cross ───
Inbred parent A X Inbred parent B
↓
Single cross A x B X Unrelated Inbred C
↓
Three-way cross (A x B) x C

─── Double Cross ───
Inbred Parent A   Inbred Parent C
X Inbred Parent B   X Inbred Parent D
↓   ↓
Single Cross A x B   X   Single Cross C x D
↓
Double cross (A x B) x (C x D)

Figure 3-7. Common hybridization methods.

Figure 3-7b. Plant breeding is simplified in corn, where the male flowers (tassel) and female flowers (silk) are separate.

Figure 3-7c. In hybrid seed corn production the tassels of the female plants
are removed to allow cross pollination from the male plant.

breeding method in which offspring are continuously crossed with one of
the parents. For example, a strawberry variety that is susceptible to anthracnose would be crossed with another variety that shows genetic resistance
to the disease. Succeeding generations are then crossed with the susceptible
parent until offspring show both the desirable traits of the susceptible
parent and anthracnose resistance.

BIOTECHNOLOGY TECHNIQUES

Biotechnology can be broadly defined as the management of biological
systems for the benefit of humanity. Today, biotechnology uses molecular
biology and molecular genetics as the basis for new and developing techniques that supplement traditional plant breeding methods. These include
cell and tissue culture, protoplast fusion, embryo manipulation, recombinant DNA techniques, and other procedures.

Micropropagation is the propagation (asexual reproduction) of plant cells
or tissues in a closed container. The cultures are grown on a growth medium
that contains essential nutrients for normal growth. Tissue culture techniques will be examined in Chapter 13. *Cell culture* involves modifying the
genetic makeup of the cell and then regenerating plants with the desired

Figure 3-8. Researchers check the progress of micropropagated strawberries. (Courtesy, Agricultural Research Service, USDA)

traits. Cell culture techniques provide for rapid detection of disease and herbicide resistance or tolerance to environmental stresses, such as salt accumulation. Cells that survive this screening process are then regenerated into whole plants, which are examined under field conditions.

Microinjection techniques involve the mechanical insertion of genetic material into single, living cells. Microscopic needles are used to inject DNA into protoplasts. Scientist have also discovered ways to fuse cells together. Cell walls are dissolved by enzymes, revealing the naked protoplasts. These techniques hold the potential for bringing together the genetic makeup of unrelated plants. For example, scientists could fuse corn and soybean protoplasts to produce a leguminous grain crop capable of producing its own nitrogen.

Recombinant DNA, or *genetic engineering*, techniques involve gene splicing, replication, and transfer of genes to other organisms. These transgenic organisms would carry in all of their cells a foreign gene that was inserted by laboratory techniques. The ability to genetically engineer new plants by using gene isolation and splicing techniques has created great excitement among scientists. Thus far, only a few genes of agronomic importance have been inserted into plants. These include genes that create insect and virus resistance, as well as herbicide tolerance. Scientists have recently inserted a gene into tomatoes that delays overripening and prolongs the shelf life of the fruit.

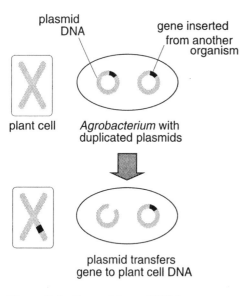

plasmid DNA

gene inserted from another organism

plant cell   *Agrobacterium* with duplicated plasmids

plasmid transfers gene to plant cell DNA

Figure 3-9. Recombinant DNA is a molecular breeding technique that holds great promise for the future.

Recombinant DNA techniques start with cutting a gene with an enzyme that behaves like a scalpel. The sliced gene is then removed and inserted into circular DNA molecules called plasmids which are found in bacteria. An enzyme is used to seal the spliced ends together. The DNA plasmid can then be inserted into a cell that has been selected for alteration. The result is a new sequence of DNA in the plant cell. These techniques will allow genotypic changes in plants that would require several years to achieve using conventional plant breeding techniques. A major emphasis of plant biotechnology is to construct genetic road maps that are necessary for successful genetic engineering programs. This plant genome research is aimed at identifying genes that affect economically important traits in food crops.

SUMMARY

Producing agronomic and horticultural crops requires a sound understanding of basic plant biology concepts. Without a working knowledge of heredity and plant reproductive processes, scientists and producers would constantly be using a trial-and-error approach to their work. These plant science fundamentals explain why some plants are self-sterile, why offspring sometimes do not carry traits from their parents, why poor pollination sometimes occurs, and why some plant species cannot be crossed. These fundamentals also drive our plant breeding programs and dictate the emerging uses of plant biotechnology.

Plant breeding programs of today are a blend of conventional plant breeding techniques and biotechnology. Molecular breeding techniques can significantly reduce the amount of time required to develop new plant varieties. Many improvements in plant characteristics have resulted from traditional plant breeding programs, and several new products have recently emerged as a result of biotechnology applications. These efforts will con-

Figure 3-10. Developing the perfect strawberry through plant breeding research. (Courtesy, Agricultural Research Service, USDA)

tinue to focus on the important nutritional and economical characteristics of agronomic and horticultural crops.

FURTHER LABORATORY INVESTIGATIONS

1. Obtain several additional samples of genetic corn with a known genotype. Determine the probable genotype of the parent lines. Select various genotypes for crossing and complete a Punnett Square for each cross to predict the genotypic and phenotypic ratios in each case.

2. Collect a variety of flowers from ornamental and crop plants. Compare their reproductive structures. How does

pollination occur in each species? Identify the four major structures in each flower.

3. Hand pollinate a variety of plant species and observe the results. Keep careful records on your pollination procedures. What factors might explain unsuccessful fertilization?

4. With a dissecting needle remove some pollen grains from the anther of a flower. Put a few drops of water on a glass slide and carefully add the pollen. Use a microscope to examine the appearance of the pollen. (A drop of thionin stain may enhance the image.)

5. Compare the rate of growth and the germination percentage of pollen from various plant species. Examine the effects of environmental conditions on the rate of pollen tube growth.

Chapter 4

PLANT TISSUE TESTING

Green Leaves

AGRICULTURAL APPLICATIONS

Maintaining the nutrient levels of crops is a critical element in plant growth and management. Since crops remove nutrients from the soil or growing medium, fertilizers must be added to replenish diminished nutrient supplies in the soil. Traditionally, soil nutrient levels have been used as an estimate of nutrients available for use by plants, but scientists discovered many years ago that not all nutrients present in the soil are available for uptake and use by plants. Growers continually seek to maintain adequate nutrient levels for plant growth so that yield (crop, flower, foliage) can approach the plant's genetic potential.

Growers, as well as the public, have become increasingly concerned about the effects of an oversupply of nutrients in the soil; thus, nutrient management has now become even more of a challenge. Adequate nutrient supplies must be maintained, yet an oversupply of some nutrients may lead to harmful environmental effects. This problem is complicated by the lack of accurate methods for assessing nutrient availability to plants. In field crops, fertilizer recommendations are based upon expected yields, as well as an estimate of the soil's capacity to supply nutrients (based upon soil type, organic matter, etc.)

In addition to soil testing, two methods have been developed for determining the nutrient content of plant tissues. Total plant analysis involves precise analytical techniques performed on plant tissues in the laboratory. The plant material is air dried and ground. Spectrometry techniques are used to test for as many as 22 nutrient elements. Many soil testing labs offer plant analysis for a small fee. However, difficulty in

65

Figure 4-1. Avoiding under-fertilization or over-fertilization is a key management practice. (Courtesy, Agricultural Research Service, USDA)

establishing standards for interpreting results and the variation in results has limited the use of plant analysis by growers.

Plant tissue testing is another procedure which has been developed for estimating plant nutrition levels. Tissue testing is a fast procedure done in the field that yields results in only a few minutes. Tissue testing is also known as sap analysis, green tissue testing, or leaf analysis. Juices from plant tissues or bits of leaf petioles or midribs are tested for nitrogen, phosphorus, and potassium. Tissue tests for analysis of other nutrients have been developed but are not widely used. Plant tissue testing provides a general estimate of plant nutrient levels. Results are useful in diagnosing nutrient deficiency problems.

TERMS

active absorption	micronutrients	protoplasm
amino acid	nitrogen (N)	sap
enzyme	phosphorus (P)	senescence
law of limiting factors	potassium (K)	soil nutrients
macronutrients	protein	xylem

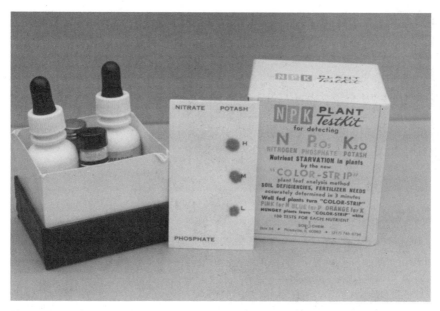

Figure 4-2. A simple tissue test can give a general indication of plant nutrition.

Researchers are now testing the accuracy of a new hand-held meter for determining the levels of chlorophyll in plant leaves. The results are then used to estimate levels of nitrogen available to the plant. This new device, developed by Minolta Camera Company, is being widely tested on both agronomic and horticultural crops. One disadvantage of the meter is that some plant varieties have their own characteristic greenness. Thus, the meter must be calibrated for that particular species and variety before readings

Figure 4-3. This new chlorophyll meter can be used to estimate the amount of soil nitrogen available to plants. (Courtesy, OACE, University of Illinois)

are taken. Up to 30 readings can be taken and stored in the meter, and an average reading can be calculated.

When used in combination with soil tests, plant tissue tests can yield reliable results and give growers useful information on plant nutrition. Fertilizers are one of the most critical and expensive inputs into any crop enterprise. The use of tissue testing and other procedures for monitoring plant nutrient levels greatly improves management of fertility levels while protecting the environment.

OBJECTIVES—QUESTIONS FOR INVESTIGATION

After completing the following laboratory exercises and studying this chapter, you should be able to answer the following questions:

1. How do plant nutrients vary by stage of plant growth? Why?
2. Why is sap from plant tissues a good indicator of nutrient availability?
3. Why should tissue tests be made at mid-day?
4. What parts of the plant should be tested? Why?
5. What factors affect nutrient levels contained in plant tissues?
6. Why are nitrogen, phosphorus, and potassium needed by plants?
7. Why does the addition of nitrogen enhance the green color of plant leaves?

LABORATORY INVESTIGATIONS

EXERCISE I.
N-P-K TISSUE TEST ON FIELD CROPS

Purpose

The purpose of this lab exercise is to determine the levels of nitrogen, phosphorus, and potassium contained in the tissues of selected field crop plants. A plant tissue testing kit will be used to approximate tissue nutrient levels.

Materials

- plant tissue samples from selected field crops (corn, alfalfa, soybeans, small grains)
- tissue testing kit (either the Urbana NPK Kit or the LaMotte Plant Tissue Test Kit for use on green plants)
- paper towels
- pliers

Procedures

Collect plant tissues to be tested. In general, the latest mature leaf should be used for tissue testing. Plant sap should be extracted from the petiole or midrib of these leaves. Plant tissue testing works well on forage crops. Tests can be made anytime after significant growth in the spring. Nutrient requirements are greatest during bloom and fruiting stages. Conduct plant tissue tests around mid-day.

Follow the procedures outlined in the plant tissue test kit instructions. Be sure your hands are clean before performing the test to avoid contaminating the results. Test 10 to 15 plants and average the results. Use only

Figure 4-4. Tissue testing can be done anytime after significant seedling growth. (Courtesy, Illinois Dept. of Agriculture)

Figure 4-5. Tissue testing can be used
on any type of plant,
including indoor plants,
field crops, and
vegetable crops.

freshly cut samples. Compare the results between plants growing in problem areas with those growing in desirable areas of the field.

Develop a data summary table for recording the results of each test. Include descriptive information on the crop, as well as date, sample number, and results. Use the interpretation guide supplied with the kit to estimate plant nutrient levels. Combine these tests with soil tests to determine if adjustments are needed in soil fertility or pH.

EXERCISE 2.
N-P-K TISSUE TEST ON GREENHOUSE/ POTTED PLANTS

Purpose

This lab exercise is designed to allow you to apply tissue testing procedures to greenhouse crops and potted plants. This includes field crops that are being experimentally grown in pots to allow better control of nutrient supplies and climatic conditions.

Materials

- tissue samples from container-grown plants to be tested (any greenhouse crop or plant, as well as field crops being grown in pots)
- tissue testing kit
- paper towels
- pliers

Procedures

Follow the same procedures as outlined in Exercise 1 above.

SCIENCE CONNECTIONS

BASES OF PLANT TISSUE TESTING

The availability of *soil nutrients* to plants and the uptake of nutrients by plants depends on many factors. Growers must use the best methods available to continually monitor the nutritional status of their crops and soils. *Tissue tests* give an important added dimension to soil test results, since they give a general indication of plant nutritional status. Just because

Figure 4-6. Tissue tests should be made in conjunction with soil tests to determine the plant's nutritional status.

a certain element is contained in the soil does not mean that it is taken in by the plant. Plant tissue tests are based on the assumption that the amount of an element present in plant tissues is a good indication of the supply of that nutrient in the plant and the soil. Results estimate the nutritional status of the plant at the time of testing.

Despite the benefits of green tissue testing, the test does have its limitations. Only water soluble forms of nitrogen (nitrate), phosphorus, and potassium are measured with this procedure. Thus, tissue tests packaged in kits measure only the nitrate form of nitrogen in the plant tissues. Soluble phosphorous represents about two-thirds of total phosphorus in young tissues and about 20% of total phosphorus in old tissues. Since all potassium is water soluble, these wet chemistry tests provide an estimate of all potassium contained in the plant tissues. Tissue test results vary considerably, which suggests that such tests should be used in combination with soil tests. Total plant analysis, which involves laboratory testing of air-dried whole plants, is used on a limited basis, again due to the variation in results and the difficulty in establishing standards for interpreting the results.

Tissue tests can be used to forecast plant nutritional problems. They can also help in assessing nutrient supplies in the soil and determining the effects of soil fertility programs. Tissue tests give a general indication of the relationship between plant nutrition and plant/crop growth.

Figure 4-7. Variation in plant growth and crop quality can be due to many factors.

Plant Tissues for Testing. The nutrient content of plant tissue has been found to vary widely, depending on the part of the plant used for the tests. Scientists have been working to develop guidelines for selecting plant tissues on various crops that will give the best indication of the actual supply of nutrients in the plant. In general, the *midrib* or *petiole* of the latest mature leaf is used for tissue testing; young leaves should be avoided. The greatest utilization of plant nutrients takes place in the upper part of the plant. Decreasing nitrogen supplies will first become apparent in these young tissues. In addition, *senescence* is associated with some nitrogen buildup as proteins break down. However, phosphorus and potassium deficiencies will first become apparent in the lower part of the plant.

Time of Testing. The nutritional needs of the plant are greatest at the flowering and fruit production stages. Thus, low nutrient readings are most likely to be found at this time. Medium to high tissue test results for nitrogen, phosphorus, and potassium at blooming time are considered adequate for most plants. Tissue tests should be made when plants are alive

Figure 4-8. Sap should be extracted from the midrib and/or petiole of mature leaves.

and growing; do not use frozen or harvested samples. The recommended time of day for tissue testing in mid-day. This is due primarily to the fluctuations in nitrogen supplies in plant tissues. During dark conditions, protein compounds break down to form soluble nitrogen compounds. This leads to an *accumulation* of nitrates during the night. In the presence of sunlight, nitrates are utilized during the synthesis of carbohydrates, amino acids, and finally proteins. Thus, tissue tests performed during mid or late afternoon will underestimate the actual supplies of nitrogen in the plant tissues.

Figure 4-9. Lower tissue test results can be expected when a crop or plant is in bloom, since nutritional needs are greatest at that time.

Environmental Conditions. Growing conditions can have a significant effect on the results of tissue tests. For example, poor soil aeration or drought conditions will underestimate the supply of nutrients in the soil, and thus the plant. Under these conditions, the plant's ability to absorb the nutrient solution in the soil is hampered. Also, higher temperatures and sunlight conditions increase plant metabolism, affecting the rate at which nutrients are taken in and utilized by plants. In addition, observe the general condition and vigor of plants and any unusual growing conditions when using tissue testing. Due the variability in tissue test results, multiple tests should be made on plants in the same field or growing area. An average of these individual tests should then be used to make nutrient management decisions.

PLANT NUTRITION

Essential Elements. An element is considered *essential* if it meets the following criteria: (1) absence of the element results in abnormal growth, injury, or death; (2) the plant is unable to complete its life cycle without the element; (3) the element is required for plants in general; and (4) no other element can serve as a complete substitute. Of the 16 elements which have been identified as essential, *nitrogen (N)*, *phosphorus (P)*, and *potassium (K)* are the most important. Large amounts of these elements must be supplied to the plant for optimum growth. The *critical nutrient concentration* is the point at which the concentration of the nutrient moves from a deficient level to an adequate level. An oversupply of nutrients can potentially have a toxic effect on plants. Those elements required in relatively large supply by plants are called *macronutrients*, while trace or *micronutrients* are required in smaller amounts.

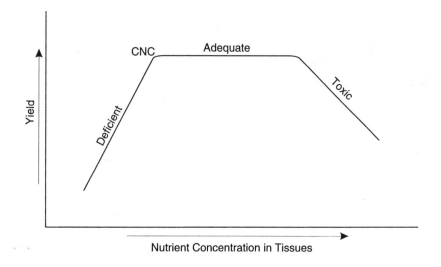

Figure 4-10. Relationship between yield and nutrient concentration in plant
tissue.

In general, an increase in the supply of essential elements is associated with an increase in growth or yield. However, plant growth is dictated by the element which has the most insufficient concentration. This *law of limiting factors* says that if the supply of all essential elements is sufficient except one, growth and yield of the plant is limited to the extent that this essential element is lacking. This principle has significant implications for tissue testing and soil fertility analysis. For example, if tissue tests on plants with yellow leaves show high concentrations of nitrogen, phosphorus, and potassium, this does not necessarily mean that the supply of these elements is sufficient. Sulfur may be the limiting factor. Once sulfur concentrations are brought to adequate levels, tissue tests may show deficient amounts of nitrogen, phosphorus, or potassium. *Luxury consumption* is the continuing accumulation of nutrients in the plant without corresponding gains in growth or yield.

Nitrogen. Nitrogen is absorbed by plants in the form of *nitrate* (NO_3^-) and *ammonium* (NH_4^+) ions. Nitrogen is a component of *chlorophyll*, with four nitrogen atoms contained in each chlorophyll molecule. Thus, the addition of nitrogen fertilizer is associated with a rapid greening effect on plant tissues. Unlike phosphorus and potassium, nitrogen is readily leached from the soil. Nitrogen also plays a critical role in photosynthesis, due to the action of chlorophyll in this process. Nitrogen is a component of *amino acids*—the building blocks of *proteins*—including *enzymes*.

Adequate supplies of plant nitrogen stimulate utilization of *carbohydrates* during protein synthesis. Inadequate nitrogen concentrations lead to the buildup of carbohydrates. This causes cell walls to thicken and growth to be stunted. Too much nitrogen creates an overly succulent plant with weak fibers. This can cause a delay in flowering. Excessive succulence is due to higher carbohydrate utilization and the formation of more *protoplasm*. Since protoplasm combines with water, a more succulent plant results.

Phosphorus. All cells contain special proteins called *nucleoproteins*. Phosphorus is an important component of these cell proteins. Nucleoproteins are in the *chromosomes* of cells. Thus, phosphorus has a direct effect on cell division and the transmission of heredity characteristics. Large amounts of phosphorus are found in seeds; it is essential for seed formation.

Phosphorus is contained in cell membranes, and thus affects the flow and retention of substances in and out of cells. Phosphorus is necessary for the release of energy from sugar molecules. Plant energy created through photosynthesis and the breakdown of carbohydrates is stored in phosphate compounds. Phosphorus is also necessary for the breaking of *high-energy bonds* in plant cells, releasing the energy required for nearly all biological processes in plants.

Potassium. Plant requirements for potassium are relatively high. If a shortage in potassium occurs, potassium is moved to the younger plant tissues, making deficiency symptoms more apparent in the lower leaves.

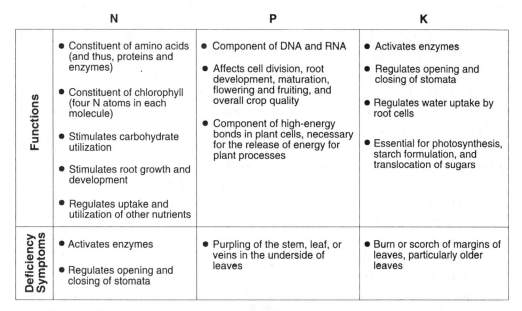

	N	P	K
Functions	• Constituent of amino acids (and thus, proteins and enzymes) • Constituent of chlorophyll (four N atoms in each molecule) • Stimulates carbohydrate utilization • Stimulates root growth and development • Regulates uptake and utilization of other nutrients	• Component of DNA and RNA • Affects cell division, root development, maturation, flowering and fruiting, and overall crop quality • Component of high-energy bonds in plant cells, necessary for the release of energy for plant processes	• Activates enzymes • Regulates opening and closing of stomata • Regulates water uptake by root cells • Essential for photosynthesis, starch formulation, and translocation of sugars
Deficiency Symptoms	• Activates enzymes • Regulates opening and closing of stomata	• Purpling of the stem, leaf, or veins in the underside of leaves	• Burn or scorch of margins of leaves, particularly older leaves

Figure 4-11. Functions and deficiency symptoms of the primary macronutrients.

Enzyme activation is regarded as potassium's most important function in plants. (Over 60 enzymes require potassium for activation.) These enzymes regulate photosynthesis, respiration, translocation, and carbohydrate metabolism.

As the most abundant *cation* in plants, potassium plays an important role in drawing water into plant roots. Plants that are deficient in potassium are more susceptible to drought due to their inability to draw in water that is available. Potassium also plays a direct role in *transpiration* and photosynthesis by regulating stomatal opening. During transpiration, *stomata* open when the *turgor pressure* of surrounding guard cells increases. During photosynthesis, stomatal opening allows for the inward movement of necessary carbon dioxide (CO_2). In general, when potassium concentrations are increased, the net effect is a decrease in transpiration and an increase in photosynthesis.

Potassium has also been found to enhance *nitrogen uptake* and protein synthesis in plants. Furthermore, the synthesis of high-energy bonds in plant cells requires potassium. Grain filling in corn, soybeans, and small grain crops is significantly affected by potassium because the presence of potassium activates the enzyme which converts sugars into starch. Finally, potassium has been shown to have a positive effect on *nitrogen fixation* in legumes.

UPTAKE AND TRANSPORT OF NUTRIENTS

Most of the soil water taken up by plants is lost through transpiration. This water loss creates an upward suction in plant tissues, drawing in additional water from the soil. Mineral elements are contained in the soil solution and their availability depends upon their chemical composition. Of the four major processes by which plants draw nutrients from the soil, *active absorption* is the only biological process. In this process, minerals are actively transported across cell membranes. Only respiring cells are capable of accumulating minerals in the form of ions through the active absorption process.

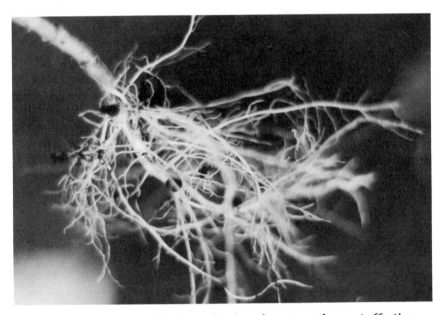

Figure 4-12. Root hairs located near the tips of roots are the most effective sites for water and mineral absorption.

The most active site for absorption of soil minerals is about ⅛ inch from root tips. Water absorption occurs about ½ inch from root tips. *Root hairs* greatly increase the absorbent surface area of roots. Root hairs are most numerous near the tips of roots. As roots mature, they lose their absorptive ability, so continual root growth is important.

Water and minerals absorbed from the soil by the roots move upward through the plant in the woody portion of the stem called the *xylem*. The xylem actually consists of dead cells that form the rigid, internal pipework of the transport system of the plant. The *negative hydraulic pressure* created

Figure 4-13. A tissue test card after testing a tomato leaf.

by water evaporation in the leaves pulls water into the roots and upward through the xylem. The *sap* of a plant consists of all plant fluids which are contained in the plant's vascular system (xylem and phloem). When conducting plant tissue tests, water and mineral salts contained in the xylem, as well as manufactured nutrients carried in the phloem, are extracted for analysis.

SUMMARY

Plant nutrition is of primary concern to growers regardless of the crop or species being cultivated. Scientists continue to seek more accurate, affordable methods of determining plant nutritional status. Soil tests are commonly used to estimate soil fertility, but they may not reflect the actual nutrient concentrations in plant tissues. Nutrients contained in plant tissues should be a better indicator of available nutrients and thus, crop growth/yield.

A number of plant tissue analysis procedures have been developed. These include whole plant analysis, sap analysis, and more recently, use of hand-held instruments for measuring leaf chlorophyll. Analysis of green plant tissues, often called sap analysis, continues to be a useful, inexpensive method of estimating plant nutritional status. This procedure involves extracting sap from leaf petioles or midribs and treating it with reagents. These wet chemistry techniques estimate the concentration of soluble forms of macro and micronutrients in the plant tissues. When used in conjunction with soil tests, plant tissue tests can be very useful in diagnosing nutritional problems and managing plant nutrition.

FURTHER LABORATORY INVESTIGATIONS

1. Apply plant tissue testing procedures to a variety of vegetable crops. Compare your results with results from soil tests.

2. Use the tissue testing kit to compare the concentration of nitrogen, potassium, and phosphorus in various parts of selected plants. Test young leaves, old leaves, recently matured leaves, upper stems, lower stems, and sections of leaves not containing the midrib. How do the results compare? What hypotheses can you list that might explain the difference in test results?

3. Use the tissue test kit to compare the nutrient concentrations in plants of the same species but at varying stages of growth. Does the concentration of nutrients in various plant parts also depend upon stage of growth?

4. Perform several tissue tests at different times of the day and under different environmental conditions. What effect does time of day, temperature, and other factors have on your results?

5. Compare the results of tissue tests after the addition of fertilizers and soil amendments. Check plant tissues at 10-day intervals following the fertilizer applications. Use a hydroponic unit to create specific nutrient deficiencies and verify nutrient concentrations with plant tissue tests.

Chapter 5

RHIZOBIUM

Dining In

AGRICULTURAL APPLICATIONS

The application of synthetic nitrogen fertilizers is one of the most expensive inputs for the production of crops. All growing plants, including cereal grains, forages, turf grasses, vegetables, woody plants, and flowers need relative large amounts of nitrogen. Nitrogen is readily accumulated by plant roots, but this uptake by plants substantially reduces the supplies of nitrogen in the soil. Even the richest soils in the crop-producing states

Figure 5-1. All plants need relatively large amounts of nitrogen for healthy growth.

Figure 5-2. Erosion and tillage lead to reduced organic matter and soil
          fertility.

of the Midwest have lost as much as 40% of their original nitrogen and
organic matter. These losses have been the result of erosion and increased
oxidation of organic matter due to tillage and drainage systems. Harvested
crops remove more nitrogen than any other nutrient from the soil. Deni-
trification and leaching also contribute to nitrogen loss from the soil.

A number of free-living, as well as symbiotic, bacteria have developed
the ability to convert (fix) atmospheric nitrogen into a form that is more
useable by plants. Only plants associated with these bacteria are able to fix
atmospheric nitrogen. The most important of these plant-bacterium relationships in agriculture involves the bacterium *Rhizobium*. This bacterium
invades the root system of legumes, which include species in the pea, bean,
and clover plant family. The presence of rhizobia enables these leguminous

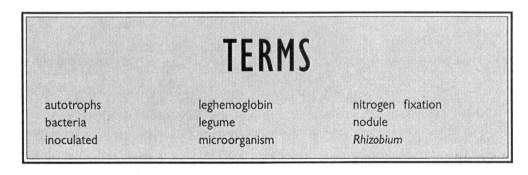

TERMS

autotrophs	leghemoglobin	nitrogen fixation
bacteria	legume	nodule
inoculated	microorganism	*Rhizobium*

Figure 5-3. Legume species, such as alfalfa, are able to manufacture their own nitrogen.

plants to manufacture their own supplies of nitrogen. Legume seeds are usually inoculated with rhizobia at planting time to ensure adequate populations of these bacteria in the soil.

The economic benefits of nitrogen fixation by leguminous plants are very important. A study in Illinois found that the average amount of nitrogen removed in harvested grain was 148 pounds per acre for soybeans and 96 pounds per acre for corn. However, well nodulated soybeans have been shown to account for 63% of the nitrogen removed in harvested grain. There are several strains of *Rhizobium*, and each is effective only on certain species of legume plants. Thus, growers must be certain to select the appropriate *Rhizobium* strain when inoculating seed. Some legumes, such as soybeans, have not been found to respond significantly to bacterial inoculation. By understanding the action of rhizobia in legume plants, growers can reduce their supplemental applications of nitrogen, thereby reducing their production costs and better safeguarding the environment.

OBJECTIVES—QUESTIONS FOR INVESTIGATION

After completing the following laboratory investigations and studying this chapter, you should be able to answer the following questions:

1. Why is the need for supplemental nitrogen reduced or eliminated in legume plants?

2. Why is legume seed inoculated?

3. Why are only legumes affected by bacterial inoculations? Why don't all legumes respond to inoculation?

4. What is a symbiotic relationship?

5. How do bacteria in the soil improve the nitrogen supply to legumes?

LABORATORY INVESTIGATIONS

EXPERIMENT I.
ROOT NODULE VARIATION

Purpose

The purpose of this lab is to demonstrate the presence of nitrogen-fixing bacteria on legume roots and compare the root nodules of various legumes. Given this purpose, what are your hypotheses for this experiment?

Materials

- multiple samples of various cultivated legumes with roots (alfalfa, soybeans, red clover, peas, peanuts, snap beans, etc.)

- samples of uncultivated (wild) legumes with roots (vetch, sweet clover, etc.)

- single-edged safety razor

Procedures

Collect the legume samples as indicated in the materials list. Plants must be actively growing. Samples from deep-rooting crops, like alfalfa, must be taken when the soil is wet, otherwise root nodules may be dislodged when removing the plant from the soil.

Soil must be washed from the roots in order to study the root system and examine the nodules. Carefully rinsing the roots with water or spraying with a fine mist should loosen loamy or sandy soils from the root system

The Wolf River apple variety from Wisconsin is one of the largest varieties maintained at the New York germplasm collection unit. (Courtesy, Agricultural Research Service, USDA)

Monitoring the nutritional status and mineral absorption of pregnant cows can help to predict the performance of young calves. (Courtesy, Agricultural Research Service, USDA)

These corn plants are growing in an aeroponic chamber, where nutrient needs of the plants are provided by a mist. (Courtesy, Agricultural Research Service, USDA)

Development of additional biological control measures is a top agenda for agricultural researchers. (Courtesy, Agricultural Research Service, USDA)

Many variables important to the agricultural industry can be investigated in the school agriscience laboratory. (Courtesy, National FFA Organization)

Special environmental controls can be created to allow scientists to study plant responses to certain conditions, such as drought. (Courtesy, Agricultural Research Service, USDA)

Animal scientists are developing a standardized animal identification system that would allow an animal to be tracked anywhere from the processor back to the producer. This cow's yellow ear tag contains a miniature electronic identification device. (Courtesy, David Riecks, University of Illinois)

Computers are used in many important ways in agricultural research, such as tracking and predicting fire blight infections in pears. (Courtesy, Agricultural Research Service, USDA)

Development of new, ultra-low-volume herbicide application methods may significantly reduce the levels of herbicide use. (Courtesy, Agricultural Research Service, USDA)

Scientists are working to develop tougher-skinned potatoes that store better. Tissue culture techniques were used to grow these potatoes. (Courtesy, Agricultural Research Service, USDA)

Seed from many plant species is produced and preserved in special collections to ensure genetic diversity in future years. (Courtesy, Agricultural Research Service, USDA)

Agricultural scientists use both laboratory and field research techniques to conduct their investigations. (Courtesy, National FFA Organization)

A research technician checks the progress of tiny peach and apple trees being grown from cells which have received new genes. (Courtesy, Agricultural Research Service, USDA)

Virus-resistant plants have been created using antisense technology, a form of genetic engineering in which cells are made to do the opposite of their genetic instructions. (Courtesy, Agricultural Research Service, USDA)

DNA strands extracted from blueberry leaves are used in gene mapping research. (Courtesy, Agricultural Research Service, USDA)

Nutrition, immunity, environment, and many other factors affect the health and performance of young animals. (Courtesy, Jimmy Clark, University of Illinois)

Soybean roots are evaluated for resistance to soybean cyst nematode. (Courtesy, Agricultural Research Service, USDA)

Samples from floral crops are screened for new viruses. (Courtesy, Agricultural Research Service, USDA)

Due to the many advances in technology that have been developed through agricultural research, animal management today is much different than even 10 years ago. (Courtesy, Agricultural Research Service, USDA)

In this laboratory the connections between parasite infections, fluctuating hormone levels, and white blood cell action are being investigated. (Courtesy, Agricultural Research Service, USDA)

Numerous steps are involved in developing safer, more effective vaccines for controlling animal diseases. This microbiologist is working on a new cattle vaccine. (Courtesy, Agricultural Research Service, USDA)

Leaf tissue from blueberry plants is collected for DNA analysis and gene mapping. (Courtesy, Agricultural Research Service, USDA)

These cultured cells have been infected with a bovine rhinotracheitis virus, which is being tested as an experimental vaccine. (Courtesy, Agricultural Research Service, USDA)

Scientists check the response of this parasite-infected calf to growth-regulating hormones. (Courtesy, Agricultural Research Service, USDA)

without damaging the nodules. However, heavy clay soils are much more difficult to remove from plant roots and intense washing may damage the root structures. Clay soils usually contain calcium carbonate, or lime. When acid is added to lime, the resulting chemical reaction produces carbon dioxide (CO_2), which helps to break up the soil and make it easier to wash from the roots. Let the plant roots with soil intact stand in a 10% acetic acid solution for about 20 minutes. Remove and wash away remaining soil with water. Less soaking time will be required for nonclay soils.

After removing soil from the roots of collected plant samples, compare the root nodules on the plant specimens. Observe size, shape, and number. Record your observations by sample number and plant species. Also note the stage of growth and other growing conditions of the samples in your data chart. Compare the root nodules on multiple plants of the same species as well as different legume species. Compare the root nodules on legume samples that were growing wild versus those that were collected from a cultivated crop.

Using a safety razor, slice open the nodules on several legume roots. Compare nodules from the various legume specimens collected. Inefficient strains of rhizobia produce nodules that are relatively small, widely dispersed, and green, white, or brown on the inside. Efficient strains of rhizobia produce nodules that are relatively large and pink or red on the inside.

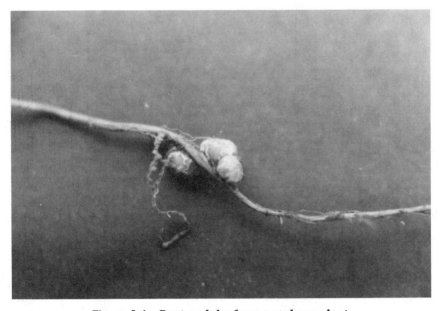

Figure 5-4. Root nodules from a soybean plant.

EXPERIMENT 2.
THE EFFECTS OF INOCULATION AND
FERTILIZATION ON NODULE DEVELOPMENT

Purpose

The purpose of this experiment is to examine the effects of added cultures of *Rhizobium* on nodule development of legume root systems. The effects of supplemental nitrogen will also be observed. Write down your hypotheses for this experiment before proceeding.

Materials

- 80 soybean seeds, 120 red clover seeds
- sterile soil
- inoculum (clover seeds may be preinoculated)
- twelve 6-inch pots
- liquid fertilizer (20-20-20)
- growing medium
- balance (optional)

Procedures

Fill pots with growing medium. Separate the soybean seeds into two equal lots and inoculate one lot (40 seeds) with the appropriate inoculum. Inoculate all red clover seeds if not preinoculated. (Other legumes may be substituted for red clover.) In four of the pots, plant 10 of the inoculated soybeans seeds in each pot. Plant the other 40 soybean seeds in the same manner. Plant 30 red clover seeds in each of the remaining four pots. Label the pots according to the treatment condition.

Add water as necessary to keep soil moist. For best results, plants should be grown in a greenhouse; however, natural growing conditions may be used, as long as all pots are exposed to the exact same germination and growing conditions. On day 21 add fertilizer to two of the red clover samples, one pot with inoculated soybean seed, and one pot with uninoculated soybean seed. Label pots accordingly. Be sure to prepare the fertilizer solution according to the manufacturer's directions and add the same amount of the fertilizer solution to each of the two pots.

Provide adequate sunlight for seedling growth after germination. Record the average plant height in each pot on days 28, 35, and 42. On day 42 record your observations about the general growth and appearance of the plants in each pot. Randomly select five plants from each pot and gently remove them with roots intact. Rinse the soil from the roots and examine them for nodules. Count the number of nodules on each plant and calculate the average number of nodules per plant in each treatment. Record your findings. Compare the size of nodules from plants in each treatment and record. Nodules may be removed and weighed. Examine your data. What conclusions do you draw? Were your hypotheses verified or rejected?

Data Summary Table

| | Soybeans | | | | Red Clover | |
| | Inoculated | | Not inoculated | | Inoculated | |
	with fertilizer	no fertilizer	with fertilizer	no fertilizer	with fertilizer	no fertilizer
average height (cm) day 28						
average height (cm) day 35						
average height (cm) day 42						
general appearance day 42						
average no. of nodules/plant day 42						
relative size of nodules day 42						

Figure 5-5. Sample data summary table for experiment 2.

SCIENCE CONNECTIONS

RHIZOBIUM

Soils naturally contain millions of *microorganisms*. As one type of microorganism, *bacteria* are simple, one-celled organisms that are the most abundant inhabitants of the soil. While most bacteria break down organic matter in the soil, some important bacteria, known as *autotrophs*, actually produce food for plants. *Rhizobium* is a rod-shaped species of aerobic, soil-inhabiting bacteria that has the unique capability of converting atmospheric nitrogen into a form that is useable by plants. Rhizobia form a *symbiotic* relationship with their host plant. Symbiosis occurs when two dissimilar organisms live together in a condition of mutual benefit. Rhizobia get their energy from the oxidation of mineral constituents, as well as from carbohydrates supplied by their host plant. In return, rhizobia supply their host *legume* plant with the nitrogen it needs for normal growth.

Rhizobia populations are influenced by the stage of plant growth and the moisture, oxygen, aeration, temperature, and pH of the soil. Up to a certain point, each of these factors positively affects the growth of rhizobia. Thus, many environmental conditions, as well as soil conditions, affect rhizobia populations. Soil acidity has been shown to be a major factor in the growth of rhizobia; however, the strains vary in their sensitivity to acid soils. For example, *R. meliloti*, the strain that invades alfalfa roots, is more sensitive than other strains to soil pH levels below 6.0. In general, soil pH should be maintained between 6.0 and 8.0 to support the greatest rhizobia populations.

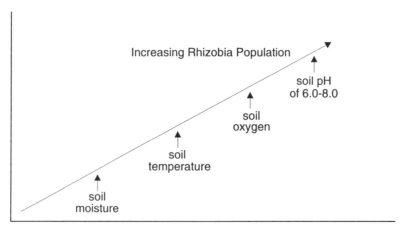

Figure 5-6. Factors that have a positive effect on rhizobia populations in the soil.

Legumes can meet their nitrogen needs from the soil if their roots have the appropriate strain of *Rhizobium* and growing conditions are favorable. *Rhizobium* bacteria are selective in the legume species that they infect. There are seven general legume groups, each affected by a different strain of the *Rhizobium* bacteria. These groups include (1) alfalfa and sweet clover,

(2) true clovers (red, ladino, white, alsike, etc.), (3) peas and vetch, (4) beans (garden, pinto, etc.), (5) cowpeas and lespedeza, (6) soybeans, and (7) lupines. In addition, some individual strains are specific to birdsfoot trefoil, crownvetch, or sainfoin.

Legume seeds are *inoculated* with rhizobia in order to increase the population of these bacteria in the soil. In general, the greater the rhizobia population, the greater the amount of nitrogen it will provide for its host plant. *Rhizobium inoculum* is sold in small packets containing a peat

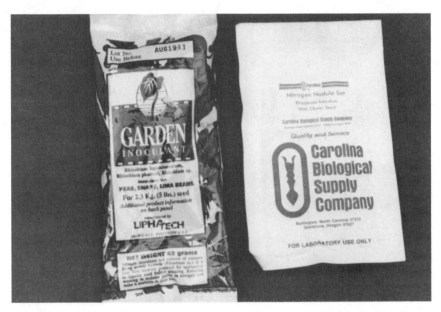

Figure 5-7. Although many legume crop seeds are pre-inoculated, rhizobium inoculum can be purchased in packets to allow growers to inoculate their seed.

moss/bacteria mixture. The contents of the packet are simply mixed with the designated amount of seed, and the inoculum sticks to the surface of each seed. Today, most forage legume seeds are preinoculated. Seed inoculant commonly contains about 100 million bacterial cells per gram of inoculant! Inoculum has a definite "shelf life," usually about six months. Without the energy sources of the host plant, the bacteria cannot survive. Unused inoculum should be refrigerated to keep bacteria viable. Most legume seeds are inoculated at planting time to ensure adequate rhizobia populations in the soil.

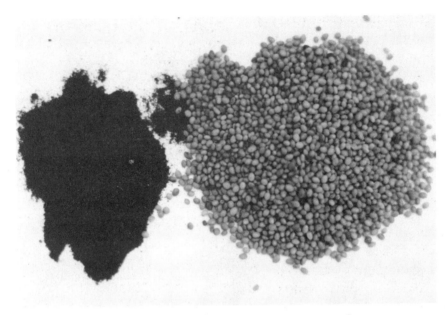

Figure 5-8. Red clover seed and rhizobium inoculant.

NODULATION

Since a large number of bacteria are present in the soil, how are rhizobia able to select the plant species which they will infect? The answer lies in the composition of cell surfaces on both the bacteria and the root hairs of plants. The arrangement of *sugar molecules* on cell surfaces allows the bacteria and the plant cells to recognize one another. Plant roots secrete a protein (*lectin*) that binds with a particular type of sugar molecule.

After the bacterium binds with the *root hair*, it stimulates the cell wall of the root hair to grow inward to form a small tube. This enables the bacterium to penetrate the root hair. The bacterium grows in the tube, which continues to penetrate cell layers in the root hair. Once the tube containing the bacteria enters the *cortex* of the root, plant cell division is stimulated and a *nodule* or small lump develops on the root surface. The rhizobia are contained inside these nodules.

As indicated earlier, rhizobia populations are affected by soil temperature. Nodules are not present on the roots of legumes during the winter months. Research has also shown that nodules slough off immediately after crop harvest and then begin to return several days after cutting. The presence of nodules does not guarantee that adequate nitrogen is being supplied to the host plant. Mature nodules tend to be relatively large, concentrated on the primary roots, and have pink or red centers. Ineffective nodules are more numerous, scattered throughout the root system, and are white, pale green, or brown in the center.

NITROGEN FIXATION

The biochemical process of converting atmospheric nitrogen (N_2) to a form that can be used by plants (nitrate, NO_3–) is called *nitrogen fixation*. A compound is referred to as "fixed" when it resists decomposition. Several groups of bacteria are important in the nitrogen fixing process, but rhizobia perform the critical first step. These bacterial cells in the center portion of the nodules on legume roots synthesize a pink substance called *leghemoglobin*. Only those nodules that contain active rhizobia will display this color.

Figure 5-9. A soybean plant with intact root system and nodules.

Leghemoglobin plays a critical role in the nitrogen conversion process within the nodules. In order for nitrogen fixation to occur, the rhizobia bacteria must exist in an near oxygen-free environment. This is accomplished by the nodule which encases the bacteria, as well as the leghemoglobin which binds to oxygen molecules that might penetrate the cortex. With the oxygen molecules "tied up," the enzyme *nitrogenase* is able to produce nitrate, which is readily used by plants.

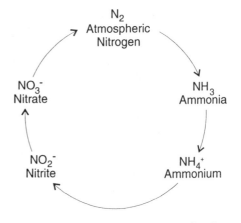

Figure 5-10. Biological nitrogen fixation in plants.

Figure 5-11. Alfalfa and clovers are the best nitrogen fixers.

The amount of nitrogen fixed by rhizobia differs according to the particular *Rhizobium* strain, the host plant, and environmental conditions. Nitrogen fixation is greatest in alfalfa and clovers, with typical rates of over 150 pounds per acre per year produced in some species. Legumes as a whole produce an average of 100 pounds of nitrogen per acre per year.

Figure 5-12. As soil nitrogen increases, nitrogen fixation by legumes decreases.

There is an inverse relationship between available soil nitrogen and legume fixation of nitrogen; thus, supplemental nitrogen is not recommended for legume crops in most cases. However, until young seedlings get established, during cold spring weather, and for rapid recovery after cuttings supplemental nitrogen is sometimes used. One theory suggests that the production of lectin is reduced as available soil nitrogen increases, thus preventing rhizobia from binding to the root hairs.

High supplies of potassium have been shown to have a beneficial effect on nodule formation and nitrogen fixation rate. Potassium enhances the transport of carbohydrates to the nodules, providing energy for the bacteria

Figure 5-13. Supplemental nitrogen is sometimes added to legume crops, helping plants quickly recover after cuttings.

to do their work. Some transfer of nitrogen from the roots of legumes to companion crops apparently occurs. Crop yields from nonlegume plants are often increased when they are grown in combination with legumes. Nitrogen is released from the roots and nodules of legumes when these plants are harvested, killed, or rotated into other crops.

SUMMARY

Maintenance of essential plant nutrients is a critical factor in plant growth and reproduction. Legumes have the unique capacity to meet some of their own nitrogen needs by converting atmospheric nitrogen into a form useable by the plant. This nitrogen fixation by legumes significantly contributes to the total nitrogen supplies in the soil. In fact, in most cases legume plants are able to fix enough nitrogen to meet their needs without the use of supplemental nitrogen.

The action of *Rhizobium* bacteria is integral to the nitrogen fixation process in legume plants. These bacteria are naturally present in soils, although legume seeds are usually inoculated with these bacteria prior to planting to ensure strong soil populations. A number of factors affect the presence of rhizobia in the soil, including soil temperature and pH. These bacteria attach to root hairs, resulting in the formation of small bumps on the roots called nodules. Inside these nodules the rhizobia lead a biochemical process which reduces free nitrogen into ammonia, and eventually into nitrate. In this symbiotic relationship between the bacteria and the host plant, the plant supplies energy in the form of carbohydrates to the bacteria and the bacteria supply the plant with an essential life nutrient.

FURTHER LABORATORY INVESTIGATIONS

1. Replicate the experiments presented earlier in this chapter using a variety of crop species. Include vegetable crops as well as other field crops. Observe and compare the nodule development on these various legumes.

2. Examine the effects of various concentrations of fertilizer on the rate of nodule development. Use greenhouse tests to examine the effects of nutrient supplied (nitrogen, phosphorus, and/or potassium) as well as the amount and concentration of supplemental nutrients.

3. Test the effects of different strains of *Rhizobium* on selected legumes. Include treatments for soil temperature, moisture, and pH.

4. Examine nodule formation at different stages of plant growth (seedling, blooming, fruiting, mature).

5. Examine live inoculum under a microscope. Culture rhizobia bacteria on nutrient agar (keep at room temperature). Compare your results with live cultures available from biological supply companies.

Chapter 6

GERMINATION

Power Surges

AGRICULTURAL APPLICATIONS

Seed germination is one of the most basic and important life processes in plants. Plant reproduction through seed germination (sexual propagation) is the primary means of crop production in field conditions. In horticultural settings, vegetative propagation (asexual reproduction) is also used for producing new plants. Reproducing plants for ornamental and food uses requires high-quality seed to ensure future generations of cultivated plants. Thus, germination is a critical process for both plant reproduction and production of seed stock for subsequent planting.

Seed production and testing is big business, with most states having seed certification programs. Government standards must be followed when producing seed for field crops (see Figure 6-18). However, the genetic purity of flower and vegetable seeds is largely regulated by seed companies. Seed is one of the major cost inputs of crop production in both crop and horticultural settings. Seed dormancy is a concern for seed producers and growers. Seeds of some species require special treatments before they will germinate.

Seed companies test seed for viability and vigor using a variety of germination tests. The standard test for seed viability is the warm germination test, although other seed viability tests are sometimes used. These include (1) the cut test, where the seed is cut in half to determine if an embryo is present; (2) the float test, in which seeds with no embryo usually float to the water's surface; (3) the TZ test, which detects living tissue in the seed; and (4) the excised embryo test, where embryos are removed from seeds and germinated on moist paper in a covered dish. The type of seed determines which of these additional seed viability tests will be performed.

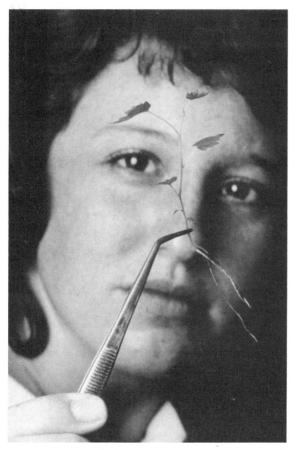

Figure 6-1. Successful seed germination is a critical stage of plant growth and reproduction. (Courtesy, Agricultural Research Service, USDA)

TERMS

aleurone layer	gibberellin	protease
amylase	hydration	protein
caryopsis	hypocotyl	radicle
coleoptile	imbibition	salt
coleorhiza	ion	scutellum
cotyledons	leaching	seed
dicot	legume	seed coat
dormancy	metabolic activity	seed embryo
endosperm	micropyle	seed viability
enzyme	monocot	shoot
epicotyl	osmotic flow	turgor
evaporation	ovule	TZ test
formazan	permeability	warm germination test
germination	phytochrome	

Figure 6-2. Seed companies contribute greatly to the development and production of new plant varieties.

Figure 6-3. A variety of laboratory seed germination tests are used to predict performance in the field or greenhouse.

Tests for seed vigor usually involve exposing a planted sample of the seed to cold temperatures (approximately 50°F [10°C]) for one week, followed by sevenday germination at 77°F (see Figure 6-18).

Seed storage is another important factor in providing high-quality seed for growers. In some plants, particularly certain tree species, embryos are shortlived (sometimes only a few days). Embryo viability is in large part a function of seed storage conditions. In general, seed stored at cooler temperatures (approximately 40°F) and low relative humidity (approximately 15%) tend to remain viable longer.

Along with seed viability, environmental conditions dictate germination percentages. Seeds from some species require just the right mix of moisture, temperature, oxygen, and light before germination will occur; other species readily germinate under a range of environmental conditions. Greenhouses allow for almost total control of growing conditions, thereby ensuring a good crop. Planting depth and seedbed preparation are major considerations. For example, soybeans should be planted 1½ to 2 inches deep. Deeper planting often results in lower emergence and poorer stands. A similar range is best for corn, with shallower planting depths used in early spring and up to an inch deeper planting in late spring. Smaller seeds should be planted closer to the soil surface. Soybean varieties are sometimes assigned an emergence score, indicating the ability of the seedling hypocotyl to

Figure 6-4. Seed size, which varies greatly, primarily determines planting
depth. Larger seeds have more food reserves and can push
through the soil farther and longer than smaller seeds.

elongate sufficiently when planting is deeper than recommended. A score of one on the fivepoint scale indicates very good likelihood of emergence.

Crusting over of the soil surface is sometimes a serious problem in the germination of various crops. To counter this problem, bedding plant seeds should be covered with sand or vermiculite after planting. USDA researchers have developed a technique for treating rice seed with gibberellic acid that elongates emerging plant parts and gives them the extra power needed to break through dry soil layers. This technique has resulted in up to a 30% increase in germination of semidwarf, dryplanted rice varieties.

For crops grown outdoors, time of planting is another critical factor in obtaining a good germination percentage. Plants are generally grouped into cool season crops that germinate at 32°F to 50°F, and warm season crops that germinate at 59°F to 79°F.

Salt buildup in irrigated soils can become a serious problem under both field and greenhouse conditions. In fact, salinity is estimated to be a problem in as much as 30% of all irrigated land in the United States, especially in the Southwest. Salt buildup in soils is also a concern in other areas of the world, including India and South America. A newly developed battery-operated measuring device can accurately measure salinity levels in the field in 60 seconds whereas previous tests took about 12 hours.

Dissolved salts accumulate in soils from irrigation water and fertilizer. Adequate drainage and sufficient watering to leach salts from the root zone and soil surface are the strategies being used by growers to decrease soil salinity. In addition, plant breed-

Figure 6-5. Many factors affect seed germination. The viability of this two-year-old seed was extremely low (only 20% germination).

Figure 6-6. Saline soils, like in this California field, reduce germination and plant health. Plant breeders are working to develop salt-resistant varieties. (Courtesy, Agricultural Research Service, USDA)

ers are working to develop salt-tolerant crop varieties. Scientists have discovered a wild tomato variety that is naturally resistant to saline soils. Using conventional plant breeding techniques, new varieties have been developed that show up to a 25% increase in salt tolerance. Because salt tolerance is a complex characteristic, genetic engineering techniques have not yet provided any answers to the salinity problem.

Of course seed is also important as a food product, and seed components are used in a variety of nonfood consumer products as well. Common products include starches and glutens from grains, and proteins and oils from soybeans, corn, cotton, sunflower, and peanut seeds. Drugs, enzymes, vitamins, spices, and condiments are obtained from embryos, endosperms, and entire seeds.

OBJECTIVES—QUESTIONS FOR INVESTIGATION

After completing the following laboratory investigations and studying this chapter, you should be able to answer the following questions:

1. How does seed germination occur?

2. Why are moisture, appropriate temperature, oxygen, and sometimes light essential for germination?

Figure 6-7. **Seed itself is the source of many important food and non-food consumer products. (Courtesy, Illinois Dept. of Agriculture)**

3. How do planting depth, time of planting, and soil conditions affect germination?

4. Why does cracked or damaged seed have lower germination rates?

5. Why do some seeds need light for germination?

6. What causes excessive buildup of soluble salts in soils?

7. What are the effects of excessive salt concentrations in soils on seed germination and seedling growth?

8. Why is a smooth seedbed necessary for the successful germination of most crop seeds?

LABORATORY INVESTIGATIONS

EXPERIMENT I.
WARM GERMINATION TEST

Purpose

The purpose of this experiment is to determine the viability of various seed samples using the standard warm germination test.

Materials

- paper towels
- resealable plastic bags (gallon size)
- 100 seeds of each sample to be tested (use a variety of field crop and vegetable seeds)
- water
- rubber bands

Procedures

Place two layers of moistened paper towels on a table and evenly space 25 seeds from a sample to be tested on top of the towels. Cover the seeds with another double layer of moistened paper towels. Fold over each edge of the towels about one inch. Roll the towels and enclosed seeds into a tube. Make four of these "rag dolls" for each type of seed to be tested. Thus, you will expose 100 seeds of each species to the warm germination test.

Place a rubber band around the top and bottom of each rag doll. Insert the rag dolls into the plastic bags, and seal to prevent moisture loss. Label

Figure 6-8. A simple warm germination test using rag dolls can be used to test
             seed viability.

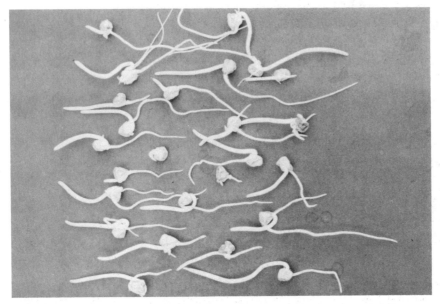

Figure 6-8b. Results of a rag doll germination test on sweet corn after four
days.

Figure 6-9. Results of a germination test. (Courtesy, Illinois Dept. of
Agriculture)

the bags by species. Place the rag dolls upright at room temperature (as close to 77°F as possible). Make sure all rag dolls are placed in identical temperature zones. If moisture loss occurs, add additional water as necessary.

Count the number of germinated seeds in each rag doll at the end of seven days and record. (You can check their progress at days three and five to observe the germination process and draw comparisons among the different species.) Calculate the germination percentage of each of the samples tested and compare.

EXPERIMENT 2.
TZ TEST

Purpose

The purpose of this experiment is to determine the viability of seed using the TZ test.

Materials

- samples of seed to be tested (10 to 20 seeds of each type, sweet corn works well)
- one gram of 2,3,5 triphenyl tetrazolium chloride (TZ)
- a small container to soak seeds
- single-edged safety razor
- paper towels
- magnifying lens (optional)
- thermometer
- hot water bath or temperature-controlled growth chamber

Procedures

Soak seeds in warm water at a temperature of 85 to 100°F (29 to 38°C) for about two hours. A longer soaking time will not harm the seed. However, if the temperature exceeds 100°F, the live embryo within the seeds may be killed.

After soaking, cut the seeds lengthwise through the center so that each half contains part of the embryo and endosperm (for corn). This will expose the full length of the germ (embryo). Place one half of each cut seed immediately into a 1% solution of TZ. Discard the other seed half. Warm the TZ solution to 85 to 100°F and let the seeds soak for 30 to 60 minutes. As an alternative, the seeds can soak at room temperature for two to four hours.

Remove seed halves from the TZ solution and wash several times with cool water. After the final rinsing, place the seeds in enough water so they are completely covered. Examine the seeds for color changes. All actively respiring parts of the seed germ (embryo) will turn red or dark pink. Darker staining indicates a higher degree of enzyme activity in the germ. Note that the endosperm and all nonliving parts of the seed do not change color. Use the guide in Figure 6-21 to estimate the viability of the seeds tested.

EXPERIMENT 3.
COLD GERMINATION TEST

Purpose

The purpose of this experiment is to test the vigor of a seed lot by exposing the planted seed to less than desirable germination temperatures followed by optimum germination temperatures.

Materials

- germination mix of potting soil and vermiculite
- 50 seeds of each type to be tested
- temperature-controlled growth chamber
- thermometer
- water

Procedures

Plant seeds in a flat containing the recommended germination mix. (A comparable germination mix may be used.) Water thoroughly. Place the flat in a 50°F environment for seven days. Remove and germinate at 77°F for three days. Record the number of strong germinations at the end of the three day warm phase. Calculate the germination percentage.

	# of replications	# seeds per replication	germination mix	cold phase	warm phase
Corn	4	50	70% water saturated potting soil/vermiculite	7 days @ 50°F	then 3 days @ 77°F
Sorghum	4	50	sand/peat mixture	7 days @ 50°F	then 3 days @ 77°F

Figure 6-10. Procedures for conducting cold germination tests for corn and sorghum.

EXPERIMENT 4.
SALINITY AND SEED GERMINATION

Purpose

The purpose of this experiment is to determine the effects of salinity on seed germination and seedling growth.

Materials

- 12 six-inch pots with drainage holes
- potting soil
- 40 seeds each of peas, beans, and sweet corn (other seed types may be substituted)
- four two-liter bottles with lids
- table salt (NaCl)
- gravel
- 50 ml beaker
- balance

Procedures

Place about two centimeters of gravel in the bottom of each of 12 pots. Add potting soil to each pot so that the soil line is about three centimeters from the top. Add one liter of tap water to each pot and allow to drain by tipping and shaking.

In four of the pots, plant 10 green bean seeds in each pot. Plant 10 seeds of the other types to be tested in each of the remaining pots. Label all pots according to seed type. Mix the four irrigation solutions by adding 0 grams of table salt to bottle one, 12 grams of salt to bottle two, 24 grams of salt to bottle three, and 36 grams of salt to bottle four. Fill each bottle with two liters of tap water to make the 0%, 0.6%, 1.2%, and 1.8% saline solutions. Label each bottle accordingly.

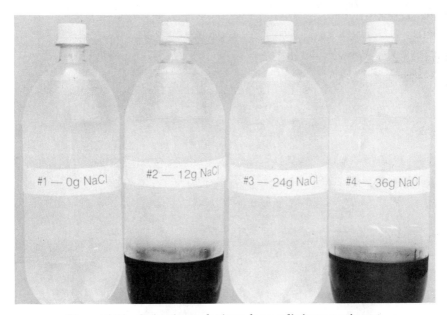

Figure 6-11. Irrigation solutions for a salinity experiment.

Label each pot of the three seed types according to the type of saline solution it will receive. Place the pots in a sunny location and keep moist by adding about 40 ml of the proper irrigation solution to each pot, preferably once a day in late morning. Seedlings should appear in five to seven days. Record the number of germinated seeds in each pot at days 5, 7, 11, and 15. Maintain the seedlings and continue watering with the appropriate solution until 15 days have passed since the seeds were planted. Using a metric ruler, calculate the average height of the seedlings in each pot at day 15. Divide the average plant height in pots two, three and four by average plant height in pot one to determine the growth ratio for the seedlings. Also on day 15, record your observations about the health of the plants in each pot.

SCIENCE CONNECTIONS

SEED ANATOMY

A *seed* is a fertilized *ovule* that contains an embryo and forms a new plant upon germination. Seeds consists of three primary parts—the *seed embryo*, the food reserve tissues, and the *seed coat*. One or more layers of tissue form the seed coat, which completely encloses the seed except for a tiny pore called the *micropyle*. The seed embryo is actually a plant in an arrested state of development. The embryo, or *germ*, consists of an *axis* and attached seed leaves called *cotyledons*. Within the seed the cotyledons are white, due to lack of the green pigment chlorophyll. The part of the axis above the cotyledons is called the *epicotyl* (plumule). The seedling stem develops from the epicotyl. The part of the axis below the cotyledons is called the *hypocotyl* and contains the embryonic root called the *radicle*.

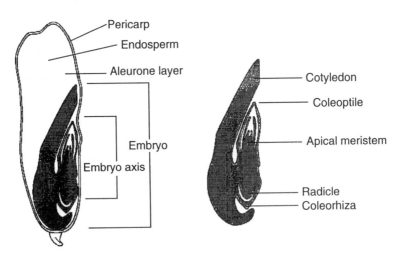

Figure 6-12. Corn seed and embryo.

A grass embryo has a single cotyledon. Thus, grasses are referred to as monocotyledonous plants or *monocots* for short. The cotyledon of a grass plant is usually called the *scutellum*. Cotyledons absorb food reserves in the seed during germination. The *coleoptile* serves as a protective sheath for the epicotyl during germination. Similarly, the *coleorhiza* functions as a protective sheath for the radicle. The fruit of a grass is called a *caryopsis*.

Figure 6-13. Bean seedling showing cotyledons and primary leaves

Unlike legume seeds, the mature fruit wall in grass seeds is usually fused with the outer seed coat.

Legume seeds are more simple than grass seeds; the cotyledons constitute most of the volume of the seed. Legumes have two cotyledons and are referred to as dicotyledonous plants or *dicots*.

The *endosperm* is the major food storage tissue in grass seed. It is adjacent to the embryo and consists mostly of starch and protein. The outer layer of the endosperm is called the *aleurone layer*. By contrast, as legume seeds develop, the endosperm is absorbed by the fleshy cotyledons. Thus, in legume seeds the cotyledons serve as the primary food reserve tissues and are high in protein.

THE GERMINATION PROCESS

Germination is the resumption of growth by a seed embryo. Technically, germination begins when the seed starts to take up moisture in a process called *imbibition*. Germination has occurred when the embryonic root emerges from the seed coat.

Germination occurs through three primary stages: (1) intake of water, (2) increase in metabolic activity, and (3) enlargement of the embryo. During storage, seeds contain 5 to 10% moisture and *respiration* is taking place at a very low rate. Although they don't look like it, the seeds are

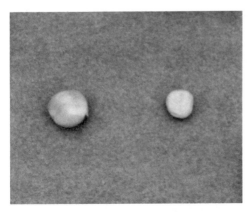

Figure 6-14. The pea seed on the left is greatly enlarged after imbibition, due to water intake and enzymatic activity.

alive! Water is absorbed primarily through the seed micropyle. Dry seeds take up water very rapidly during the first 12 hours, raising the water content to between 30 and 40%. Water uptake is due to the *hydration* of large molecules within the seed until they are restored to full *turgor*. Cells become more turgid, or rigid, due to the pressure exerted against the cell wall by their increased water content. Water intake is associated with an increase in respiration within the seed. Respiration is necessary for cell division to take place. Thus, oxygen must be present for seed germination to occur.

Phase two of the germination process involves rapid increases in *metabolic activity* and mobilization of stored *food reserves*. These changes are not apparent from the outside of the seed, but they allow for cell multiplication and growth. The cotyledons or endosperm contain the food reserves

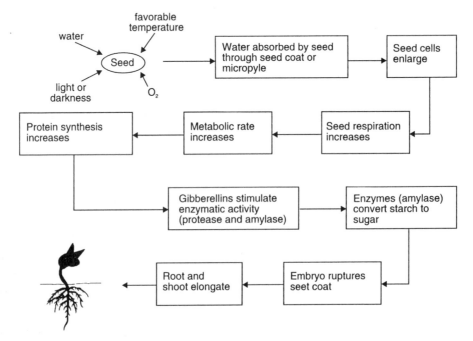

Figure 6-15. The germination process.

of the seed. These reserves consist of large molecules of *starch* and *protein* that are insoluble in water. Starch provides energy for germination, and storage proteins are later converted to amino acids. These food reserves must be broken down into smaller, water-soluble molecules that can be used by the plant. Water alone cannot accomplish this conversion.

The embryo produces a water-soluble chemical called *gibberellin*, which stimulates production of *enzymes* that break down food reserves in the endosperm. Gibberellin is one of a large group of naturally occurring plant hormones. In the presence of water the enzyme *amylase* breaks down starch reserves to glucose and maltose, sugar compounds readily usable by the embryo. In cereal grains (e.g., wheat, oats, etc.) evidence suggests that starch breakdown begins near the outermost layers of the endosperm in the aleurone layer. The enzyme *protease* is mobilized and works to break down storage proteins into amino acids. The soluble sugars and amino acids produced by enzymatic action are then transported to cell division, growth, and differentiation sites at the tips of the root and shoot.

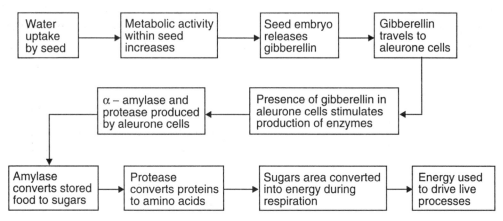

Figure 6-16. How enzymes are produced during germination.

The third phase of seed germination involves an increase in metabolic processes. The embryonic axis grows by cell division and enlargement. The embryo ruptures the seed coat, and the *shoot* emerges from the soil and begins manufacturing food for the plant via *photosynthesis*. Until this point, energy for germination comes entirely from reserves in the seed endosperm or cotyledons. Thus, seed size dictates the life span of the seed during germination and determines planting depth. The root pushes into the soil and begins to take up water for transport to other plant tissues. Germinating seeds have tremendous power as they burst through the seed coat and soil.

This power is derived from the *osmotic pressure* that develops within the cells of the seed as water is absorbed during the germination process.

Dormancy is a lack of seed germination despite the presence of favorable conditions for germination. Dormancy is primarily due to embryo dormancy or tough seed coats that do not allow water to penetrate. Seeds with tough seed coats are scarified (mechanically scratched), soaked in sulfuric acid, or treated with heat. Embryo dormancy, which is common in woody plants, is often treated by controlling temperature or moisture levels.

Requirements for Germination

Planting depth and date dramatically affect the success of germination. Germination occurs when adequate moisture, appropriate temperature, and oxygen are present. In addition, some plant species require light for seed germination. *Water* is necessary for activation of the metabolic processes of germination, such as the breakdown of food reserves. Soil moisture levels should be between *field capacity* and *permanent wilting point*. Soil field capacity represents the ideal soil moisture level in which water is held loosely by soil particles and is readily absorbed by the seed. By contrast, at the permanent wilting point soil water is held so tightly by soil particles that it is unavailable for absorption by the plant and eventual uptake by the developing roots. Water is adsorbed onto soil particles called colloids. A smooth seedbed increases the surface area of the soil particles and provides greater opportunity for the seed to come in contact with the water films held by soil colloids.

Respiration is an essential element of seed germination. Thus, an adequate supply of *oxygen* is required (an exception is rice). If oxygen supply is reduced, such as in flooding conditions or poorly drained soils, seed germination and seedling growth will be severely retarded. Soil pores become filled with water rather than oxygen, and oxygen becomes less available to the germinating seed. During respiration, sugars are broken down and energy is released to support the metabolic processes.

While water activates the germination process, *temperature* regulates the metabolic reactions necessary for successful germination. Most plant species have an acceptable temperature range that supports optimum germination. In general, higher temperatures are associated with an increase in metabolic activity and seed germination.

Some seeds, such as lettuce, tomato, tobacco, and many grasses have a *light requirement* for germination. For most of these seeds the presence of light, even low levels for only a few minutes, is enough to initiate the

Crop	Minimum (°F)	Optimum (°F)
Corn	50	75
Oats	35	65
Pea	40	75
Snap bean	60	85
Sorghum	50	75
Soybean	50	70
Squash	60	95
Tomato	50	85
Wheat	35	65

Figure 6-17. Soil temperatures suitable for germination of various crops.

germination process, assuming other necessary conditions are present. These seeds contain a photoreceptor called *phytochrome* that sends signals to the seed that initiate or halt the germination process. Scientists now believe that probably five genes direct a seed or plant to make phytochrome. This protein enzyme is sensitive to red (580 to 700 nanometers) and far-red light (700 to 800 nanometers). This amazing pigment is green when in its red-sensitive form and blue when sensitive to far-red light. Germination is promoted by red light and stalled by far-red light. Phytochrome is photo-reversible, that is, it switches back and forth depending upon the wavelength of light it encounters. Phytochrome acts as a molecular switch that controls germination and flowering.

Germination Testing

The *warm germination test* is the standard test for *seed viability* run by seed testing centers and seed producing companies. Procedures for conducting the warm germination test are established by law for some common field crops. Although slight variations exist from species to species, the warm germination test usually involves a seven-day period at 77°F and 100% humidity. The common germination medium or material is paper toweling or a similar product. Germination percentages for a viable lot of seed should be greater than 90%.

The Association of Official Seed Analysts has established criteria for assessing germination when using the standard warm germination test. For corn, germination percentage is determined by excluding germinations that show the following defects.

1. Small, late-germinating seedlings

2. Split or shredded leaves

3. Shoot defects—coleoptile split, damaged or stunted shoot, leaf less than one half the length of the coleoptile

	# of replications	# seeds per replication	germination material	# days	temperature*
Corn	4	100	paper towels	7	77°F
Sorghum	4	100	between moist paper blotters	10	alternating 68°F (6 hours dark) and 86° (8 hours light)
Soybeans	4	100	Kimpak	7	77°F
Alfalfa	4	100	between moist paper blotters	7	68°F

*all warm tests conducted at 100% humidity

Figure 6-18. Legal requirements for conducting the warm germination test for selected field crops.

4. Mesocotyl defects—spirally mesocotyl, lesions, shoot trapped in seed coat

5. Root defects—missing primary root, insufficient roots

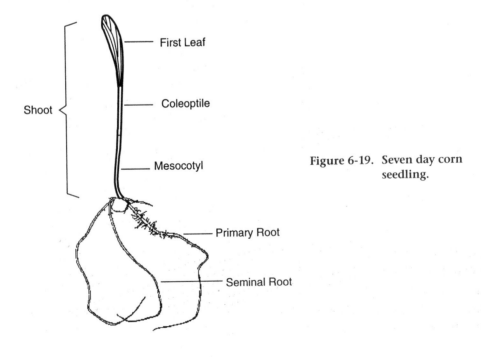

Figure 6-19. Seven day corn seedling.

Germination percentage in beans is determined by excluding germinations that show the following defects.

1. Small leaf size and weak epicotyl
2. Root defects-stubby or missing primary root, insufficient roots
3. Damaged primary leaves
4. Thickened hypocotyl
5. Cotyledons missing or shriveled
6. Hypocotyl defects, lesions

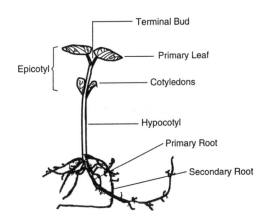

Figure 6-20. Seven day bean seedling.

For cereal grains the following defects are considered when determining germination percentage.

1. Root defects—one or two seminal roots, short seminal root
2. Shoot defects—short shoot, leaf less than one-half the length of the coleoptile
3. Detached endosperm
4. Leaf defects-split or damaged coleoptile, split or shredded leaf

Another test for seed viability is the *TZ test*. In this test seed samples are treated with the chemical 2,3,5 triphenyl tetrazolium chloride. A 1% solution of TZ is prepared. (TZ is a white powder that is colorless in water.) In order for the TZ to become activated it must come in contact with living tissue (the embryo) within the seed. Thus, seeds are soaked to soften the seed coat and activate the germination process. (Remember, water intake is the first phase in seed germination.) Seeds are then split in half so that each half contains a lengthwise dissection of the embryo. One half of each seed is then placed in the TZ solution.

When TZ comes in contact with living tissue it changes to the red or deep pink chemical *formazan* as a result of *enzymatic activity* in the seed germ. These enzymes are only present in live seed tissues. Thus, seeds with dead embryos will not stain red, although they may show some slight staining. In living tissue, the level of staining reflects the amount of enzymatic activity—the darker the stain, the higher the degree of activity. When the entire germ of the seed stains red, the seed is alive and capable of germinating. The endosperm in monocots does not stain red, since it does not contain active enzymes early in the germination process. In dicotyledons no separate endosperm exists and the entire seed stains red. The difficulty in using the TZ test is interpreting the results, since critical parts of the embryo must stain red if the seed is, in fact, viable. Many seed

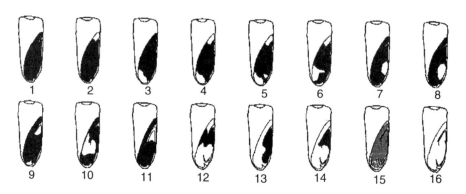

Black areas indicate stained and living tissue; white areas represent unstained and dead tissue.

No. 1.	GERMINABLE.	Entire embryo stained bright red.
Nos. 2-4.	GERMINABLE.	Extremities of scutellum unstained.
Nos. 5-6.	GERMINABLE.	Extremities of scutellum unstained; non-critical portions of radicle unstained.
Nos. 7-8.	NON-GERMINABLE.	Area where seminal roots originate is unstained.
No. 9.	NON-GERMINABLE.	Pumule unstained.
No. 10.	NON-GERMINABLE.	Central portion of scutellum and area of seminal root development unstained.
No. 11.	NON-GERMINABLE.	Plumule and radicle unstained.
No. 12.	NON-GERMINABLE.	Unstained area on lower scutellum and radicle extends into region where seminal roots develop.
No. 13.	NON-GERMINABLE.	Scutellum entirely unstained
No. 14.	NON-GERMINABLE.	Scutellum and radicle unstained.
No. 15.	NON-GERMINABLE.	Stain very faint pink.
No. 16.	NON-GERMINABLE.	Entire embryo unstained.

Figure 6-21. Interpreting the TZ test for seed viability in corn.

testing laboratories currently use the TZ test as a supplement to the required warm germination test, since the results of the TZ test are not as reliable.

Salinity

The buildup of salt compounds in soils is a major concern in all irrigated growing conditions, both indoors and outdoors. *Salts* are essentially compounds that do not contain carbon, hydrogen, or oxygen. Although plants require certain salt constituents for growth, some soils contain such large concentrations of soluble salts that yields are decreased. Most of the naturally present soluble salts in soils come from the weathering of minerals at the earth's surface. Irrigation water and fertilizers add salt to the soil solution. Fertilizers primarily consist of ammonium nitrate and potassium sulfate, which are forms of salt. Salts of primary concern are chlorides, sulfates, and sodium. Soil salinity is determined by the electrical conductivity of a solution extracted from a soil sample.

When salts dissolve in water they form *ions* (positively or negatively charged atoms) that substitute sodium for plant nutrients such as calcium and magnesium that are normally taken in by the plant root system. In addition, excessive salt concentrations in the soil create a tighter bond between soil particles and water films, thus restricting the ability of the

Figure 6-22. Soil salinity becomes a problem where rainfall is low and water must be supplied by irrigation. (Courtesy, Agricultural Research Service, USDA)

plant to absorb the soil water. In saline soils only about 10% of the soil water at field capacity is available to the plant, compared to about 50% in nonsaline soils. Increased uptake of salt ions reduces the *osmotic flow* of water into plant roots and cells. Salinity damage to seedlings often resembles damping off injury, in which seedlings die during, or shortly after, germination. Plants vary in their sensitivity to saline soils. Germinating seeds should not come in contact with fertilizers because of the negative effects of salt on water intake.

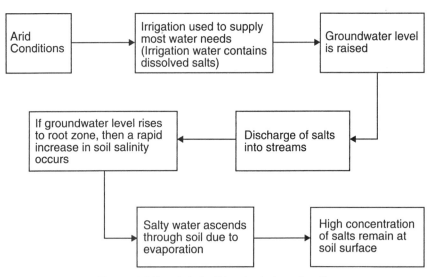

Figure 6-22b. **Salt buildup in irrigated soils.**

Restricted drainage caused by either slow *permeability* or a high water table is the principal factor in the formation of saline soils. Irrigation increases salinity by raising the ground water level, causing an accumulation of salts in the root zone due to *evaporation* of water in the upper soil layer. As water evaporates from the soil, salts are drawn upward through the soil and a high concentration of salt remains at the soil surface. *Leaching* is the downward pulling of materials (in this case salts) through the soil by percolating water. Irrigation practices should involve adding enough water to permit some drainage and promote the leaching process. Less frequent watering, using a larger volume of water, helps to reduce soil salinity. When watering plants in containers, about 25 to 50% of the irrigated water should drip from the bottom of the growing container. Thus, in irrigated growing conditions, enough water must be applied to leach out accumulated salts and replenish water lost by *transpiration* and evaporation.

Figure 6-23. Salt buildup in soils/growing media can retard germination and stunt seedling growth.

CHAPTER SUMMARY

Seed germination is the process of seed embryo growth and emergence from the seed coat. While germination appears to be a simple, straightforward process, many hidden biological and metabolic processes take place beneath the seed coat. Germination occurs in three primary phases: water intake (imbibition), mobilization of food reserves, and emergence of the root and shoot. The primary requirements for germination are water to initiate the germination process, and appropriate temperature to activate the metabolic processes of germination. Oxygen is also required for seed respiration, and some seeds require exposure to light for germination to be initiated. These seeds produce a plant pigment called phytochrome that is able to sense the presence of light and turn the germination process on or off. Some seeds possess a natural dormancy and require special treatment before germination will occur.

Germination testing is of major importance in seed production and certification. Seeds are tested for viability and vigor using both the warm test and the cold test. When using the warm germination test, the number of strong germinations is counted to determine the germination percentage. Criteria have been established for interpreting germination tests. The TZ test is also used to supplement the warm test, but its results are less reliable and difficult to accurately interpret. The cold test is used to determine the germination capacity of the seed under less than ideal conditions.

Although they vary in design, all seeds contain three essential components: the embryo, the food reserve tissues, and the seed coat. In grass seeds, the endosperm and embryo are separate. In dicotyledonous plants the seed leaves contain the food reserves, and no distinct endosperm is present. The enzymes amylase and protease play an important role in the seed germination process by breaking down stored starches and proteins into forms useable by the seed for energy and growth. The seed embryo produces a plant hormone, gibberellic acid, which stimulates the release and production of these enzymes.

FURTHER LABORATORY INVESTIGATIONS

1. Excise the embryos from several seed samples and place on moist paper in a covered dish. Place at room temperature and watch for signs of life, such as greening of tissues or separation of cotyledons.

2. Soak soybean, corn, and large vegetable seeds to soften the seed coats. Split each seed in half lengthwise, ensuring that each half contains a full length of the embryo. For dicots, split the seed between the two cotyledons. Examine the embryonic axis of the seed under a stereomicroscope and locate the parts of the embryo.

3. Conduct experiments to determine the effects of light, temperature, moisture, oxygen, storage period, and planting depth on seed germination. Seeds such as radish and lettuce may be germinated in petri dishes. For dark conditions, wrap samples in aluminum foil. For anaerobic conditions, place seeds in water or line a jar with paper towels and put steel wool in the center. Place seeds between the paper towels and the side of the jar, add water, and seal with a tight-fitting lid. (Oxidation of the steel wool depletes the supply of oxygen in the jar.) For each experiment make sure that all conditions (variables) except the one(s) to be measured (dependent variables) are controlled. For example, in an experiment

on the effects of planting depth on seed germination, make sure that temperature, moisture, and all other factors that affect germination are the same for all trials.

4. Conduct an experiment to determine the effects of the seed embryo on seed germination. Cut 15 cereal grain seeds (barley, wheat, etc.) transversely so that one half contains the embryo and the other half contains the endosperm. Discard the embryo halves. Place five endosperm halves in a petri dish and cover. Keep dry. Place five halves in another petri dish on filter paper, add eight milliliters water and cover. In the third petri dish place five endosperm halves on filter paper and add eight milliliters giberrellic acid solution. In a fourth petri dish place 10 whole grains of the selected seed on filter paper and add water only. Label each dish and store at room temperature for three days. Prepare a starch-gelatin plate by mixing a 10% gelatin solution in hot water with 0.5% corn starch. Pour into a petri dish. Place one or more seeds halves from each of the three treatments into separate quadrants of the petri dish. Cut the germinated whole seeds transversely and place one or more endosperm halves in the fourth quadrant. Allow to stand for at least six hours. Flood the dish with iodine solution. The two treatments containing amylase (the germinated seed and the endosperm with gibberellic acid added) will not indicate a presence of starch (the iodine turns clear or amber). In these treatments the gibberellic acid stimulated the production of amylase, which converted the endosperm starch to sugars.

5. Examine the osmotic pressure exerted by germinating seeds by filling a jar about threefourths full with an equal amount of bean seeds and dry sand. Shake the jar to mix the sand and beans. Pack the sand tightly. Fill the jar to the top with sand. Wet the sand, but don't flood it. Screw the lid on snugly and place the jar on a pan. Observe what happens in a few hours. As an additional experiment, plant seeds along the side of a clear container and observe the seed germination process and emergence of the root and shoot.

Chapter 7

PHOTOSYNTHESIS AND RESPIRATION

Growing Like Crazy

AGRICULTURAL APPLICATIONS

Plant growers must have a working knowledge of how a plant produces and uses energy for growth and reproduction. By controlling the environmental factors that affect energy producing and using processes in plants, growers can produce crops with more desirable characteristics. For example, many management practices center around the grower's desire to control light intensity and/or duration, thus affecting the nature and quality of

Figure 7-1. The growth and appearance of crops and plants can be managed by controlling environmental factors, such as light intensity.

the final product. Field crops planted in rows running east and west utilize light more effectively, due to less selfshading by the crop. Apple growers prune trees to ensure that plenty of sunlight reaches the center branches of the trees, resulting in uniform fruit production.

Shading plants is also an important management practice in certain floral crops. Shading reduces light intensity and/or duration, which decreases temperatures in growing areas and reduces the plant's water needs.

Figure 7-2. Greenhouses allow many environmental factors to be controlled, while still taking advantage of natural sunlight.

TERMS

absorption spectrum	glucolysis	photon
C₃ plant	glucose	photosynthesis
C₄ plant	Krebs cycle	pigment
carbon dioxide (CO₂)	light compensation point	respiration
chemical energy	light energy	senescence
chlorophyll	light intensity	starch
chloroplast	light quality	stomata
chromatography	light saturation point	wavelength

Scientists have discovered that plants are light-sensitive, and growers can use this knowledge to control flowering, growth, and reproduction. Some greenhouse or indoor crops are best grown with artificial light. In these cases growers must select the best combination of artificial light sources to ensure optimum plant growth.

Managing crop fertility is another important grower practice that has major implications for crop production. Again, by understanding the function of certain nutrients in plant growth, growers can maintain the plant nutrient levels that support optimum plant energy production. Crop density (plant populations) also has an impact on plant growth in several important ways. Growers must use seeding rates that are most productive and cost efficient for particular soil moisture and fertility conditions. Compacted or poorly drained soils, low-moisture soils, and high temperatures all have adverse effects on plant growth and must be carefully managed by growers.

In general, as plant photosynthesis increases, plant growth and crop yield also increase. Scientists are continuing to explore the intricate details

Figure 7-3. High intensity discharge (HID) lamps provide the best quality of artificial light.

Figure 7-4. Compacted, waterlogged, or poorly drained soils have adverse
            effects on plant growth.

of photosynthesis and other plant metabolic processes so that growers can
continue to improve their management practices. For example, plant breeders
are seeking ways to increase light-absorbing pigments in plants in the hope
that subsequent increases in photosynthesis and plant growth may be real-

Figure 7-5. Taking photosynthesis readings in a pecan orchard. (Courtesy,
            Agricultural Research Service, USDA)

Figure 7-6. By adjusting a plant's tolerance to temperatures through plant breeding, we may someday grow all the vegetables for a salad at the same time of year and in the same location.

ized. Agricultural researchers are exploring ways to custom design important crops for different climates. Through plant breeding techniques, new cotton varieties may be developed that tolerate cooler night temperatures, resulting

Figure 7-6b. A researcher compares the growth of two cotton plants subjected to different night temperatures. (Courtesy, Agricultural Research Service, USDA)

Figure 7-7. Scientists have recently discovered that as tomatoes begin to turn
red, a ripening enzyme called beta mannanase is produced,
breaking down cell walls and causing the fruit to soften.

in greater yields. Someday all the vegetables for a salad may be grown in
one location at the same time.

Harvesting, storage, and processing techniques used for fruits, vegetables, and other plant products are designed to counter the plant's natural

Figure 7-8. Refrigeration slows respiration in plant tissues and fruits, thus
extending shelf life.

ripening and aging processes. Refrigeration, cooking, and processing serve to reduce or stop respiration in plant/fruit tissues. Temperature and environmental control practices during storage periods are crucial to maintaining the quality of many fruit, vegetable, and floral crops. In addition, harvesting dates and techniques used for many plant food products are based upon knowledge of fruit ripening processes after picking. That's why tomatoes and most fruits are picked somewhat green, while citrus can be picked when ripe without rapid decline in fruit quality after harvest.

OBJECTIVES—QUESTIONS FOR INVESTIGATION

After completing the following laboratory exercises and studying this chapter, you should be able to answer the following questions:

1. How do plants produce and use energy needed for plant growth and fruit production?
2. In general, why do only green plants undergo photosynthesis?
3. What environmental factors may be controlled to increase photosynthesis and plant growth?
4. Why do sunlight and artificial light sources have different effects on plant growth?
5. How do plants absorb the light needed for photosynthesis?
6. What gives plants their green color?
7. What is the relationship between photosynthesis and respiration?
8. Why does refrigeration extend the life of fruits, vegetables, and floral products?

LABORATORY INVESTIGATIONS

EXPERIMENT I.
FACTORS AFFECTING PHOTOSYNTHESIS

Purpose

The purpose of this experiment is to investigate the effects of environmental and plant factors on the photosynthetic activity of plants.

Materials

- leaves from a green plant (potted plant, shrub, etc.)
- leaves from a variegated plant (coleus, philodendron, etc.)
- black construction paper
- Lugol's iodine solution
- ethyl alcohol
- beaker
- small saucepan
- hot plate
- petri dishes
- Vaseline (petroleum jelly)
- goggles

Figure 7-9. Setup for the experiment on the effects of light on photosynthesis.

Procedures

Effects of Light. Black construction paper (or other opaque material) will be used to cover the top and bottom of several leaves on the selected plant. Cut the paper about twice the size of the leaf to be covered. Fold the construction paper in half and cut a hole in the top half. Use the construction paper like a book cover to enclose the leaves. Secure the cover with paper clips. Place the plant in a good light location for several days. Remove the covering and note any visible differences in the covered and uncovered portions of the leaf.

Extract chlorophyll from the covered leaves by immersing the leaves first in boiling water and then in boiling alcohol. The alcohol will turn green as the chlorophyll is extracted.

Caution: *Alcohol is flammable! To avoid fire, place a beaker of alcohol in a saucepan of water and heat slowly. Alcohol boils at a lower temperature than water.*

After the leaf has lost its green color, remove it from the boiling alcohol and place it in a petri dish. Flood the leaf with Lugol's iodine solution. The parts of the leaf containing starch will turn dark.

Effects of Carbon Dioxide. Coat the top and bottom sides of one-half of several leaves on the stock plants with petroleum jelly. Place the plants in good light conditions for several days. Re-

Figure 7-10. Do variegated leaves differ in photosynthetic activity when compared to plants with completely green leaves?

move the coated leaves and test for the presence of starch using the procedure described above. Record the results.

Effects of Chlorophyll. Remove several leaves from some variegated plants. Prepare sketches of each leaf showing the green and white portions. Test each leaf for starch using the same procedures as above. Compare the tested leaves with your original sketches.

Effects of Water. While maintaining good light conditions, withhold water from a potted plant until signs of wilt are evident. Remove one of the wilted leaves and test for starch.

EXPERIMENT 2.
EFFECTS OF LIGHT QUALITY ON PLANT GROWTH

Purpose

The purpose of this experiment is to examine the effects of different light colors (wavelengths) on photosynthesis. Photosynthesis rate will be estimated by measuring plant growth.

Materials

- four tomato plants or other herbaceous plants with large leaves (plants should be of same type and size)
- one clear and three colored cellophane, plastic, or acetate sheets (red, green, blue)
- four cardboard boxes or other lightproof containers (or each plant can be placed in an aquarium wrapped in colored cellophane); these containers must be large enough to allow some growing room for the plants placed inside them.

Procedures

Cut an opening in the top of each of the four boxes slightly smaller than the sheets of cellophane. Punch small holes in the sides of each box to provide air for the plant. Place a plant in each of the four boxes and tape the cellophane over the opening of each box. Place all four plants in similar growing conditions and in a location with adequate light. Ideally,

Figure 7-11. A cardboard box can be adapted for use in the light quality experiment.

the design should allow for watering as needed without removing the colored cellophane sheets. Keep the cellophane sheets in place for two weeks and record observations every three days. Plot the average height of each plant for the various wavelengths of light.

SCIENCE CONNECTIONS

PHOTOSYNTHESIS

Photosynthesis is the process by which plants build up and store the energy needed for life processes. In essence, it is the conversion of *light energy* to *chemical energy*. It is also the means by which the plant obtains carbon, a principal component in plant tissues. In the presence of light, carbon dioxide and water combine to form a sugar molecule and oxygen is released as a by-product. Photosynthesis is represented by the formula below:

$$6 \ CO_2 + 12 \ H_2O + \text{light energy} \rightarrow C_6H_{12}O_6 + 6 \ O_2 + 6 \ H_2O$$

carbon   water   glucose   oxygen   water
dioxide

Figure 7-12. Photosynthesis also occurs to some extent in the stem, flowers, and fruit of a plant.

Chlorophyll is a green pigment contained in the *chloroplasts* of green plants. All higher plants and algae contain chlorophyll, but only green plants contain chloroplasts. Photosynthesis takes place in the chloroplasts-subcellular structures that contain plant pigments. Although photosynthesis occurs primarily in the leaves of plants, it also occurs to some extent in the stems, flowers, and fruit tissues. Leaves seem to have the ability to position themselves so that their surfaces are at right angles to incident light.

Photosynthesis is an extremely complex process that takes place in two successive steps: the *light reactions* (Hill reaction) and the *dark reactions* (Calvin cycle). The light reactions are not influenced by temperature, while the dark reactions are. In the light reactions, light strikes chlorophyll molecules and initiates the energy conversion process. Water molecules are split, oxygen is produced, energy-storing molecules (ATP) are created, and the carrier molecule $NADPH_2$ is created.

The dark reactions take place if the products of the light reactions are present, regardless of whether light is present. In the Calvin cycle, carbon dioxide is combined with five-carbon sugars to produce six-carbon sugars, such as *glucose*. Some of these sugars are recycled, while others are stored as *starch* (as in potatoes) or chains of simple sugars. Molecules of ATP and $NADPH_2$ provide the energy and chemical mechanisms for driving the dark reactions.

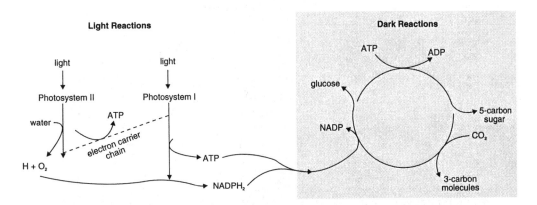

Figure 7-13. Basic photosynthesis reactions.

Plants are grouped as C_3 and C_4 plants based upon whether they produce a three-carbon or four-carbon acid during the Calvin cycle. C_3 plants have lower net photosynthetic rates and include cereal grains, soybeans, tomatoes, cotton, tobacco, and peanuts. C_4 plants have higher net photosynthetic rates and include corn, sorghum, sugarcane, millet, and many of the broad-leaved weeds. C_4 plants are more efficient users of carbon dioxide and water than C_3 plants.

Figure 7-14. In general, C_4 plants are more efficient than C_3 plants in using the sun's energy.

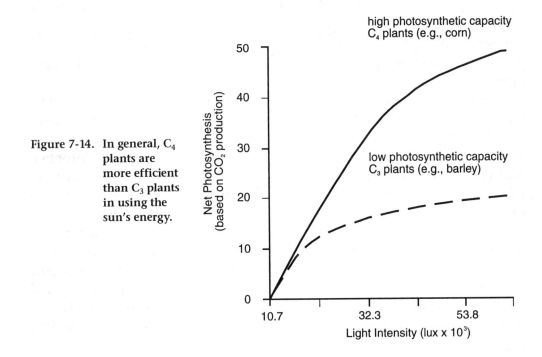

Figure 7-15. Corn, sorghum, and sugarcane have higher net photosynthetic rates than soybeans and cotton.

Requirements for photosynthesis include: (1) a living, green plant, (2) light, (3) carbon dioxide, (4) and water. Plant species vary widely in the amount and intensity of light needed for photosynthesis. Light quality (wavelength) also greatly affects the photosynthetic process. Plants take in carbon dioxide from the atmosphere through the *stomata*. (Note: The stomata will be discussed in detail in the next chapter.) The carbon dioxide then goes into solution with water and is diffused through cell walls into the cytoplasm. Scientists have estimated that an acre of corn takes in over 5,500 pounds of atmospheric carbon dioxide in a single growing season! Only a fraction of the amount of water absorbed by plants is used in photosynthesis. However, water is the source of oxygen, which is released as a by-product in photosynthesis.

Factors Affecting Photosynthesis

Photosynthesis is affected by (1) light quality, intensity, and duration; (2) carbon dioxide concentration; (3) temperature; (4) water availability; and (5) plant development. More information about the effects of light on photosynthesis will be presented later in this chapter. The percentage of *carbon dioxide* (CO_2) in the atmosphere is normally about .035%. Researchers have found that when this percentage is increased to about 0.10%, the rate of photosynthesis nearly doubles for some plant species. In a greenhouse or laboratory, carbon dioxide concentrations may be controlled. In fact, many greenhouse crops, such as roses, orchids, and carnations, are commercially grown in enriched carbon dioxide environments. In field crops the density and height of the crop canopy has some effect on carbon dioxide concentrations.

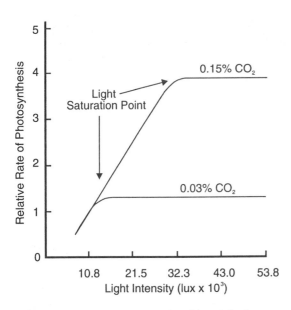

Figure 7-16. CO_2 concentration is positively related to photosynthetic activity and light saturation point.

The effect of *temperature* on photosynthesis varies by plant species. When light is a limiting factor, temperature has little effect on the rate of photosynthesis. However, for many species, the rate of photosynthesis doubles for each $50°F$ increase in temperature up to a certain point. Beyond this point, increasing temperature has a negative effect by causing the stomata to close and respiration to rise. C_3 crops close their stomata on hot days to prevent the loss of moisture. The result is a decrease in photosynthesis, due to the reduced availability of carbon dioxide. Corn and other C_4 crops do not experience afternoon stomatal closure. However, scientists have recently discovered that corn does take a photosynthesis "nap" on warm, dry afternoons. The photosynthetic rate drops by about 30%, which is apparently due to a lack of humidity around the leaves.

Plants take in carbon dioxide from the atmosphere through the stomata in the leaves. When *soil moisture* is low or when the plant has difficulty keeping its water needs met on hot days, the stomata close. This restricts the intake of carbon dioxide, which greatly reduces photosynthetic rate.

When plants undergo *senescence*, or biological aging, the rate of photosynthesis drastically decreases. When the plant produces flowers and begins to set seed, photosynthesis in mature leaves drops sharply. In some species, when the seeds are totally mature photosynthesis ceases completely and the foliage dies. In the growing plant, research suggests that the sites of growth and metabolism (called sink tissues) actually place demands on

Figure 7-17.   Tomato and other C_3 plants close their stomata on hot days.

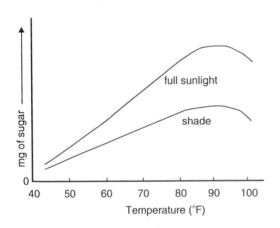

Figure 7-18. General relationship between
temperature and rate of
photosynthesis.

Bell Peppers	74-105
Cotton	73-90
Cucumbers	86-90
Field Corn	77-88
Petunias	65-84
Potatoes	62-73
Soybeans	65-84
Spinach	50-63
Tomatoes	68-78
Wheat	62-73

Figure 7-19. Temperature
range (°F)
for
optimum
growth of
common
crops.

Figure 7-19b. A researcher tests the theory that crops have a thermal kinetic window where optimum growth occurs. (Courtesy, Agricultural Research Service, USDA)

Figure 7-20. Photosynthesis in mature leaves drops sharply when flowers are formed and fruit is set.

Figure 7-21. Plant maturation is associated with rapidly decreasing photosynthetic rate until photosynthesis completely stops.

fully expanded leaves for photosynthetic products, resulting in an increase in the rate of photosynthesis.

Light and Photosynthesis

The sun's energy is transmitted to Earth as electromagnetic waves of varying *wavelengths*. Visible light is that portion of the *electromagnetic spectrum* between 400 and 780 nanometers. However, plants respond to a slightly larger portion, 300 to 800 nanometers. The sun's white light, as we see it, actually consists of all the colors of the visible spectrum. Light energy, or *photons*, is absorbed in green plants primarily by chlorophyll pigments. *Pigments* are molecules that absorb certain colors of light. After absorbing a photon of light, these pigments are transformed into a more highly energized, excited state. This extra energy can be lost as heat, reemitted as fluorescence, transferred to another molecule, or used in a chemical reaction. Photosynthesis primarily involves the last two kinds of energy loss.

Red and blue light are the most effective in photosynthesis. Thus, in artificial light conditions, plants must receive ample red and blue light to support photosynthesis. (Because they produce less heat and a greater proportion of their light is useable by plants, fluorescent and high density

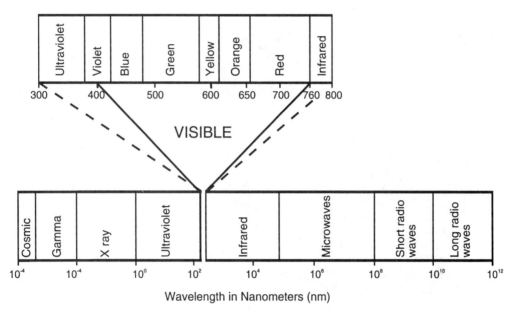

Figure 7-22. The electromagnetic spectrum of radiant energy. Plants respond to light between 300 and 800 nm, known as the photosynthetic active radiation (PAR) spectrum.

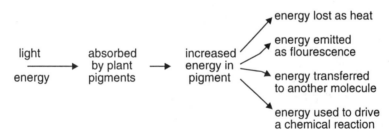

Figure 7-23. Ways a plant can use light energy absorbed by plant pigments.

discharge lamps are preferred to incandescent tungsten lamps.) Chlorophyll appears green because it primarily absorbs red and blue light and reflects green light. The two types of chlorophyll, termed *chlorophyll-a* and *chlorophyll-b*, differ in their ability to absorb light of varying wavelengths. In addition to chlorophyll, *carotenoids* and *xanthophylls* play an accessory role in light absorption. These accessory pigments transfer their absorbed light energy to chlorophyll-a, improving the plant's overall ability to absorb and use light energy.

The pattern of light absorption (called the absorption spectrum) is

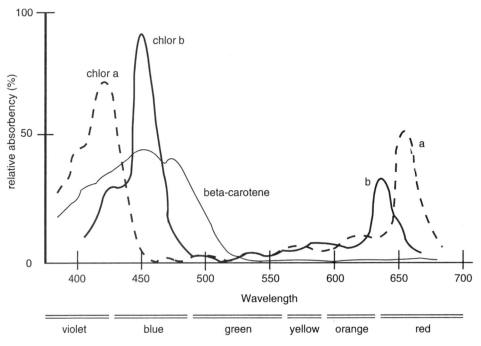

Figure 7-24. Absorption spectrum of plant pigments.

unique for each plant pigment due to its molecular structure. This differing structure also allows plant pigments to bind differently to fibers. Thus, these pigments can be placed in solution and separated into distinct bands on an absorbent material, a process called *chromatography*.

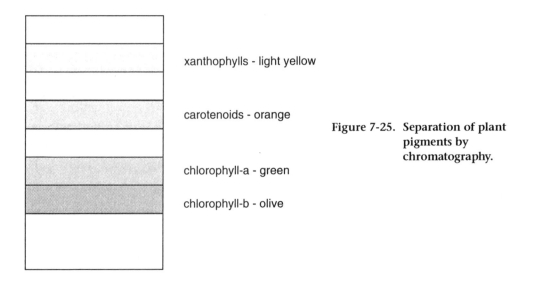

xanthophylls - light yellow

carotenoids - orange

chlorophyll-a - green

chlorophyll-b - olive

Figure 7-25. Separation of plant pigments by chromatography.

Photosynthesis involves two *photosynthetic units* that consist of about 300 molecules each. Chlorophyll-a molecules form the reaction center of these two units, called Photosystem I and Photosystem II. Each photosystem has a slightly different wavelength of maximum absorption.

Light quality, intensity, and duration are all important factors in plant growth and photosynthetic rate. *Light quality* refers to the color, or wavelength, of visible light. Due to its shorter wavelength and higher frequency, blue light (about 450 nanometers) contains nearly two times the energy of the same number of photons of red light, and would thus be considered of higher quality.

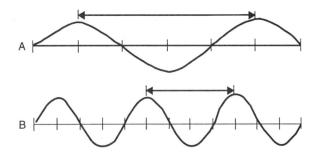

Figure 7-26. Radiant energy is emitted through waves. The length of a wave of light is depicted by the arrows. The shorter wavelength and higher frequency of B makes it more energetic than A.

Light intensity is a measure of the brightness of light, expressed in footcandles (FC), or luxes (.093 FC). Most plants require at least 100 to 200 footcandles of light to maintain adequate rates of photosynthesis. Some plants, including most field crops, some fruit trees, and many turf grasses, require high light intensities. On the other hand, many ornamentals are shade-loving plants. White or blanched asparagus and celery are grown by shielding light from the growing plant, thus reducing chlorophyll development. Light is required for the development of the darker plant pigments found in the outer layers of many fruits and vegetables.

In general, when compared to high light intensity conditions, leaves of a plant will grow longer and thinner under light of lower intensity. When grown in low light intensity conditions, many plants will become *etiolated* (elongated, spindly), due to the effects of light on the distribution of growth hormones within the plant. A light intensity in which the exchange

Figure 7-27. Shade-loving plants require lower light energy than other
plants.

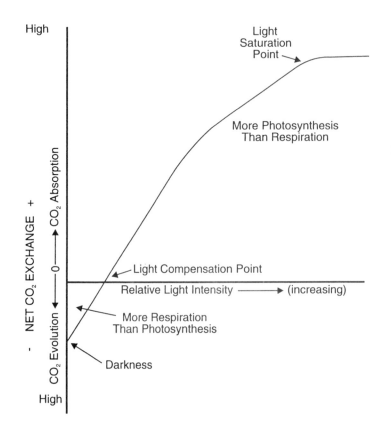

Figure 7-28. Increasing light
intensity has a
strong, positive
effect on
photosynthesis
until the
plant's light
saturation
point is
reached.

Figure 7-29.   Plants that receive less light than they need become etiolated.

of carbon dioxide during photosynthesis and respiration is equal is known as the *light compensation point*. At some point beyond this, the plant reaches a *light saturation point* in which increases in light intensity do not result in significant increases in photosynthesis.

The duration of light has a proportional impact on rate of photosynthesis. In general, the longer the *light duration*, the greater the rate of photosynthesis and plant growth. Photoperiodism refers to the specific light duration requirements of plants in order to initiate flowering. The days to maturity of crop species is a factor of the photoperiodism of the particular variety under cultivation.

RESPIRATION

Respiration is the release of energy captured and stored through photosynthesis. During respiration, carbohydrates are converted to carbon dioxide, water, and energy. This released energy is the source of energy for the plant's life processes. Respiration is the step-wise degradation of sugar molecules, with each step releasing small amounts of energy. Respiration is represented by the following chemical reaction:

$$C_6H_{12}O_6 + 6\ H_2O + 6\ O_2 \rightarrow 6\ CO_2 + 12\ H_2O + \text{energy}$$

$$\text{glucose} \quad \text{water} \quad \text{oxygen} \quad\quad \text{carbon} \quad \text{water}$$

$$\text{dioxide}$$

Respiration occurs continuously in all living cells. Oxygen is not needed to initiate respiration, but oxygen is needed to complete the process. Through the process of *glycolysis*, the glucose molecule is transformed and then split, eventually producing pyruvic acid as an end product. After removal of carbon dioxide the pyruvic acid undergoes the complex *Krebs cycle*, which produces small amounts of energy at successive stages. After movement through an electron transport chain, ATP (energy) molecules, oxygen, and carbon dioxide are the final products of respiration. About 40% of the original energy stored in the glucose molecule is then stored in the ATP molecules.

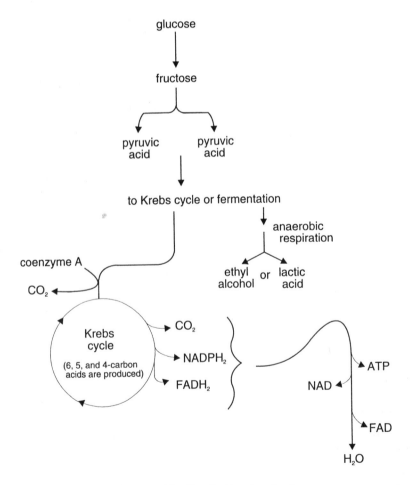

Figure 7-30. Respiration in plants.

Factors Affecting Respiration

Plant respiration is affected by temperature, oxygen, and water availability. Temperature has a very strong effect on rates of respiration, with respiration increasing two to four times with each 50°F increase in temperature. As respiration increases, more sugar molecules are "burned" by the plant, and a decrease in plant weight results (unless offset by photosynthesis). Again, respiration occurs continuously in plants, while photosynthesis occurs only in the presence of light. Lower nighttime temperatures decrease respiration, increasing overall plant growth. In fact, most plants grow best when nighttime temperatures are about 9°F cooler than daytime temperatures.

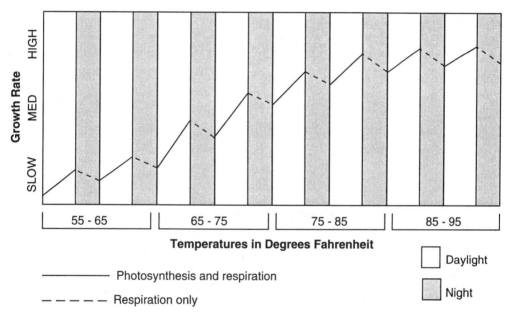

Figure 7-31. Relationship between photosynthesis and respiration as influenced by temperature and light.

Respiration rates in fruits and vegetables have been found to dramatically increase at harvest. Since no additional sugars are being produced through photosynthesis, degradation of the fruit occurs relatively rapidly as stored sugars are burned during respiration. Environmental conditions of storage strongly influence the rate of this ripening (respiration) and degradation process.

Water is necessary for respiration and photosynthesis to take place.

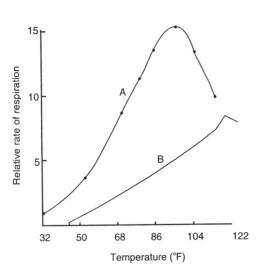

Figure 7-32. Relationship between temperature and respiration rate in (A) germinating seed and (B) potato leaves.

Water is also the driving medium for the important enzymatic reactions that take place during respiration and other plant metabolic processes. Thus, as plants become water-stressed, most metabolic processes are drastically slowed. However, in seed storage, water concentrations of less than 10% must be maintained to ensure seed viability and prevent germination.

In general, respiration decreases as oxygen concentrations decrease. Compacted or waterlogged soils thus reduce respiration. In addition, anaerobic respiration can begin to occur in flooded growing conditions, resulting in the production of lethal ethyl alcohol or lactic acid. However, in food storage settings, reducing oxygen concentrations is generally desirable because this reduces respiration rate. In commercial warehouses, oxygen concentration is reduced to 1 to 3% through the addition of nitrogen.

CHAPTER SUMMARY

Photosynthesis and respiration are the two most basic life processes in plants. During photosynthesis, plants synthesize sugars, which are either transported to sites of growth and metabolism or stored for later use as both sugar and starch. The photosynthetic process requires carbon dioxide, water, and light energy to produce sugar, water, and oxygen. A number of plant pigments, primarily two types of chlorophyll, absorb the light energy necessary to drive the photosynthetic process. Photosynthesis occurs in cell chloroplasts, which are only contained in green plants. This conversion of light energy to chemical energy occurs through a set of light reactions and a subsequent set of dark reactions.

Photosynthesis is affected by light quality, intensity, and duration; carbon dioxide concentration; temperature; water availability; and stage of

Table 7-1
Comparison of Photosynthesis and Respiration

Photosynthesis	Respiration
1. Stores engery in sugar molecules	1. Releases energy from sugar molecules
2. Uses carbon dioxide and water	2. Releases carbon
3. Increases weight	3. Decreases weight
4. Occurs only in light	4. Occurs in either darkness or light
5. Light energy trapped by chlorophyll	5. Energy released
6. Occurs only in cells containing chlorophyll	6. Occurs in all living cells
7. Occurs in chloroplasts (in eukaryotic cells)	7. Occurs in cytoplasm (glycolysis) and mitochondria (aerobic respiration)
8. Produces oxygen in green plants	8. Utilizes oxygen (aerobic respiration)
9. Produces ATP energy from light	9. Produces ATP with energy released from sugar
10. ATP and NADP used mainly for synthesis of sugar	10. ATP and NADP used for many reactions

Figure 7-33. Due to respiration, most fruits and vegetables ripen rapidly.

plant development. In general, light and temperature are associated with proportional increases in photosynthesis. Carbon dioxide concentrations and water availability also increase photosynthetic activity. Blue and red light are best absorbed by photosynthetic plant pigments, and thus, have the most positive effect on photosynthesis and plant growth.

In many ways respiration can be thought of as the opposite of photosynthesis. During respiration, energy is released from sugar molecules and used by the plant to drive life processes in the plant. Glucose is converted to carbon dioxide, water, and energy with the aid of several important enzymes. This process is affected by temperature, water, and oxygen. When the buildup of sugar molecules during plant photosynthesis exceeds the burning of sugar molecules during respiration, plant growth occurs. After fruits and vegetables are harvested, ripening and subsequent degradation occur because sugar molecules are not being replenished by photosynthesis.

FURTHER LABORATORY INVESTIGATIONS

1. Place several potted plants in total darkness. Remove a plant after 1, 4, 12, 24, and 48 hours, testing each one for starch as an indicator of photosynthetic activity.

2. Compare the effects of different light sources on photosynthesis (growth). Treatments should include sunlight, incandescent light, fluorescent light, and grow lights. Effects of duration and intensity of light source can also be examined. All other growing conditions should be the same for all treatments in the experiment.

3. Examine the effects of light quality on seed germination. Place 50 pre-soaked lettuce seeds in petri dishes lined with wet blotters. Wrap dish C (the control) in aluminum foil—the no light condition. Wrap dishes A and B with two layers of red cellophane. Place dish A under a clear, dim fluorescent light for five minutes then wrap in aluminum foil. Wrap dish B with two additional layers of blue cellophane, giving it two red and two blue layers of cellophane. Place dish B under an incandescent lamp for 15 minutes, then wrap in foil. Store

all three dishes at room temperature for seven days. Record the number of germinations and percentage of germination for each light treatment. (Note: This experiment is similar to research conducted by USDA scientists that led to the discovery of phytochrome. In your experiment, dish A received 5 minutes of red light, dish B received 5 minutes of red light and 15 minutes of far-red light, and dish C received no light.)

4. Separate photosynthesis pigments by chromatography. Select one or more leaves from herbaceous plants. Cut the chromatography paper into strips about one inch wide and six inches long. Handle by the edges only. Place a leaf near the end of the chromatography paper and crush the leaf on the paper using a wooden stick or coin. Crush the leaf until a dark, thin line develops. (Thin lines give better pigment separation.) Remove the leaf and allow the line to dry completely. Pour 70% isopropyl alcohol into a beaker until the fluid line is about one-half inch high. Wrap the nonstained end of the chromatography paper around a pencil and use a paper clip or tape to secure. Lay the pencil on top of the beaker and adjust the paper so that only the very end is touching the alcohol. Do not wet the green line. Make sure the paper is not touching the sides of the beaker. Cover with plastic wrap to avoid evaporation. Allow the liquid to rise within about one-half inch of the top of the paper. Remove the paper and allow to air dry. Repeat the procedure using leaves of different colors.

5. Design several experiments to test the effects of storage conditions on the shelf life of various fruits and vegetables. Independent variables could include storage temperature and available oxygen.

Chapter 8

TRANSPIRATION

Sweating Plants?

AGRICULTURAL APPLICATIONS

The difference between poor, average, and record crop yields is primarily due to the amount and timing of soil water supply. Unfortunately, proper watering is probably the most misunderstood cultural practice. For maximum plant growth and crop yield, the soil must be able to supply the growing plant's water needs. This is complicated by the fact that much of the water taken in by plant root systems is lost through leaf tissues (transpiration). Since leaves are major food and horticultural products, cultural

Figure 8-1. Supplying the right amount of water to a plant is difficult.

Figure 8-2.   Crop yield is directly related to moisture availability.

practices that ensure the water content of freshly harvested products must be used.

Soil moisture fluctuates widely, especially in outdoor growing conditions, and a deficit or surplus of water usually exists. A good water management program seeks to avoid extremes in water availability through a variety of means, including irrigation, adequate drainage, improved soil absorption and water holding capacity, and reduced water evaporation from soil surfaces. The selection of the proper practices to use depends upon the type of soil and environmental growing conditions. Growers can use tensiometers to track soil moisture levels.

TERMS

adhesion	evapotranspiration	spongy mesophyll
cohesion	guard cell	tensiometer
cuticle	osmosis	transpiration
diffusion	osmotic pressure	transpiration stream
epidermis	plasmolysis	turgor

Figure 8-3. A deficit or surplus of water usually exists.

Figure 8-4. Mulch helps the soil retain moisture, thus increasing the
availability of water to the plant.

Transpiration conditions largely determine a plant's water needs. Growers use various management practices to control these conditions, to the extent possible. For example, some greenhouse and nursery plants are shaded to reduce water losses due to transpiration. Transplanted seedlings in the greenhouse are often shaded for the same reason. Greenhouse cooling systems are also designed with this objective in mind.

Some plants transpire large amounts of water. It is estimated that a corn plant loses four gallons of water per week through transpiration. Mature trees can transpire 20 to 100 gallons per day, and an acre of corn is estimated to transpire 350,000 gallons of water per growing season! Consequently, the amount of water needed in a growing season varies by plant species. Corn needs 12 to 24 inches of rain in a single season. The plant's water needs must be met through rainfall and/or irrigation.

In general, irrigation must be frequent enough to keep the growing medium moist and leach out accumulating salts. In addition to manual watering, drip and mist irrigation systems are commonly used in greenhouses. Watering and potting practices must ensure that adequate soil moisture is maintained in plant root zones. Microirrigation has become more widely used in maintaining landscape plant materials. To prevent losses in field crops, more and more growers are using irrigation, even in regions where annual rainfall is adequate. Since rainfall amounts are often inadequate when the plant's water needs are the highest, irrigation can result in significant yield increases. Irrigation also provides good dividends in double-cropping by helping to get the second crop off to a strong start. Water stress early in the growth cycle can

Figure 8-5. Trees can transpire up to 100 gallons of water per day!

Figure 8-6. Crops in double-cropping systems often need irrigation. (Courtesy, National FFA Organization)

reduce yields by adversely affecting pollination. The type of soil may determine the need for irrigation; sandy and claypan soils often require irrigation.

OBJECTIVES—QUESTIONS FOR INVESTIGATION

After completing the laboratory investigations and studying the remaining parts of this chapter, you should be able to answer the following questions:

1. How are moisture supplies used up by living plants?

2. How does transpiration occur?

3. What factors affect the rate of transpiration?

4. Why are high humidity levels most desirable for plant growth?

5. How does soil moisture affect transpiration rate?

6. How does water stress affect plants?

LABORATORY INVESTIGATIONS

EXPERIMENT I.
EFFECTS OF LEAF SURFACE AREA AND
AIR MOVEMENT ON TRANSPIRATION RATE

Purpose

The purpose of this experiment is to determine how transpiration rate is affected by leaf size and number, as well as air movement.

Materials

- four 50 milliliter graduated cylinders (or large test tubes or vials with metric rulers taped to the side)
- modeling clay or four corks or rubber stoppers
- cuttings from a large-leafed, herbaceous plant (bean, geranium, poinsettia, etc.)
- water
- electric fan

Procedures

Select leaves of similar size from your stock plants. Take four stem cuttings—two with one leaf each, and two with three or four leaves each. Leaf stems must be long enough to extend well below the water line in the graduated cylinder or test tube. Insert one stem in each of the four graduated cylinders. Gently pack modeling clay around the stem at the cylinder opening to prevent evaporation losses. Be careful not to crush the stem. As an alternative, make a hole in four corks or rubber stoppers. The stem must snugly fit into the hole to minimize evaporation. Push the cutting through the hole and cut off the stem under water to prevent air pockets in the stem. At least two inches of the stem must extend beneath the stopper. Record the water level in each cylinder.

Place all four cylinders under the same environmental conditions (temperature, light, etc.). Place two of the cylinders (one with a single leaf and one with multiple leaves) in front of a low speed fan. Record the water level in each cylinder on a daily basis for one week. Summarize your data in a chart or graph.

EXPERIMENT 2. EFFECTS OF LIGHT ON TRANSPIRATION

Purpose

The purpose of this investigation is to determine the effects of light quality, intensity, and duration on transpiration.

Figure 8-7. Setup of transpiration experiment 1.

Materials

- four 50 milliliter graduated cylinders (or large test tubes or vials with metric rulers taped to the side)

- modeling clay or four corks or rubber stoppers

- cuttings from a large-leafed, herbaceous plant (bean, geranium, poinsettia, etc.)

- water

- electric fan

- incandescent, fluorescent, grow lights, and HID lights, if available

Figure 8-7b. After only 20 minutes in the sun, the cutting on the left is badly wilted because it cannot pull in water fast enough to keep up with transpiration losses.

Procedures

Follow the same procedures used in Experiment 1 to set up this experiment. Be sure to record the beginning water level for each treatment. Rather than using a fan to stir the air, the effects of different light sources on transpiration will be compared. All environmental conditions should be the same except for the presence/type of light. Place one treatment in the dark for two days and record the water level in the cylinder. Other stem cuttings should be placed under each type of light available (incandescent, fluorescent, grow lights, HID, and sunlight). Expose leaves to their respective treatments for 48 consecutive hours, recording water levels at 24 and 48 hours. Treatments should

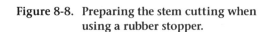

Figure 8-8.   Preparing the stem cutting when using a rubber stopper.

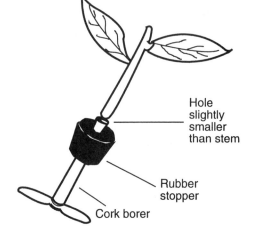

Hole slightly smaller than stem

Rubber stopper

Cork borer

be replicated to increase the reliability of your results. Summarize your data in chart and/or graph form.

Light other than that provided by the treatment must be eliminated. For example, place the incandescent light treatment in a room where all other light can be blocked out. A foil-lined aquarium or other special container may be used. **Avoid using flammable containers!** Light intensity is a function of type of light plus distance of the light source from the plant. Position incandescent lights far enough away from the plant materials to prevent heat damage.

SCIENCE CONNECTIONS

TRANSPIRATION

Water loss through the leaves of plants is known as *transpiration*. Over 90% of all water absorbed by the plant's root system is given off through transpiration. The underside of leaves contains a large number of pores called *stomata*, that open and close under certain conditions. (Some plants, including many crop plants, also have stomata on the upper side of their leaves.) Water vapor escapes through these stomata. Stomata also permit the inward movement of atmospheric carbon dioxide, a necessary element in photosynthesis. When closed, stomata limit water loss from the plant, but carbon dioxide intake is also restricted under these conditions.

The leaf is a network of veins that function as an important part of the plant's transport system. Leaves have distinct upper and lower sides. The *cuticle* is a waxy coat on the outer surface of leaves that helps reduce water loss from plant tissues. Some leaves have hairy surfaces, that reduce air flow around the leaf surface. This, in turn, reduces transpiration rate. The entire plant is covered with a continuous cell layer called the *epidermis*. Beneath the upper epidermis are the palisade cells, which are rich in chloroplasts. Beneath the palisade cells is the *spongy mesophyll*. This area of the leaf allows

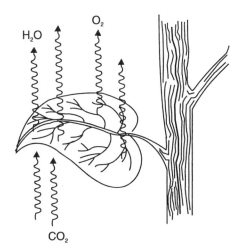

Figure 8-9. Transpiration and gas exchange in leaves.

Figure 8-10. The network of veins in a leaf constitutes a critical part of the plant's transport system.

Figure 8-11. The stem and leaves of some plants are hairy, which helps to slow transpiration rate.

for the exchange of gases in photosynthesis and transpiration. Finally, the lower epidermis contains many stomata, through which water vapor and gases are exchanged.

Osmosis and *diffusion* are the primary means by which plants absorb water from the soil and release water through transpiration. Diffusion is the movement of molecules (in this case, water) from a region of higher concentration to a region of lower concentration. Transpiration water losses occur by diffusion. Osmosis is the diffusion of water through a differentially permeable membrane. Water enters cells by osmosis. After initial absorption by the root hairs and epidermis, water travels across several membranes until it moves into the xylem. It is then transported to the leaves where much of it is diffused through the stomata.

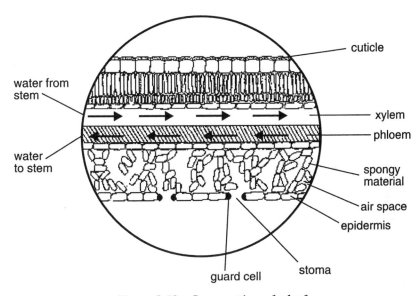

Figure 8-12.   Cross section of a leaf.

The upward movement of water from the roots to the leaves is known as the *transpiration stream*. As water is lost from the outer leaf tissues, water then moves into the water deficient cells from adjacent cells. This osmotic ripple effect occurs backwards (from the leaves to the roots), creating a suction of sorts that has the effect of pulling more water into the plant through the root system. Differences in *osmotic pressure* between cell layers drive this continuous uptake of water from the soil. Current theory suggest that this intake and upward transport of water throughout the plant is due to the physical properties of water. *Cohesion* is the attraction between like

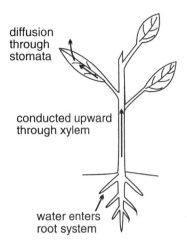

diffusion through stomata

conducted upward through xylem

water enters root system

Figure 8-13. Water flow through a plant.

molecules (i.e., two water molecules). *Adhesion* is the attraction between unlike molecules (i.e., water and plant tissues). The cohesion-tension theory suggests that water rises in plants due to its adhesion to capillary walls in plants and to itself. (Try several experiments to illustrate the cohesive and adhesive properties of water.)

Growers can keep track of soil moisture with *tensiometers*, which measure soil moisture tension (SMT). Tensiometers are best suited for use in sandy and loamy soils. They provide an estimate of how hard the roots are working to extract moisture from the soil. As the soil becomes drier, water is pulled from the tensiometer and SMT increases. The reduced water volume in the instrument creates a partial vacuum which is registered on the gauge. After irrigation or rainfall SMT decreases as soil moisture is replenished. The vacuum in the tensiometer draws water back into the instrument.

Water in the leaves evaporates into the air spaces in the leaf and then diffuses through the stomata into the atmosphere. Transpiration is regulated

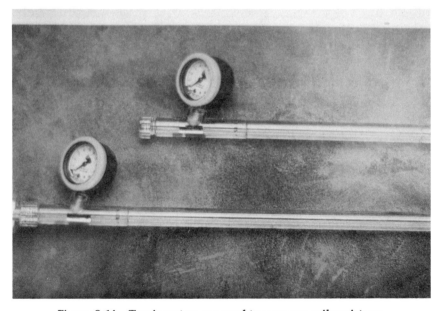

Figure 8-14. Tensiometers are used to measure soil moisture.

by the stomata. This evaporation of water molecules from the surface of leaves helps to cool the plant on hot, sunny days. Stomata are surrounded by *guard cells*, which open and close due to changes in cell firmness, or *turgor*. As cells lose water content, they lose their turgidity. This water loss is associated with shrinkage of the protoplasm from the cell wall, a process known as *plasmolysis*. Plasmolyzed cells have lost their turgidity, but if water re-enters the cell before permanent damage is done, then the cells become turgid once again. Loss of cell turgidity can be due to low water availability or high salt concentrations in soil water.

Figure 8-15. **After 15 minutes the tomato stem in the salt solution (right) loses turgidity.**

FACTORS AFFECTING TRANSPIRATION

Light, carbon dioxide concentrations, and water content in plant tissues affect the stomata, which control transpiration rates. In addition, air movement and humidity affect the opening and closing of the stomata. The guard cells surrounding the stomata have rather elastic walls that are thicker on the side next to the stomatal pore. Thus, changes in turgor pressure of the guard cells cause the stomatal pores to open and close. When the turgor pressure of the guard cells is low, the cells become "limp," which allows the stomatal pore to close. When turgor pressure of the guard cells is high, they become rigid and the stomatal pore opens. The action of the guard

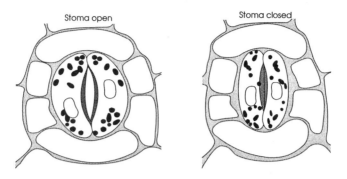

Figure 8-16. Stomata with turgid guard cell and pore open (left) and flaccid guard cell with pore closed (right).

cells is similar to a pair of curved balloons that are tied together at each end. When the balloons are only partially inflated, they are limp and close together. But when they are fully inflated, they are rigid and curved apart.

When plants become water stressed, they begin to wilt. This low turgor pressure leads to closing of the stomata. The plant thus conserves water supplies during dry conditions. However, closure of the stomata also stops photosynthesis, since the needed carbon dioxide must enter through the stomata. This, in turn, reduces carbohydrate manufacture and slows plant growth and metabolism. On hot, sunny days, herbaceous plants often wilt slightly, but they usually recover at night if soil water supplies are sufficient.

Evaporation losses through transpiration and from the soil are known as *evapotranspiration*. In some regions farmers use known evapotranspiration rates to guide their irrigation practices. Higher evapotranspiration results in greater water stress

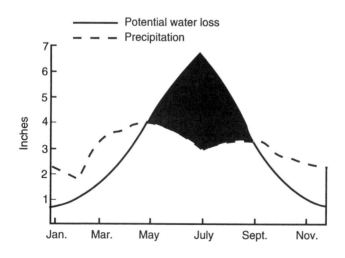

Figure 8-17. Average moisture precipitation and potential moisture loss from a growing crop.

in plants. In addition to slowing down plant metabolism, water stress has a negative effect on pollination in some crops. In corn the emergence of corn silks is delayed, coupled with a shortened period of pollen shedding. The net effect is a shorter time frame during which pollination can occur. Research has shown that corn yields can be reduced by as much as 40% when visible wilting occurs on four consecutive days when silks are emerging.

Light has a major effect on transpiration. In most plants the stomata are open during the day and closed at night. If light in-

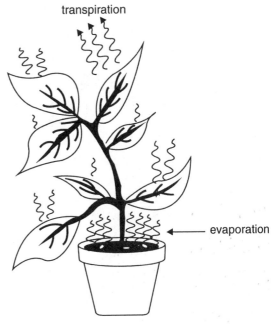

Figure 8-18. Evapotranspiration includes evaporation of water from the soil surface and diffusion of water through stomata in the leaves.

Figure 8-19. Water stress in corn shortens the pollen shedding period, reducing pollination success.

tensity is low, transpiration is also low. An increase in potassium ions in the guard cells leads to an increase in osmotic flow of water into the guard cells from adjacent cells. The resulting increased turgor of the guard cells causes the stomata to open and transpiration to rise. As noted in the previous chapter, an increase in *carbon dioxide concentration* leads to an increase in photosynthesis, which is associated with greater intake of carbon dioxide through the stomatal pores. However, plant respiration increases with an increase in temperature, and when resulting carbon dioxide concentrations reach a certain point, the stomata close.

Several other factors have a significant effect on transpiration rates. As temperature rises, transpiration rate increases (approximately twice as much from 68 to 86°F). Higher humidity decreases transpiration, due to a slowdown in diffusion. Wind tends to sweep away water molecules as they diffuse from leaf surfaces, thus reducing humidity at the leaf/air surface and increasing transpiration. However, studies have shown that wind speeds greater than 15 mph lead to stomatal closure.

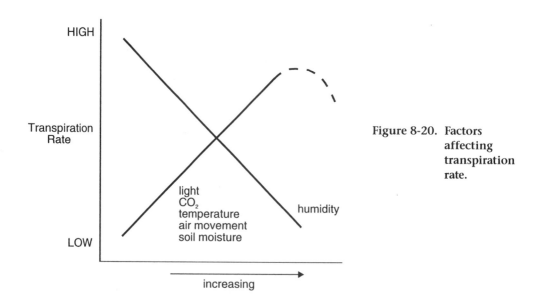

Figure 8-20. Factors affecting transpiration rate.

CHAPTER SUMMARY

Most of the water absorbed by the root systems of plants is lost into the atmosphere through the leaves of plants. This transpiration is controlled by tiny pores, usually found on the underside of leaves. Most plants open their stomata during the day and close them at night. Many factors affect the rate of transpiration in plants; light and water availability exert the greatest influence on transpiration rate. Temperature, humidity, air movement, fertility (potassium concentrations), and carbon dioxide concentration also have a significant effect on rate of transpiration.

Guard cells form the stomatal pores and open and close due to turgor pressure. As water content of the guard cells increases, turgor pressure increases and the guard cells open. Plants transpire relatively large amounts of water. Evapotranspiration includes water losses due to both transpiration and evaporation from the soil. Percolation of water through the soil accounts for other water losses. As plants transpire, additional water is pulled from the soil solution into the roots due to osmotic and diffusion pressure differences throughout the plant and between the root tissues and soil water. Water management is one of the most important and basic aspects of plant growth and crop production, with water availability having direct effects on yield. Growers use a variety of management strategies to control soil moisture levels and transpiration rates.

FURTHER LABORATORY INVESTIGATIONS

1. Cover the soil surface of a potted plant with aluminum foil. Enclose the plant in a glass jar or container. Place in normal growing conditions for three days. Observe condensation of water on the interior of the glass container. (What would happen if the plant were kept in the container for a week or more?)

2. Place several wilted celery and carrot sticks in a container of water. Place other wilted samples in a 10% salt solution. Observe the results. Explain the changes that occurred in each of the samples.

3. Design and conduct an experiment to measure the effects of temperature, humidity, and soil type on rate of transpiration. In addition, the effects of wind speed can also be examined.

4. Examine the effects of various plant factors on transpiration rate. Plant characteristics might include species, leaf surface area, stage of growth, and leaf age.

5. Design and test a method of measuring transpiration rate for an entire growing plant. Typical potted plants, as well as field crops grown in pots, can be tested. The entire plant must be enclosed in a waterproof, translucent material. A method of collecting and measuring the amount of water transpired must also be developed. Transpiration and evapotranspiration rates can be compared.

Chapter 9

TROPISMS

Give Me Light!

AGRICULTURAL APPLICATIONS

Growers have long observed that growth patterns of both the above- and below-ground parts of plants respond to environmental stimuli. When disoriented, plants have the fascinating ability to right themselves and resume a vertical direction of growth. The orientation of seeds (horizontal, vertical, right side up) has no effect on the ability of the germinating seed to send out an upward growing shoot and downward growing root. Whether

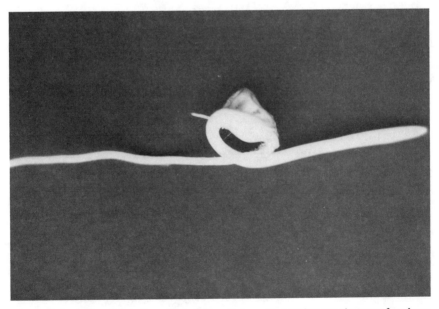

Figure 9-1. Regardless of seed position, the seed's gravity-sensing mechanisms head the root and shoot in the right directions.

Figure 9-2.   The horizontal position of fruit tree branches encourages
            flowering and dwarf-like growth.

the seed falls to the soil surface by natural means or is placed on or in
the soil by a farmer or grower, the position of the seed (other than depth)
has no effect on germination and seedling development. Young plants that
have been knocked down by wind, rain, or animals are able to almost
immediately redirect their growth in a vertical direction. Even mature
plants, whose cells have reached their growth potential, are able to return
to an upright position for flowering and fruit production. Gravitational
forces influence the direction of shoot and root growth, but these forces
may be offset by other factors. For example, branches of fruit trees are

TERMS

amyloplast	hydrotropism	root cap
auxin	node	statocytes
coleoptile	photoreceptor	thermotropism
geotropism	phototropism	thigmotropism
gravitropism	riboflavin	tropism

sometimes trained to a more horizontal position, which encourages flowering and a dwarf-like response.

Sunlight strikes practically all foliage on outdoor plants and crops during a single day. This is fortunate because direction of growth in plants is altered if the plants receive uneven light duration and intensity. Artificial lighting provided in greenhouses and homes must be designed with this phototropic response in mind. Indoor plants placed near windows will show undesirable growth patterns. In addition, landscape plant material located next to a wall or shaded by larger plants may exhibit unusual growth patterns due to uneven exposure to light. A north-south orientation of greenhouses also results in self-shading of plants, reducing intensity and evenness of light exposure. Providing an even light source is one of the most important management practices for cultivation of indoor crops and plants.

Figure 9-3. Providing an even light source is a major problem when growing indoor plants.

Roots have been shown to grow toward water. In field crops such as corn, well drained soils result in deeper root growth. Crops with deeper roots are better able to withstand drought. In irrigated conditions water need not be precisely placed at the root zone; some margin of error exists because of the root system's capacity to "find" available water in the soil.

Figure 9-4. These day lilies were shaded by shrubs and trees, causing the flowers to bend toward the afternoon sun.

OBJECTIVES—QUESTIONS FOR INVESTIGATION

After completing the following experiments and other activities designed by your teacher, you should be able to answer the following questions:

1. How do germinating seeds and plants maintain an upright orientation for growth?

2. Why do plant shoots grow upward and plant roots grow downward?

3. How do germinating seeds and plants respond to changes in gravity?

4. In terms of direction of growth, how do plants respond to light source? Why?

5. How do root systems respond to the location of available soil water?

LABORATORY INVESTIGATIONS

EXPERIMENT I.
GEOTROPISM

Purpose

The purpose of this experiment is to examine the effects of gravity on root and shoot growth during seed. germination.

Materials

- 18 corn seeds
- cardboard pieces (three approximately 5 inches x 5 inches)
- chlorine bleach, 5% solution
- straight pins (12)
- three resealable plastic bags (one gallon size)
- four pieces of wire, each piece 9 inches long
- paper towels

Procedures

Soak the corn seeds in chlorine bleach (5% solution) for about 30 minutes to kill any mold spores that might be attached to the seeds, then soak the seeds overnight in water. Select 12 of the seeds (the ones that appear to have absorbed the most water).

Arrange four of the seeds in a circle on each of three pieces of cardboard. Pin each seed to the piece of cardboard so that the tip of each seed points toward the middle of the circle. Place two folded, moist paper towels in the bottom of each of the three resealable bags. Bend the pieces of wire into a rainbow shape, and hook the ends over the edge of the cardboard. Use two pieces of the wire on each of two cardboard pieces (A and B). Place cardboard pieces A and B with the mounted seeds in a separate plastic bag and seal it. Place the third piece of cardboard (C) with mounted seeds in a bag without the wire expanders.

Hang bag C in an upright position in a dark place to avoid the influence of light. Place bag A on a flat surface. Bag B should be secured upside

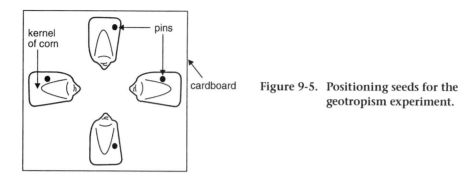

Figure 9-5. Positioning seeds for the geotropism experiment.

down with the expanded portion of the bag facing downward. All three bags should be placed in the same location at room temperature. Inspect the bags daily and record the rate of germination and direction of growth of the roots and shoots.

EXPERIMENT 2. PHOTOTROPISM

Purpose

The purpose of this experiment is to observe the effects of an uneven light source on the growth patterns of seedlings.

Materials

- four pots of germinating seeds or young seedlings (corn, etc.)
- four light-proof cardboard boxes

Procedures

Make a small window in a different side of each of the four cardboard boxes. Line each box with black construction paper to prevent light from reflecting inside the box. After the seedlings have emerged, place one pot in each of the four boxes. Observe the plants every two days and note the growth patterns (size, orientation, leaf color and shape, etc.) of each plant.

SCIENCE CONNECTIONS

PHOTOTROPISM

The growth of plants in response to external stimuli is known as plant *tropism*. Of these external stimuli, light and gravity exert the most effect on plant growth. In outdoor settings light and gravity uniformly impact the growing zones of plants. This promotes equal rates of cell elongation on all sides of the shoot or root, resulting in vertical upward or downward growth. This vertical growth is possible because the concentrations of plant growth regulators is balanced. Tropic responses are due to an imbalance of growth regulators as a result of some external stimulus.

Phototropism is the growth response of a plant toward light. Most plants are positively phototropic; the shoot tips grow toward the primary light source. The bending of the stem apex toward light is caused by differential cell growth—greater cell elongation on the darker side of the stem.

Plants have several distinct *photoreceptor* mechanisms which allow a growth response to light to occur. Most of the research to date has been conducted with grass plants; very little is known about how the photosensing mechanisms function in broad-leaved plants. The *coleoptile* tip contains *auxin*, a plant hormone that promotes cell elongation. In grass plants the active photoreceptor, *riboflavin*, is also located at the tip of the coleoptile. However, the curved phototropic growth response actually takes place 5 to 10

Figure 9-6. This bean seedling shows a typical phototropic response.

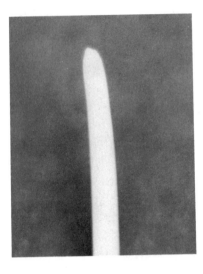

Figure 9-7. The coleoptile from a germinating corn seed contains the shoot's photo-sensing mechanism.

millimeters below the shoot tip in the *growing zone* of the plant. Riboflavin, a yellow pigment that senses light, initiates a transport system that moves auxin away from the lighted side of the stem and toward the shaded side of the stem. Thus, the greater accumulation of auxin on the shaded side of the shoot/stem results in greater *cell elongation* on the shaded side and a curvature of the shoot toward the light source.

Scientists have discovered that the shoot of some plants does not always grow toward the light source. Initially, a positive phototropic response is observed, but as light intensity or duration increases the phototropic response ceases, then becomes negative, and then becomes positive once again! The reasons for these growth patterns in response to light are not known.

GEOTROPISM

Plants also grow in response to gravitational forces. This is known as *geotropism* or *gravitropism*. As a result, plant shoots and roots grow vertically, regardless of the slope of the soil surface. Thus, the shoot and root must be equipped with some sort of gravity-sensing mechanism that allows the plant to adjust its growth as its position changes.

Like the light-sensing mechanism in plants, the gravity-sensing mechanism is also located in the tip of the root and shoot. Specialized cells called *statocytes* are found in the *root cap*, as well as throughout the plant stem. Statocytes contain clusters of starch grains, called *amyloplasts*, which rather quickly settle to the lower side of the statocyte cells as the position of the plant is altered. If the root cap is removed, the root no longer responds to

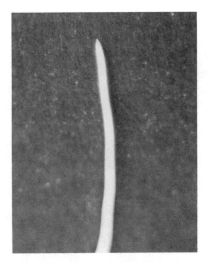

Figure 9-8. The tip of the root cap contains the
gravity-sensing mechanism in roots.

gravitational forces. The degree of geotropic response varies by plant species
and even within plant tissues of the same species.

Plant stems are considered to be negatively geotropic, while roots are
positively geotropic. When plants are placed on one side, root cells on the
opposite side of the gravitational stimulus elongate and produce a downward
growth response toward the gravitational pull. By contrast, shoot cells on
the same side of the gravitational pull elongate to a greater extent, creating
an upward curve in stem growth. How the amyloplasts actually stimulate

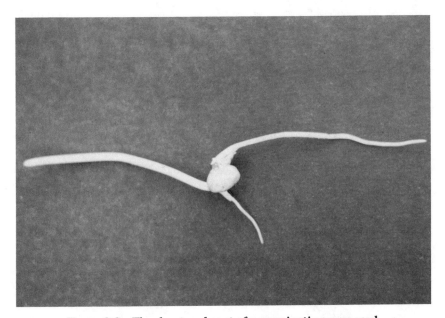

Figure 9-9. The shoot and root of a germinating corn seed.

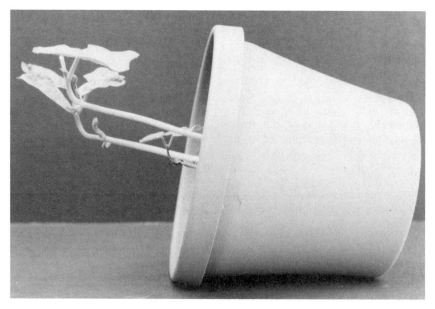

Figure 9-10.   Upward growth of a bean shoot after being placed on its side for
                eight hours.

Figure 9-11. This oak seedling encountered an
               obstruction and redirected its
               growth, exhibiting a
               thigmotropic response.

differential cell elongation is not well understood, although scientists have discovered that redistribution of auxin leads to differential cell elongation. Placing a plant under a centrifugal force, which counters the effects of gravity, prevents the starch grains from settling. The root and shoot then grow horizontally, instead of following the usual vertical growth pattern in response to gravity.

Stems of mature grasses are still able to exhibit a geotropic response even though they have in essence exhausted their growth potential. When these plants are knocked down by nature, people, or animals they are able to regain their upright position by initiating differential growth in a stem *node*. This is a fascinating response, given that the nodes otherwise do not contribute to plant growth. Apparently the amyloplasts play the same role in node curvature as they do in root response to gravitational pull.

OTHER TROPISMS

Phototropism and geotropism are the two primary growth responses of plants to external stimuli. A plant's growth pattern is usually a function of the combined effect of these two stimuli. Plants exhibit a number of other tropic responses. *Hydrotropism* is a growth response to water. In general, roots exhibit a positive hydrotropic response to water. *Thigmotropism* is a growth response to a solid object. This includes a diverted growth path, as well as a coiled growth pattern that is seen in vine-type plants. The roots of common weed plants grow horizontally under colder temperatures and more vertically when temperatures are

Figure 9-12. Coiling vine-type plants actually grow around an object they encounter as a tropic response.

warmer. This is termed *thermotropism*. Plants have been shown to alter their growth patterns in response to chemicals, trauma, electricity, and other stimuli. How plants produce these tropic responses is not well understood.

CHAPTER SUMMARY

In addition to major metabolic processes that continually occur in plants, external stimuli also have a direct influence on patterns of plant growth. Light (intensity and duration) and gravitational forces alter the direction of root and shoot growth. The growth response of plants to external stimuli is known as tropism. Phototropism and geotropism usually work in combination to control growth patterns. Growers must account for the consequences of plant tropisms, especially in indoor and greenhouse plants and crops where appearance of the plant is of primary concern.

Plants have light-sensing and gravity-sensing mechanisms in their root and shoot tips that sense environmental stimuli and initiate respective adjustments in plant growth. Phototropism and geotropism are both due to an imbalance in cell elongation in the shoot or root growing zone. Plants produce a curved growth pattern toward a light source due to a greater concentration of auxin on the shaded side of the shoot. The plant's light-sensing mechanism initiates a redistribution of this plant hormone, which is produced in the tip of the coleoptile. Geotropic responses are due to the action of specialized cells called statocytes. Starch grains contained in these cells settle near different parts of the cell membrane as the position of the plant changes. When the plant is placed in a horizontal position, the starch grains settle to the lower side of the cell wall, resulting in greater cell elongation in that area and resumed vertical growth. Plants have been found to exhibit a number of other tropic responses, many of which are not well understood.

FURTHER LABORATORY INVESTIGATIONS

1. Conduct a hydrotropism experiment to examine the direction of root growth in relation to water source. Make a hole in the bottom of a box and place a piece of medium-mesh screen wire over it. Add one-half inch potting soil or germinating mix and plant three to four

corn seeds. Cover with another one-half inch of soil and moisten. Place the box over a dry dish or saucer. Prepare a second box in the same manner and place it over a dish of water. (The water should be within one-fourth inch of the screen.) Compare the direction of root growth for each treatment.

2. Obtain a large potted plant and observe the effects of placement of irrigation water on root growth. Water the plant as needed on only one side of the growing medium for a four to six week period. Note the position of the plant in the pot. Carefully remove the plant from the pot and slowly remove the growing medium from the roots. Observe the pattern of growth of the root system in relation to the placement of water in the pot.

3. Examine the effects of location and spacing of the light source on growth pattern and overall growth. Vary the distance of the light source from the plants, as well as the spacing of individual lights. When different types of artificial light are provided, will the plant grow toward a certain type of light?

4. Determine the effects of the root cap on direction of growth of the root in germinating seeds. Prepare seeds for a warm germination test. After the roots have emerged (as soon as two days), carefully snip off the root cap and/or coleoptile from some germinating seeds and observe the direction of growth of the root and shoot. Compare root growth of normal germinating seeds with those that have had the root cap removed. Remove half of the root cap on another group of germinating seeds and observe the subsequent direction of growth.

5. Design a device to negate the effects of gravity on plant growth. A record turntable or any other slowly rotating mechanism will work. Attach small potted plants to the rotating surface and leave it turning for one day. Observe the direction of growth of the plant shoots.

Chapter 10

HYDROPONICS

Look Mom, No Soil!

AGRICULTURAL APPLICATIONS

Since the mid 1970s, hydroponics has gradually gained acceptance in the United States as a viable and profitable approach for commercial vegetable crop production. The primary hydroponic vegetable crop is lettuce, but a variety of other crops are also grown hydroponically. These include tomatoes, cucumbers, eggplant, peppers and herbs. Commercially grown hydroponic vegetables are usually grown in greenhouses, which allows for

Figure 10-1. Greenhouses are used to provide the needed environmental control for commercial hydroponics.

185

good control of many environmental conditions affecting plant growth and overall production. Marketing is a major concern for hydroponic vegetable crop growers.

In a hydroponic production system more plants can be grown in less space than under field or soil culture conditions. In addition, hydroponic food crops mature faster and yield more. Some believe that hydroponically grown vegetables have a better flavor and overall higher quality than soil-grown vegetables. Hydroponics also provides vegetables at times when fresh, field-grown crops are not available. Soils used in greenhouse vegetable production gradually become more difficult and expensive to sterilize; this is not a concern with hydroponics. In some hydroponics systems, water and fertilizer are conserved because they are recirculated through the system. Hydroponics also allows for crop growth in areas where suitable soils are not available.

Whether plants are grown hydroponically or in soil, they still need proper temperature, light, humidity, and nutrition. In addition, production can be increased by raising other factors, such as carbon dioxide concentration, to above normal levels. Since commercial hydroponic crops are grown in greenhouses, many of the key environmental factors are easily controlled.

Maintaining the appropriate supply of nutrients to hydroponically grown plants is probably the most critical management practice in soilless plant culture. Management of micronutrient levels and solution pH are especially difficult. Thus, accurate preparation of stock solutions is crucial

TERMS

aeration	continuous flow system	nutrient film technique
aeroponic	drip irrigation	(NFT)
alkaline	gravel culture	nutrient solution
anions	hydroponics	open hydroponic system
bag culture	immobile nutrients	pH
bare root system	microorganism	sand culture
cations	mobile nutrients	soilless culture
chlorosis	necrosis	substrate system
closed hydroponic system	noninfectious disease	trickle irrigation

Figure 10-2. Some companies operate large-scale hydroponic systems. (Courtesy, Illinois Dept. of Agriculture)

Figure 10-3. Lettuce growing in a water culture system. (Courtesy, Marty Frick)

to effective soilless crop production. Water quality is a constant concern. Many commercial growers use automatic equipment to monitor salinity and pH, as well as temperature. Maintaining adequate oxygen levels for plant roots is also a major concern for hydroponic growers.

Hydroponics also can be used successfully by the hobbyist or home-owner for growing vegetables, flowers, herbs, and spices. As long as certain growth conditions are met, hydroponic system designs are limited only by the grower's imagination. Different techniques may be used to adjust the scale and type of operation in the home or business. These include sand culture, gravel culture, bag culture, aeroponics, raceways, nutrient film technique, and others.

Hydroponics is widely used as a research technique because it allows for better control of growing conditions, including temperature, humidity, light, and carbon dioxide. In addition, hydroponics provides for better control of concentration, form, and presence of nutrients than soil. Thus, hydroponics has many research applications because it allows scientists to exert better control over variables in experiments. Hydroponics is well suited to seed germination, since the soil-borne fungus that causes damping off injury is not present.

Much research is being conducted on ways to improve the performance and cost-effectiveness of hydroponic production systems themselves. NASA has conducted hydroponic experiments in space. Hydroponics offers in-

Figure 10-4. Hydroponics is an excellent research tool. (Courtesy, Fred Below)

triguing possibilities for space-grown food. New methods of marketing hydroponically grown crops are also being explored.

Plant breeders continue to seek new cultivars that are well suited to soilless crop production. Mildew resistant cucumbers and tomatoes that are resistant to salinity and root disease have been developed thus far. Cucumber cultivars that set fruit without pollination and bear almost all female flowers have been developed. Scientists are also examining the effects of various pruning and pollination techniques on some vegetable crops grown in soilless conditions.

Figure 10-5. The effectiveness of various hydroponic systems is one area of hydroponic research. (Courtesy, Illinois Dept. of Agriculture)

New greenhouse designs are being developed and tested that allow for better temperature control and space utilization. Root zone warming is a new development, based upon the discovery that as long as plant roots are kept warm, air temperatures can be significantly cooler than normal without negative effects on the plant.

OBJECTIVES—QUESTIONS FOR INVESTIGATION

After conducting the laboratory exercises included in this chapter and completing other activities assigned by your teacher, you should be able to answer the following questions:

1. Why are plants able to survive and grow without soil?
2. How do plants obtain essential mineral elements necessary for growth and fruit production?
3. What effect does the pH of the nutrient solution have on plant growth?
4. Why is oxygen pumped into the nutrient solution in most hydroponic systems?
5. What effects do nutrient deficiencies have on plants?

LABORATORY INVESTIGATIONS

EXPERIMENT I.
A COMPARISON OF SOIL VS. SOILLESS PLANT CULTURE

Purpose

The purpose of this experiment is to observe the response of plants grown hydroponically and compare their growth with that of plants grown in soil.

Materials

- hydroponic system suitable for growing multiple plants (aquarium, styrofoam container, etc.)
- aerator
- styrofoam board for a lid
- complete, water-soluble fertilizer
- Jiffy-7 pellets or floral foam
- seeds (lettuce, spinach, etc.)
- plastic tray or flat
- pH meter or litmus paper
- soil/growing medium

Procedures

Prepare the hydroponic unit and place it in a location that provides adequate light and temperature. If using a clear container, such as an aquarium, cover the sides with foil to prevent algae growth in the nutrient solution. Prepare the nutrient solution, following the directions provided by the manufacturer for mixing. Allow tap water to sit for two days before using in the hydroponic system to allow for the removal of chlorine. Alternatively, a chlorine removal agent can be purchased at a pet supply store. Fill the container with the nutrient solution, making sure the solution level reaches the bottom of the lid. Check the pH of the nutrient solution and adjust if necessary.

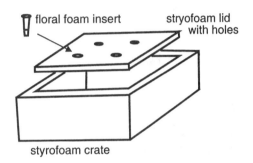

The lid will need to float on top of the nutrient solution if you are using Jiffy-7 pellets. Expand the Jiffy-7 pellets by adding water. Cut holes in the styrofoam lid to hold the Jiffy-7 pellets or floral foam plugs. Foam plugs should extend two to three inches below the styrofoam

Figure 10-6. Styrofoam packing crates or coolers work well for small-scale production and research programs.

Figure 10-7. Rockwool, foam plugs, and a variety of other means are used to secure plants.

into the nutrient solution. (Foam plugs work well with coolers and styrofoam crates that have a fixed lid position.) Holes should be six to eight inches apart and provide a snug fit for the pellets or plugs. The holes should be slightly tapered from top to bottom to prevent the plug or pellet from pushing through the lid. Place the pellets or foam plugs into the holes. Place two seeds in each pellet. After germination, thin to a single plant in each pellet or plug. Aerate the nutrient solution and replace the solution every two weeks to ensure a continuous balance of nutrients.

Plant the same number of seeds in a flat containing soil. Keep the soil moist by covering the flat with plastic until the seeds emerge. Provide adequate water and nutrients, using the same water-soluble fertilizer used to make the hydroponic nutrient solution. Compare the growth of the seedlings grown under each condition. Record observations such as height, appearance, color, and general health.

EXPERIMENT 2.
THE EFFECTS OF NUTRIENT CONCENTRATIONS
ON HYDROPONIC PLANT GROWTH

Purpose

The purpose of this experiment is to examine the effects of macronutrient concentration on plant growth and general health.

Materials

- hydroponic system (for single or multiple plants)
- seedlings for transplanting into the hydroponic system (lettuce, etc.)
- nutrient solutions, each deficient in a single macronutrient
- pH meter or litmus paper

Procedures

Each hydroponic container will receive a different nutrient solution. Prepare the containers as described in Experiment 1. Add the nutrient solutions to the containers. Clearly label the containers according to the type of nutrient solution they contain.

Maintain the nutrient solutions by aerating and replace with fresh solution every two weeks (or longer depending upon the type of hydroponic setup). Keep a record of the experiment, including the date started, beginning size and condition of plants, height, and overall appearance (noted weekly). Continue the experiment for six weeks. Summarize the results in chart and/or graph form.

When conducting experiments on hydroponics, keep a log (scientific journal) of all activities associated with the experiment. Include treatment descriptions, pH levels, type and amount of light, temperature, humidity, seeding and transplanting dates, nutrient concentrations, when the nutrient solution is changed, and any other factors pertinent to the experiment.

SCIENCE CONNECTIONS

HYDROPONICS

Plants do not need soil to grow—just the mineral nutrients and support they provide. *Hydroponics*, or *soilless culture*, is a method of growing plants in which the nutrients needed by the plant are supplied by a *nutrient solution* (water with dissolved nutrient salts). The term "hydroponics" was coined by California researcher William Gericke in the 1930s when he captured the media's attention with 25-foot-tall tomato vines grown in nutrient solutions. Today, greenhouses are used for hydroponic crop production so environmental growing conditions can be controlled. Plants can be grown with or without a medium (substrate) to support the root system, although some means of securing the plant is always provided.

Hydroponic growing systems offer several advantages over soil culture techniques. Plant nutrition is completely controlled through prepared nutrient solutions. Yield per unit area is greater, since plants may be spaced closer together. Because hydroponic systems pump the necessary nutrients right to the plant, roots do not spread as much as they do in soils, where they must seek out their water and nutrient supplies to a greater degree. The need for weed, disease, and insect control is greatly reduced or eliminated, due to the absence of soil. In most systems no water loss occurs through percolation through a growing medium. High humidity environments minimize water losses due to evaporation, and total water loss approximates transpirational water loss.

Hydroponic fruits tend to be more firm and have a longer shelf life. These fruits transport better, and in some cases, have higher vitamin content. Over-fertilization is prevented, and no leaching of salts into the soil occurs.

Figure 10-8. Hydroponic systems can be simple and relatively inexpensive. (Courtesy, Paul Heasley)

Figure 10-9. A simple hydroponic unit can be made from an aquarium.

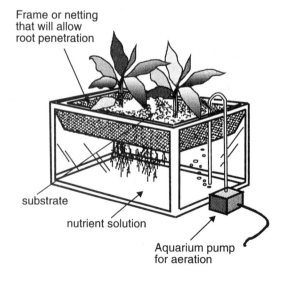

Frame or netting that will allow root penetration

substrate

nutrient solution

Aquarium pump for aeration

Hydroponically grown plants generally mature faster and yield better than those grown in soil.

Methods of hydroponic gardening and crop production vary from the simplest design imaginable (a glass jar) to large scale, complex systems. However, all designs are variations on the same theme of growing plants without soil. *Open hydroponic systems* do not recover the nutrient solution, which is commonly provided to plants by *drip* or *trickle irrigation*. *Closed hydroponic systems* recover and recirculate the nutrient solution. A sufficient supply of oxygen must be available to the roots, and this is often accomplished by some means of artificial *aeration*.

Hydroponic Systems

Hydroponic systems are also classified according to the use of substrate materials. *Substrate systems* include *sand culture*, which involves growing plants in sterilized sand and with individual drip irrigation. *Gravel culture*, in which irrigated plants are grown in gravel for mechanical support, is a seldom-used technique today in commercial hydroponic systems. Rockwool is a commonly used substrate for germinating seeds and growing hydroponic crops. Rockwool is a porous material made from basalt, an inert rock. *Bag culture*, a popular substrate technique, utilizes plastic bags that are filled with a substrate, such as rockwool, peatlite, and sawdust. Drip irrigation is commonly used. Bags either lay flat on the floor or are secured in an upright position, which requires less space.

Figure 10-10. Cotton growing in a sand culture system.

Figure 10-11. PVC pipe is often used in small-scale recirculating systems. (Courtesy, National FFA Organization)

Figure 10-12. Plants can be grown aeroponically. These Hungarian wax peppers are growing in hanging columns. (Courtesy, Marty Frick)

Bare root systems use no medium or substrate for root development or mechanical support; however, rockwool cubes are often used as a starter material. There are several types of bare root systems. Deep flow or *continuous flow systems* are made up of shallow pools with panels containing plants floating on the surface. In *aeroponic systems* plant roots are suspended in air, and a fine mist of oxygen-rich nutrient solution is sprayed on them at regulated intervals. *Nutrient film technique (NFT)* is a popular bare root system that uses a recirculating, shallow stream of nutrient solution which moves through channels in which the plants grow. Roots are usually covered with a plastic sheet.

Today, plastics are used in nearly every type of commercial soilless cultivation. Their advantages include corrosion resistance, light weight, thermal insulating qualities, ability to hold liquids and gases, and low maintenance. However, plastics stretch more easily than other materials, and some may exhibit phototoxic effects. Thus, plastics must be carefully selected to fit the hydroponic system.

PLANT DISEASES IN SOILLESS CULTURE

Plant species vary in their sensitivity to soilless cultivation. Cucumbers are extremely sensitive to high salts, low light, cool temperatures, and low humidity. Tomatoes are also very sensitive to low light. Disease resistance is especially critical when selecting tomato cultivars for hydroponic production.

Plant diseases may be caused by either unfavorable environmental conditions (*noninfectious diseases*) and/or *microorganisms*. Common causes of noninfectious diseases include low or high temperatures, chemical injury, air impurities, nutrient deficiency, nutrient oversupply, and oxygen deprivation around roots.

Four types of microorganisms can cause diseases in greenhouse crops: *bacteria, fungi, viruses,* and *nematodes*. Bacteria can deplete the oxygen supplies in the nutrient solution. Fungi usually feed upon plant tissue after an injury, resulting in a spot or rot symptom. Viruses are of particular concern since they are responsible for a wide range of plant disease symptoms. Virus injury usually results in lower crop yield and poorer quality fruit. Viruses are transmitted from one plant to another by insects, man, and other means.

pH OF THE NUTRIENT SOLUTION

The *pH* of the root environment in most soilless systems usually becomes more *alkaline* with time. A pH of 5.5 to 6.5 is suitable for most plants. At higher pH ranges some micronutrients become less available for uptake by the root system. The increase in pH is due to the fact that plants absorb *anions* (NO_3-, PO_4-, and SO_4-) at a faster rate than cations ($Ca+$, $Mg+$, $K+$), resulting in an increase in hydrogen ions. Commercial hydroponic systems monitor pH constantly, and adjustments are made automatically. In small scale research or home hydroponics, pH can be determined by litmus paper, an indicator solution, or a pH meter. Vinegar can be used to lower the pH level in small hydroponic systems.

Figure 10-13. In both research and production hydroponic systems the pH of the nutrient solution must be carefully monitored.

PLANT NUTRITION

Essential plant nutrients must be provided through the nutrient solution. Water and nutrients from the solution are absorbed by root hairs through the process of osmosis. *Nutrient deficiency symptoms* often become apparent only after the deficiency is acute and yield has been reduced. When *mobile nutrients*, such as nitrogen and phosphorus, become deficient, they move from older leaves to new leaves to support leaf expansion. Thus, deficiency symptoms first appear in the older leaves. A deficiency of *immobile nutrients*, such as calcium and boron, appears first in the new, faster growing leaves. A lack of chlorophyll causes yellowing of leaves and is termed

Symptoms	Element Deficient

1. Symptoms most apparent in older or lower leaves
  2. Generalized leaf symptoms (includes veins)
    3. Leaves light green to yellow, especially down midrib
    3. Leaves with reddish or purple margins
  2. Localized symptons (interveinal or mottled)
    3. Interveinal chlorosis (striping in monocots);
      curling of leaf margins
    3. Mottled or chlorotic leaves with necrotic spots
      4. Necrosis on leaf margins, necrotic spots between veins
      4. Affected spots generalized, rapidly enlarging;
        white spots on corn leaves; shortened stem internodes
	Nitrogen
	Phosphorus
	
	Magnesium
	
	Potassium
	
	Zinc

1. Symptoms localized and most apparent in newer or bud leaves
  2. Terminal buds die; tips of new leaves distort
    3. Top growth severely stunted, giving plants the
      appearance of being cut off at the top; root
      laterals stunted
    3. Leaves become thickened, curled, and brittle;
      young leaves yellow or redden in some legumes;
      root tips necrotic
  2. Terminal buds remain alive
    3. Young leaves permanently wilted (withered tip)
    3. Young leaves chlorotic, not wilted
      4. Scattered necrotic spots; interveinal chlorosis,
        bleaching in severe iron deficiency
      4. General chlorosis of young leaves
	Calcium
	
	Boron
	
	Copper
	
	Manganese
	or Iron
	Sulfur

Figure 10-14. **Visual diagnosis of plant nutrient deficiencies is difficult, but a key can be used in combination with plant analysis and soil tests.**

chlorosis. Necrosis refers to death (browning) of plant tissue. *Mottling* is a patchy development of deficiency symptoms.

Plants need 16 different chemical elements for healthy growth. Carbon, hydrogen, and oxygen are taken from the air, while the other 13 must be supplied through the nutrient solution. This includes six macronutrients (nitrogen, potassium, phosphorus, calcium, magnesium, and sulfur) and seven micronutrients (iron, manganese, boron, zinc, chlorine, copper, and molybdenum). The concentration and form of each mineral nutrient must be carefully controlled by the hydroponic grower. Nitrogen, potassium, and iron are among the nutrients of most concern in hydroponic systems. The availability of many nutrients decreases as the nutrient solution becomes more alkaline. This is particularly true of some micronutrients, such as manganese and iron.

CHAPTER SUMMARY

While commercial hydroponics production has been significant in sev-

Figure 10-15. Hydroponics is extensively used in plant nutrition research.

Figure 10-16. Lettuce is one of the most popular hydroponic crops.

eral other countries, hydroponics has been relatively slow to take hold in the United States. However, commercial interest in hydroponics has been increasing in recent years. There is evidence to suggest that, among other advantages, hydroponically grown crops have higher quality and yield. Much research is underway to determine the most effective and efficient hydroponic systems. In addition, hydroponics is used as an important research tool to provide more controlled investigation of many crop production factors.

Hydroponics is the soilless culture of plants. As such, all nutrients needed by the plant must be supplied in the nutrient solution. In solution hydroponics, plant roots are immersed in the nutrient solution, restricting oxygen concentrations in the root zone. Thus, aeration of the nutrient solution is required for normal root respiration. Growers must provide 13 different nutrients to the growing plant; some of these are of much greater concern than others. Solution pH tends to increase over time because anions are absorbed by plant roots at a faster rate than cations. Growers must continually monitor pH, especially in bare root systems, and make adjustments as necessary.

Many types of hydroponic systems are used in commercial, research, and home gardening settings. As opposed to an open system, in a closed system the nutrient solution is collected and recirculated. All hydroponic systems involve soilless cultivation; however, some systems use substrate materials to anchor the plant, while others use a bare root system. Many design options exist within these two major types of hydroponic systems. Plastics are extremely important to hydroponics and are used in many of the most popular systems today. Disease resistance is a major concern of hydroponic growers. Diseases may be the result of environmental limitations or microorganisms.

FURTHER LABORATORY INVESTIGATIONS

1. Compare the effectiveness of different hydroponic systems. Create your own system design and test its utility.

2. Examine the effects of nutrient solution pH on plant growth and overall appearance. Make sure that all other variables in the experiment are controlled. The same

concentrations of the same nutrients should be present in each nutrient solution.

3. Compare the performance of different species in a soilless growing condition. Use the same nutrient concentration in all nutrient solutions.

4. Determine the effects of aeration on plant growth in various hydroponic systems. Levels might include continuous aeration, nighttime aeration, daytime aeration, and alternating day aeration.

5. Examine the effects of light intensity and duration, temperature, and humidity on hydroponic plant growth.

Chapter 11

PLANT RESPONSES TO HERBICIDES

Shields Up!

AGRICULTURAL APPLICATIONS

Weeds compete very strongly with crop plants for available nutrients, moisture, and light. Controlling weeds is an ongoing challenge in any crop production situation. Certain growing conditions promote vigorous weed growth and make control more difficult. While perennial weeds are often difficult to control because of their deep, spreading roots, annual summer

Figure 11-1. Weeds can be extremely difficult to control, as seen in this field of drilled soybeans. Economic losses due to competing weeds can be significant.

and winter weeds can have a greater negative impact on crop profits. Economic losses are due to reduced yields, lower product quality, and increased production costs related to herbicide application and other control methods. Weed control measures are most effective during the early stages of crop growth, and scouting of crop areas within two weeks after planting is a common practice. The economic impact of chemical treatment of weeds is especially crucial to large scale producers. This impact is measured in terms of herbicide cost, as well as increases in crop yield as a result of weed control treatments.

More than 100 organic herbicides are currently used in the United States for weed control in field and vegetable crops, ornamentals, and turf. In some states over 90% of all crop acres are treated with herbicides. In addition, herbicides are commonly used by homeowners to control weeds in lawns and turf.

Chemical weed control began with the development of 2,4-D in the 1940s. Herbicide applicators must pass certification exams before they can purchase and apply certain herbicides, known as restricted-use herbicides. Misapplication or poor selection of herbicides can be costly, in both economical and environmental terms. Applying too much herbicide can actually damage the crop intended to be protected from weed competition. Misapplication can also cause damage to crops and plants in surrounding areas and lead to an accumulation of herbicides in soils and crops. Build-up of herbicidal residues in ground water is becoming a concern in the major crop-producing states of the Midwest.

Growers use a variety of methods for controlling weeds and reducing the potentially high economic losses that may result from weed competition.

TERMS

adjuvant	herbicides	postemergence
bioassay	integrated pest	preemergence
carryover	management (IPM)	retention
contact herbicide	interception	selective herbicide
cuticle	mode of action	soil texture
cutin	nonselective herbicide	systemic herbicide
economic injury level	organic matter	translocated herbicide
epidermis	phloem	translocation

Figure 11-2. Scientists continue to work to develop weed control methods and products that are safe and effective. (Agricultural Research Service, USDA)

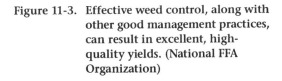

Figure 11-3. Effective weed control, along with other good management practices, can result in excellent, high-quality yields. (National FFA Organization)

These methods include crop rotation, drilling versus row cropping, early planting, and mechanical, biological, and chemical control. In recent years, growers have begun to use a combination of control methods as a result of environmental concerns. Integrated pest management (IPM) uses a combination of control methods and often involves reduced levels of herbicide use. IPM is an example of a sustainable agriculture practice—one that is environmentally prudent.

In field crops herbicides may be applied to the soil before planting and then incorporated into the soil using field cultivators or disks. Pre-emergence herbicides are applied to the soil after planting but before emergence of the crop seedlings. Postemergence herbicides are applied after the crop has emerged. The effectiveness of each of these types of herbicides depends on a number of factors, including timing of application, rainfall, temperature, and humidity.

OBJECTIVES—QUESTIONS FOR INVESTIGATION

After completing the laboratory investigations and studying the remaining parts of this chapter, you should be able to answer the following questions:

Figure 11-4. Herbicides may be applied before planting, before crop seedling emergence, or after emergence. (Illinois Dept. of Agriculture)

1. How do herbicides work within the plant to cause injury or death?
2. How do herbicides enter the plant?
3. Why are some herbicides selective in the plants they affect?
4. Why do some herbicides cause injury to only the plant parts they contact while others are translocated throughout the plant?
5. How do climatic conditions influence herbicide effectiveness?
6. How do plant characteristics affect herbicide activity?
7. Why is timing, method, and rate of herbicide application important?

LABORATORY INVESTIGATIONS

EXPERIMENT I.
EFFECTS OF HERBICIDES ON CROPS AND PLANTS

Purpose

The purpose of this experiment is to examine herbicidal activity on a mixture of crop and weed plants. The experiment will consist of two elements: soil-applied herbicides will be selected and used in one phase of the experiment, while the effects of foliar-applied herbicides will be examined as the second element of the investigation.

Materials

- nine 4-inch pots with drainage holes
- various broadleaf and grass crop seeds
- weed seeds
- dry soil
- various soil-applied and foliar-applied herbicides (Note: Select herbicides that are least toxic and not classified as restrictive use. Suggestions include Eradicane, Pursuit, and Sutan+ as soil-applied herbicides. 2,4-D and Roundup can be used for the foliar-applied treatments. Other herbicides that are more commonly used in your local area can be tested. Ask growers in your community to give you small amounts of leftover herbicides. Be sure to obtain a label for the herbicides you use.)
- water

Procedures

Fill each pot to about one inch from the top with dry soil. In each pot plant three seeds of each crop species (use two broadleaf and one grass species). Plant one-half teaspoon of each of two or three weed seeds. Weed seeds may be obtained from local sources: the Cooperative Extension Service, Crop Improvement Associations, and some seed companies. Add soil to each pot to cover planted seeds.

Label each pot as follows: 1—control; 2, 3, 4—unincorporated Eradicane, Pursuit, and Sutan+; 5, 6, 7—incorporated Eradicane, Pursuit, and Sutan +; 8, 9—foliar-applied 2,4-D and Roundup. (Note: Each pot will be treated with only one herbicide.) Using a 100 milliliter graduated cylinder, add a measured amount of water to the control (pot 1) to thoroughly moisten the soil. Note the amount of water added. Moisten pots 2,3, and 4 with the same amount of water. Then apply 1 milliliter of the appropriate herbicide solution to each pot, as indicated by the label. Use a pipet and apply in drops. (Note: Mix the herbicide with the correct proportion of water as directed on the label.)

For pots 5, 6, and 7 add 1 milliliter of the herbicide solution to the premeasured amount of water needed to moisten the soil for each pot. Water each pot with the water/herbicide solution, making sure that the herbicide used corresponds to the label on the pot. Check plants every two to three days for three weeks and note emergence patterns and injury symptoms. After three weeks compare the roots of the various crops and weed plants.

For pots 8 and 9 allow seeds to germinate and plants to reach a height of about six inches. Following label directions, apply 2,4-D and Roundup to each pot as labelled. Examine the plant response and injury symptoms of the various plants in each pot for a period of two weeks.

EXPERIMENT 2.
DIFFERENTIAL EFFECTS OF HERBICIDES

Purpose

The purpose of this experiment is to examine the differential effects of herbicides on a mixture of broadleaf and grass plants. In addition, the effects of rate of herbicide coverage will be observed.

Materials

- monocotyledon and dicotyledon seeds (corn, beans, oats, etc.)
- three planting flats
- growing medium
- five potted, broad-leaved plants of the same species (field crop or horticultural plants)
- selective and nonselective herbicides (2,4-D, Roundup, etc.)
- glass rod
- plastic wrap

Procedures

Fill the planting flats with the growing medium. Mix the monocot and dicot seeds together. Plant an equal amount of the seed mixture in each of the three flats. After the seedlings have reached a height of about six inches, spray the plants in one flat with a selective herbicide and label accordingly. Spray the plants in the second flat with the nonselective herbicide and label. As with all experiments, record the date and rate of application. Plants in the third flat will remain untreated and will serve as the control. Record your observations of plant injury on a daily basis for a period of two weeks.

Select two of the potted, broad-leaved plants. Using the glass rod, apply one drop of the selective herbicide to one side of the stem of one plant and label it A. In a similar manner apply a drop of the nonselective herbicide to the stem of a second plant labelled B. Record your observation of plant injury and response on a daily basis for two weeks.

Select two of the remaining potted, broad-leaved plants. (The fifth plant may be used as a control.) Label one pot as "complete" coverage and the other as "single leaf" coverage. For the complete coverage plant, spray 2,4-D over the entire foliage of the plant until it drips. For the single leaf treatment select one of the largest leaves on the plant, and mark the stem with a piece of tape. Isolate this leaf from the other leaves on the plant with plastic wrap. Spray this single leaf with 2,4-D until it drips. When the leaf begins to dry, remove the plastic wrap. Note the condition of each plant at the time of herbicide application and every two days throughout the experiment. (You may want to take pictures to record the gradual effects of the herbicide.) Observations should include, species, height, number of leaves, extent and nature of injury, and so on.

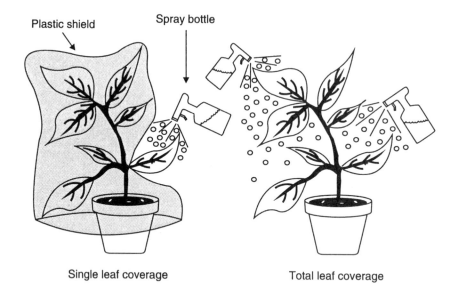

Figure 11-5. Treatment groups for rate of coverage (Experiment 2).

EXPERIMENT 3.
HERBICIDE BIOASSAY

Purpose

The purpose of this experiment is to determine if herbicide residues are present in selected crop soils.

Materials

- soil samples from suspected fields
- small growing containers (pots, cartons, etc.)
- oat seeds
- water

Procedures

Prior to planting, collect soil samples from suspected fields. Sample the soil to a six-inch depth and separate the samples into two sections: 0 to 3 inches and 3 to 6 inches. Label all samples. Take several samples (the

Figure 11-6. A herbicide bioassay, designed to test for the presence of herbicide residues in the soil, should be run prior to replanting.

Figure 11-7. Soil samples for bioassays should be taken six inches deep and separated into the upper three inch and lower three inch zones.

smaller the growing area, the more samples per unit area are needed) and mix together to form a composite sample. Take additional samples from areas where excessive herbicide residues are suspected and keep these samples separate from other samples. About four quarts of soil are needed for each bioassay. Sample an untreated area to be used as a check soil (the control).

Run the bioassay when samples are taken; a time delay may allow herbicide residues to decrease. Allow the samples to air dry, if necessary, until they can be worked easily. Punch holes in the bottom of the growing containers to allow drainage. Fill two or more containers (a set) with soil from each of the samples to be tested. Place the soils from the 0 to 3 inch depth in one set of containers and soil from the 3 to 6 inch depth in another. Also fill a set of containers for the check soil and the soil where excessive residues are suspected.

For Triazine Residues. An oat bioassay works best for atrazine and simazine residues. Place about 15 oat seeds in each set of growing containers and cover the seeds with about one inch of soil. Moisten the soil and place containers in adequate growing conditions. Sunlight is essential. Water as necessary. Injury symptoms should become apparent within 10 to 14 days. These include chlorosis (yellowing) and necrosis (browning) of the leaves. Symptoms usually start at the tips of leaves and develop toward the leaf base. Smaller amounts of triazine residue will only stunt the plant. Compare the growth and appearance of plants with those growing in the check soil.

Figure 11-8. An indoor bioassay using ryegrass.

Other Residues. Bioassays can be performed for other herbicides using similar techniques. The procedure for detecting the herbicide residue is determined by the mode of action of the specific herbicide. For example, if the herbicide inhibits root development, then a root bioassay should be used. Wheat and oats are good indicator plants for many herbicides. Include several plant species in the bioassay, including the crop to be grown, to give a better range of susceptibility to herbicide injury.

SCIENCE CONNECTIONS

CLASSIFICATION OF HERBICIDES

Most *herbicides* in use today are derived from organic compounds. Herbicides may be classified by one or more of the following characteristics: type of action, chemical composition, method of application, and species of plants affected. For example, *selective herbicides* are effective in controlling a limited number of plant species, while *nonselective herbicides* destroy all vegetation. In addition, *contact herbicides* kill only the portions of plants that they contact, while *systemic* or *translocated herbicides* are absorbed into the plant's vascular and root system and destroy the entire plant.

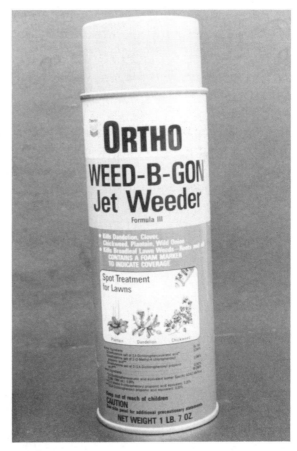

Figure 11-9. Most of the popular broadleaf weed killers contain 2, 4-D as the active ingredient.

Figure 11-10. The timing of herbicide applications is critical for effective weed control.

HERBICIDE APPLICATION

Herbicides may be applied to the soil either before planting (*preplant*) or after planting but before crop emergence (*preemergence*). Some herbicides are applied after crop emergence (*postemergence*). Producers sometimes use both soil-applied and foliar-applied herbicides for weed control.

The performance of herbicides depends upon temperature, rainfall, humidity, maturity of crop and weeds, soil characteristics, and chemical concentration. Higher temperatures elevate metabolic rates in plants, thus speeding up the injurious effects of the herbicide. However, temperatures above 85°F also result in greater volatilization and decomposition of chemicals due to sunlight. Higher humidity also increases herbicide uptake and action. Young plants are more susceptible to herbicide injury.

Soil-applied herbicides are usually incorporated into the soil by using field cultivators or tandem disks. Even *incorporation* often requires two passes with the incorporation implements. Herbicide applied to wet soils may be unevenly incorporated and result in less effective weed control. Incorporated herbicide should be placed one to two inches below the soil surface—the zone where most weed seeds are located. Deeper incorporation reduces proximity to germinating weed seeds and dilutes the herbicide. For preemergence herbicide, one-half to one inch of rainfall is needed within 10 days of application to move the herbicide into the soil.

Figure 11-11. Many factors, including climatic conditions and weed
characteristics, determine herbicide effectiveness.

Figure 11-12. Soil texture, organic matter, and pH affect rates of application
and persistence of herbicides in the soil.

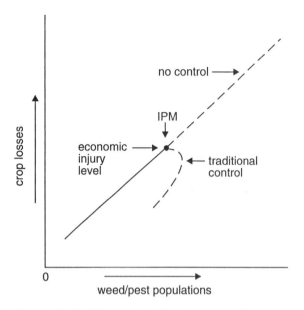

Figure 11-13. When using IPM, growers strive to hold crop losses and weed/pest populations at the economic injury level.

Soil texture and percentage of *organic matter* affect application rates for soil-applied herbicides. Higher amounts of organic matter increase the absorptive capacity of the soil. In addition, clay soils hold the herbicide in smaller soil pores. In these soils the soil water solution, which contains the herbicide, is less easily absorbed by the plant roots and weed seeds. Thus, a higher rate of herbicide application must be used to obtain the desired effects. The amount of herbicide taken up by plant roots depends upon the concentration of herbicide in the soil solution and the amount of water transpired by the plant.

Integrated Pest Management (IPM) is a crop pest-management strategy that uses a combination of measures to control pests, including weeds. The goal with IPM is to keep pest populations below the *economic injury level*, defined as the point where crop losses due to the pests are equal to the cost of control. In IPM chemicals are still used, but often in reduced quantities, in an effort to protect humans, wildlife, and the environment.

HERBICIDE CARRYOVER

Herbicide *carryover* refers to the persistence of the herbicide in the soil after harvest or at the next scheduled planting date. Carryover is a function of soil texture, pH, and organic matter, as well as chemical composition of the herbicide and the concentration applied. For example, atrazine and simazine may persist in the soil after cool, dry seasons and where soil pH is greater than 7.3. These conditions reduce microbial populations in the soil, a major means of herbicide breakdown. The solubility of various herbicides also affects their carryover potential. Recommended recropping intervals have been established which allow sufficient breakdown of soil herbicides and thus, prevent injury to the subsequent crop.

Table 11-1
Persistence of Selected Herbicides in the Soil

Herbicide	Persistence	Means of Decomposition
2,4-D	1-6 weeks	microbial
Paraquat	persistent	photodecomposition
Simazine	>1 year	hydrolysis, microbial
Atrazine	5-12 months	microbial, hydrolysis, photodecomposition
Glyphosate	nonpersistent	microbial, leaching
Trifluralin	16-24 weeks	microbial

Source: *CRC Handbook of Pest Management in Agriculture,* 1991.

Two methods are used to determine if herbicide residues exist in a certain soil. These include a laboratory soil chemical test and a *bioassay,* done either in the field or indoors. In essence, a bioassay predicts potential crop injury due to herbicide carryover in the soil. A bioassay does not indicate the amount of herbicide in the soil, but rather if sufficient herbicide residue is present to harm a sensitive crop. Crops vary in their sensitivity to various herbicides, as shown below:

For triazine: (relative degree of crop sensitivity)
ryegrass > alfalfa > oats > wheat > soybeans > sorghum > corn

For clomazone: (relative degree of crop sensitivity)
oats = wheat = alfalfa > sunflower > sorghum > corn > soybeans

Some herbicides, such as glyphosate, are nonpersistent in the soil, while others may remain in the soil for weeks or months before they dissipate. Herbicides dissipate from the soil by several means, including microbial, volatization, photodecomposition, chemical, hydrolysis, and leaching. The chemical composition of the herbicide largely affects the dissipation method(s).

MODE OF ACTION

Contact herbicides kill only the treated portion of the plant. Good coverage is essential, and a rain-free period of at least several hours is needed to ensure complete uptake. Contact herbicides do not move into the phloem, but rather diffuse across leaf membranes toward the leaf margin. Systemic, or translocated, herbicides enter the phloem and are transported throughout the plant. The movement from the xylem to the phloem is due to differences in pH between the two membranes. Once ions enter the *phloem*, they are trapped due to the higher pH. Systemic herbicides are most effective when applied on actively growing weeds.

Mode of action refers to the metabolic action or enzyme system through which the herbicide destroys the plant. Some herbicides exert toxic effects on plants through more than one mode of action. The mode of action in some herbicides is not known. Herbicide mode of action can be classified as shown in Table 11-12.

Table 11-2
Mode of Action of Selected Herbicides

Mode of Action	Herbicide	
Meristematic inhibitors	Dual	Lasso
	Eradicane	Sutan+
	Prowl	Treflan
	Poast	Roundup
	Pursuit	Scepter
Photosynthetic inhibitors	Atrazine	
	Bladex	
	Princep	
	Spike	
Growth regulators	Banvel	
	2, 4-D	
	MCPA	
Contact herbicides	Paraquat	
	Basagran	
	Buctril	

Root mitotic inhibitors prevent normal cell division by affecting cell replication. As a result, root growth is severely inhibited and the plant is stunted. Stems and leaves may turn purple due to a potassium deficiency. Examples include Sonalan and Prowl.

Shoot inhibitors affect cell growth and division, but the specific site of action is not known. Affected plants appear stunted and have crinkled leaves. Seedlings may leaf out underground and grass leaves may not unfurl correctly. Examples include Dual, Eradicane, and Sutan.

Photosynthetic inhibitors block the photosynthetic reaction within cells so that captured light cannot be converted to chemical energy. Soil-applied herbicides of this type move throughout the plant. Older leaves lose their color first. Leaf veins are the last to lose their green color. Foliar-applied herbicides of this type are usually nonmobile within the plant but have the same general effect on plant tissues. Examples include atrazine, Bladex, Basagran, and Buctril.

Enzyme inhibitors disrupt the normal function of the acetolactate synthase (ALS) enzyme. This, in turn, inhibits plant metabolism and cell division. Symptoms include bushy root growth, purple leaves and stems, and overall plant stunting. Veins turn brown and leaves become yellow from the outer edges in toward the veins. Examples include Pursuit, Classic, Scepter, Accent, Pinnacle, and Beacon.

Membrane disrupters tear down internal cell membranes, preventing these cells from manufacturing energy. These herbicides cause water spots to develop, which cause the leaf to lose color and the tissue to die. Examples include paraquat and Blazer.

Pigment inhibitors prevent the formation of chlorophyll. Affected tissue turns white or light green. Both new and old leaves may be affected. Examples include Command and Zorial.

Hormone type herbicides affect growth in the newest leaves and stems by affecting protein synthesis and normal cell division. Treated plants are stunted and malformed. Calluses may form and the plant may become brittle. Examples include 2,4-D, Banvel, and Stinger.

Meristematic lipid inhibitors prevent formation of lipid cells in the shoots of grass plants. Treated plants become stunted and the growing point of the plant dies first. Examples include Poast, Assure, and Option.

Most soil-applied herbicides are either photosynthetic or meristematic inhibitors. Weed seedlings may contact the herbicide as they grow through the soil, or the herbicide may move through the soil to the weed root system.

HERBICIDE SELECTIVITY

As noted earlier, a selective herbicide is one that kills some plants and leaves others unharmed. Three terms are important in understanding uptake and *selectivity* of foliar-applied herbicides. *Interception* refers to initial herbicide contact on leaves. *Retention* is the percentage of intercepted spray that remains on the leaf surface. The movement of herbicide throughout the plant is termed *translocation*. Herbicide selectivity is based upon a number of factors, including dosage, retention, differential wetting, orien-

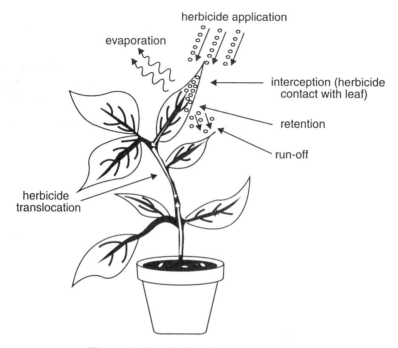

Figure 11-14.   Herbicide uptake by plants.

Figure 11-15.   Younger weeds are more susceptible to herbicide injury, due to a
thinner cuticle.

tation of leaves, location of growing point, timing and method of application, herbicide composition, and plant physiology.

In order for foliar-applied herbicides to be absorbed by plant tissues, they must first pass through the plant's outermost layer of cells, called the *epidermis*. These epidermal cells secret a fatty substance called *cutin*. The *cuticle* is actually a thin membrane of cutin that covers all aerial parts of the plant. The thickness of the cuticle has a great deal to do with a plant's susceptibility to herbicides. The cuticle is usually thinner on younger plants, thus increasing retention and making them easier to control with herbicides.

Figure 11-16. Leaf characteristics have much to do with herbicide interception, retention, and uptake.

Retention on the surface of a leaf is affected by drop angle, momentum of drops, drop size, leaf angle, and nature of the leaf surface (e.g., hairy versus smooth). The shape and arrangement of the cutin particles varies by plant species. Small spray drops are retained better. Wetting agents (also called *adjuvants*) may be added to the herbicide to aid in spray retention.

Scientists have concluded that after herbicides penetrate the cuticle, they enter the plant through the guard cells, hairs, and veins (in broadleaves). Surface tension of liquids appears to prevent entry through the stomata. Herbicide selectivity is largely due to differential wetting.

CHAPTER SUMMARY

Weeds are a major nuisance to plant growers. Since the 1940s growers have been using herbicides as a primary means of controlling weeds. Herbicides represent a relatively large investment for growers and can lead to greater crop growth and yields. Many herbicides are available today. They can be classified by selectivity, method of application, and mode of action.

Many factors affect herbicide selectivity. Susceptibility to a herbicide is primarily a matter of differential wetting, which is caused by a number of plant and herbicide characteristics. Herbicide modes of action include meristematic inhibitors, root or shoot meristematic inhibitors, photosynthetic inhibitors, membrane disrupters, enzyme inhibitors, and pigment inhibitors. Soil texture and organic matter affect application rates of soil-applied herbicides, as well as extent of carryover. Carryover is defined as the persistence of a herbicide after harvest or at the next planting date. One easy way to test for herbicide carryover is to conduct field and indoor bioassays.

FURTHER LABORATORY INVESTIGATIONS

1. Examine the effects of soil pH, soil moisture levels, temperature, humidity, light, and plant species on herbicide action and effectiveness.

2. Treat weeds around your home and on school property and observe plant responses. Identify plant injury symptoms and chemical classification for treated samples.

3. Examine the effects of herbicide action when site of application and concentration are varied.

4. Using similar growing conditions and plant species, test the effectiveness of various herbicides.

5. Conduct herbicide bioassays for residues from other types of herbicides (i.e., dinitroaniline, imazaquin, chlorimuron, etc.).

Chapter 12

GROWTH REGULATORS

Getting in Shape

AGRICULTURAL APPLICATIONS

Plant growth regulators include both plant hormones and nonnutrient substances that affect plant growth and development. These plant growth regulators are widely used in agronomic and horticultural settings and include auxins, gibberellins (GA), cytokinins, abscissic acid, and ethylene.

Auxins influence plants in many ways and, in general, cause cell enlargement. Stimulation of root growth in stem cuttings is one of the many common uses of auxins. Auxins are also used to cause uniform flower set

Figure 12-1. Early fruit drop is prevented by applying an auxin spray.

in fruit trees, increase fruit set in tomatoes, initiate shoots and roots in tissue culture (when used with cytokinins), and prevent sprouting in woody ornamental plants. Interestingly, auxins can also be used to thin excessive fruit set in apples and olives. Apple, pear, and citrus growers apply a synthetic auxin to keep fruit on the trees a few extra weeks before fruit drop to allow further ripening. A combination cytokinin/GA spray is used in commercial apple orchards to enhance the elongated shape of some varieties. Apical dominance is due to the distribution of auxin in plant stems. By pinching back the tips of stems, growers can produce fuller, better shaped plant materials. Some herbicides, such as the commonly used broadleaf weed killer 2,4-D, are actually auxins.

Gibberellins also have widespread application in agriculture. USDA scientists have recently found that soaking semi-dwarf rice seeds for just five minutes in gibberellic acid (GA_3) results in stronger and more uniform germination. This is especially important where rice is planted in dry fields and seeds planted even one-fourth inch too deep may not germinate. In Arkansas alone, the nation's top-producing rice state, over 500,000 acres of the GA_3 treated seed were grown in 1992. Researchers have discovered that growth promoters can be used to either extend or break seed dormancy depending upon the concentration. Scientists have also learned that coating citrus with GA is an effective defense against fruit fly damage, a major concern in maintaining postharvest quality.

Gibberellic acid is commonly used in the grape industry to thin blossom clusters and dramatically increase berry size. Plant breeders have found that GA stimulates the production of male flowers in cucumbers, which is useful in developing hybrid seed. GA is also used to increase the size and crispness of celery stalks.

TERMS

abscissic acid (ABA)	cuticle	guard cells
abscission	cytokinins	lateral buds
apical dominance	endosperm	metabolism
apical meristems	ethylene	osmotic forces
auxins	gibberellins (GA)	plant hormone
cell division	growth inhibitors	stomata
cell membrane	growth regulators	translocation

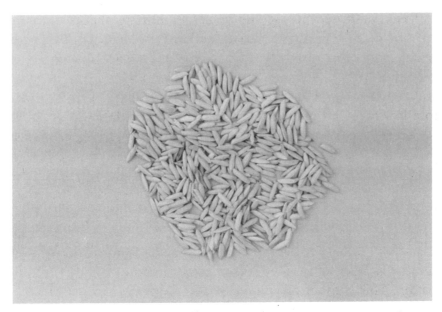

Figure 12-2. Gibberellic acid is effective in breaking seed dormancy and promoting germination.

Growth inhibitors have essentially the opposite effect of auxins and gibberellins. A number of synthetic growth retardants have widespread commercial use. Applications of B-Nine, Cycocel, and A-Rest are used on chrysanthemums, poinsettias, and lilies to produce more compact plants

Figure 12-3. A number of synthetic growth inhibitors are used to produce more compact flowering plants.

with an increased number of blossoms. Cycocel has also been used to prevent lodging of wheat by shortening the plant stem. Growth retardants are used to place nursery plants in a state of dormancy during shipping to preserve quality.

Ethylene is another plant growth regulator that has widespread application in agriculture. Ethylene promotes flowering, fruit ripening, and leaf abscission; tree and vine fruits are easier to harvest after applications of ethylene. Ethylene is widely used by food wholesalers to ripen fruit uniformly before shipping. Ethylene has also been used to make cotton harvesting easier by slowing vegetative growth. Ethylene sprays stimulate the production of female flowers on plants such as cucumbers and pumpkins, thereby increasing yield. Scientists are now developing a film to be sprayed on fruits to slow the ripening process, which is stimulated by ethylene.

OBJECTIVES—QUESTIONS FOR INVESTIGATION

After completing the experiments contained in this chapter and other activities provided by your teacher, you should be able to answer the following questions:

1. What are plant hormones and growth regulators?

2. How do growth regulators work within plants?

3. What effects do growth regulators have on plants?

4. How does the timing and application of growth regulators affect their action on plants?

LABORATORY INVESTIGATIONS

EXPERIMENT I. EFFECTS OF ROOTING HORMONE ON ROOT DEVELOPMENT

Purpose

The purpose of this experiment is to examine the effects of rooting hormone on root development in stem cuttings. Both use and concentration of rooting hormone will be examined.

Materials

- young, healthy potted plant(s) for taking cuttings
- propagating knife
- plastic bag
- small pots for growing cuttings
- rooting medium (sphagnum moss, sand, etc.)
- rooting hormone (Rootone, etc.)
- water

Procedures

Fill two pots with the selected rooting medium for each treatment to be used (e.g., control, hormone concentration). Take enough stem cuttings (three to five inches long) from the stock plant(s) to equal twice the number of treatments included in your experiment. If necessary, place the cuttings in a plastic bag to keep them moist.

Prepare a set of two cuttings for each of the treatments to be used. This should include two with no hormone applied (the control) and two for each concentration tested. Rooting hormones can be used as either a wet dip or a powder. Be sure to follow label directions when preparing the hormones. A fungicide may be added to some hormone treatments to examine its effects on preventing root rot.

Plant each cutting in the propagating pots and clearly label each pot as to the treatment it contains. Water to settle the medium and place all pots in a good growing location with adequate light, temperature, and moisture. Covering the cuttings with plastic or placing cuttings under a mist system will keep the rooting medium moist. After one week remove one plant in each treatment and gently rinse the rooting medium from the roots. Compare the length and overall size of the developing root systems for each cutting and record. After another week remove the second cutting in each treatment and make the same observations.

EXPERIMENT 2.
EFFECTS OF GIBBERELLIC ACID ON
SEED GERMINATION

Purpose

The purpose of this investigation is to examine the effects of GA on the rate of germination of various seeds. GA concentration will also be examined.

Materials

- gibberellic acid, 10 ppm and 100 ppm
- various seeds (lettuce, radishes, peas, etc.)
- plastic, resealable bags (quart size)
- paper towels

Procedures

Fold three paper towels so they will fit into the plastic bags. Saturate one towel with plain water (the control), one with a solution of 10 ppm of GA, and one with a solution of 100 ppm of GA. Place the wet towels inside the plastic bags. Place 10 seeds of each seed type in each of the three bags (on top of the towels). Keep seed bags in a lighted area at room temperature for one week. Observe the germination rate of each seed type on a daily basis and record your observations. Note the first day of germination and number of seeds germinated.

SCIENCE CONNECTIONS

TYPES OF PLANT GROWTH REGULATORS

Plant *growth regulators* include both naturally occurring and synthetic plant hormones, as well as nonnutrient, synthetic materials that influence plant growth and development. A *plant hormone* is an organic compound that is produced in minute quantities in one part of a plant and then translocated to another part of the plant where growth and development are modified. A plant hormone can have many different effects on plant growth, which are often dependent upon the concentration used and the presence of other plant hormones. Five major classes of hormones are recognized today: auxins, gibberellins, cytokinins, abscissic acid, and ethylene.

Auxins

Auxins are plant hormones whose most important and distinguishing effect is cell elongation. Plants produce auxin primarily in the *apical meristems*, buds, and other growing parts. Auxins were the first plant hormones discovered, and scientists now believe that plants produce several auxins. However, indoleacetic acid (IAA) is the most commonly used naturally occurring auxin. Several synthetic auxins are also in use, including 2,4-D, indolebutyric acid (IBA), and naphthaleneacetic acid (NAA).

The *translocation* of auxins in plants occurs only from the apical meristems downward toward the base of the plant. Scientists believe that this unique trait accounts for the *apical dominance* seen in most plants. The higher concentration of auxin in the tips of stems is believed to suppress the development of *lateral buds*. However, research shows that auxins must be continuously present in the apex of the stem in order for lateral bud growth to be suppressed.

Auxins attach to cell walls and activate a series of processes that lower the tensile strength of the *cell mem-*

Figure 12-4. Auxins are transported only downward, from the apical meristem toward the base of the plant.

Figure 12-5. Leaf and fruit abscission (shedding) can be delayed by treating with auxins.

Figure 12-6. Tropisms are due to the differential distribution of auxins in plant tissues.

brane. This allows the cell to enlarge. Auxins are acid in nature. The increased acidity in cell membranes created by auxins makes the cell wall less resistant to stretching due to *osmotic forces.*

Auxins are commonly used to promote root growth, both in traditional propagation methods and in micropropagation. Auxins are also believed to delay *abscission* (shedding) of leaves and maturing fruits. How auxins work to slow the breakdown of the thin layer of cells in the abscission zone is not well understood. Applications of NAA on some fruit trees delays development of the abscission zone, and thus, delays premature dropping of fruit.

Tropisms, a growth response of plants to external stimuli, are the result of differential cell growth caused by unequal distribution of auxin around plant stems (see Chapter 9). Auxins are effectively used for thinning fruit blossoms, resulting in larger fruit, and in growing seedless grapes. Again, the precise mechanisms of action are not well understood, although embryo abortion appears to be the net effect.

Gibberellins

Gibberellins (gibberellic acid or *GA*) stimulate stem growth even more dramatically than auxins. In addition to promoting cell elongation, GA also stimulates *cell division* and controls enzyme release. Applications of GA can transform a dwarf plant into one of normal size. In addition, GA produced in the embryo during the germination of cereal seeds moves to the aleurone layer surrounding the *endosperm*, activating the synthesis of enzymes (see Chapter 6). This enzymatic action is essential for successful germination. For this reason, GA is applied to barley during the malting stage of brewing to increase the enzyme content of the malt. This, in turn, leads to early release of sugars from the endosperm, resulting in higher alcohol production.

Over 70 different gibberellins (labelled GA_3, GA_7, etc.) have been discovered in various plant tissues. Despite nearly identical chemical structures, a plant species will respond to only certain types of gibberellin. Commercial supplies of GA are obtained from the fungus *Gibberella fujikuroi*. Applications of GA in grape vineyards increase berry size by thinning clusters and increasing internode length, allowing more space for the fruit to grow.

As suggested earlier, gibberellins promote seed germination, even for some difficult-to-germinate seeds. Researchers have also found that GA can replace the need for red light in the germination of some lettuce varieties. As a result of USDA research, GA-treated rice seed is now commercially available and widely accepted by growers. Designed especially for semi-dwarf, dry-planted varieties, the GA treatment elongates emerging plant parts. The result is more even germination and stronger germination at a deeper planting depth.

GA, a naturally occurring plant hormone, has been used for over 40 years on citrus crops. GA keeps the peel tough, and therefore, resistant to molds. Scientists are now exploring the use of GA in preventing fruit fly damage based upon the effect GA has on the citrus fruit peel. GA tends to keep the peel green, and growers could use the ripening hormone ethylene to bring the fruit to its normal color.

Cytokinins

Cytokinins have a number of effects on plants and plant tissues, including cell enlargement and division, tissue differentiation, dormancy, and retardation of leaf senescence. However, their most significant effect is the promotion of cell division. Unlike auxins, roots supply cytokinins upward toward the shoots. Natural cytokinins are most abundant in seeds, fruits, and roots. In tissue culture, the balance of auxins and cytokinins dictate whether cells will develop into shoots, roots, or remain undifferentiated. Cytokinins slow the process of senescence by preventing the breakdown of chlorophyll in the leaves.

Figure 12-7. A combination of cytokinins and GA is used in commercial apple orchards to enhance the elongated shape of some apple varieties.

Abscissic Acid

Abscissic acid (ABA) is the only natural *growth inhibitor* within the category of plant growth regulators. ABA counteracts the effects of gibberellin during seed germination. It also promotes dormancy in seeds and buds, and flowering in some short-day plants. Scientists believe that ABA prevents seeds from germinating while they are still in the fruit. ABA also plays an important role in maintaining water supplies within the plant. When a plant becomes water stressed, greater amounts of ABA are produced by the plant tissues. This, in turn, interferes with the availability of potassium in the *guard cells*, causing the *stomata* to close. Increased water supplies breakdown ABA, and the stomata reopen.

ABA has the net effect of "shutting down" the metabolic processes in plant cells. Once ABA concentrations are

Figure 12-8. Abscissic acid concentrations in seeds prevent germination.

reduced, normal plant *metabolism* resumes. Scientists have discovered that ABA levels must be reduced before seed and bud dormancy can be broken.

In the last 40 years, a number of synthetic growth inhibitors have been developed and used commercially in the horticulture industry. These materials block gibberellin production or action within plants. They slow down plant growth, creating smaller, more compact plants that usually have darker, more attractive foliage and more flowers. Daminozide (B-Nine) retards growth and stimulates flowering in some plants, including chrysanthemums, bedding plants, and azaleas. Chlormequat (Cycocel, CCC) is used to reduce the height of poinsettias and prevent lodging in wheat. Other synthetic growth inhibitors are effective in reducing the height of bulbous, potted plants and reducing shoot growth.

Ethylene

Ethylene, unlike the other natural plant hormones, is a water-soluble gas that moves readily throughout the plant. The *cuticle* prevents loss of ethylene from plant tissues.

Ethylene is produced in ripening fruits, senescent flowers, plant meristems, and at sites where plant or fruit injury occurs. Ethylene and ethylene-releasing chemicals such as ethephon are widely used to promote fruit ripening and flower initiation. The abscission-producing effects of ethylene also make it useful in harvesting tree fruits. Ethylene has the same effect on leaf abscission.

Ripe fruits produce ethylene and cause the ripening of other fruits that are held in the same container. This is why a piece of spoiled fruit in a fruit container seems to speed up ripening and eventual spoilage of other pieces of fruit in the container. Since ethylene is a gas, its effects are greater in enclosed areas. The effects of ethylene also explain why "green" fruit placed in an enclosed container ripens more rapidly and evenly than other fruit.

Ethylene enhances the ripening of most fruits, with the exception of strawberries. Fruits such as apples, bananas, and tomatoes produce a relatively large amount of ethylene gas and carbon dioxide as they ripen. Thus, adequate ventilation is necessary to prevent unwanted ripening. Ethylene

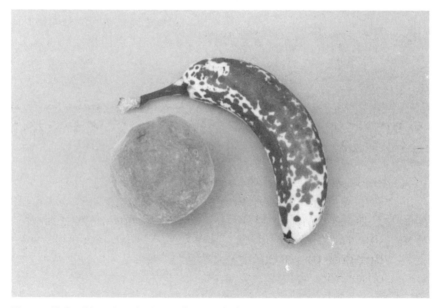

Figure 12-9. Ripening fruit produces ethylene. The more ethylene produced, the faster the ripening process.

production surges when plant tissues are cut or bruised, speeding the ripening process. Scientists are working on a protective film for fruit that would inhibit uptake of oxygen, and thus, slow respiration and ripening. Plant tissues also need oxygen to produce ethylene.

CHAPTER SUMMARY

Plant growth regulators include natural and synthetic compounds that affect growth and development. The five types of plant hormones are auxins, gibberellins, cytokinins, abscissic acid, and ethylene. Some natural hormones, like giberrellin, are widely used in agriculture. Others have limited use due to the expense and/or difficulty involved in obtaining adequate supplies. A number of synthetic growth inhibitors have been developed and are widely used in food and horticultural crops.

Plant growth regulators vary in their effects on plant growth and development. These effects are often due to the presence of other growth regulators. Auxins, gibberellins, and cytokinins promote plant growth, while abscissic acid acts as a growth inhibitor. Ethylene is important in fruit ripening and senescence, speeding up both processes. Auxins are commonly used as rooting stimulants. Giberrellins promote vegetative growth but also have a dramatic effect on seed germination. Cytokinins have important research applications in tissue culture. Abscissic acid promotes dormancy and helps plants survive water stress conditions by affecting stomatal opening. Ethylene has widespread commercial use for harvesting tree fruits and stimulating even ripening in fruits.

FURTHER LABORATORY INVESTIGATIONS

1. Soak seeds in 0 (water), 100, 1,000, and 8,000 ppm GA solutions for various time periods (5 minutes, 1 hour, 5 hours, and 15 hours). Remove seeds from the GA solution and plant. Observe germination rate and seedling growth rate for a period of 21 days and record your observations every two days.

2. Take two small, freshly cut twigs from a large-leafed evergreen shrub. Recut the stems under water and im-

mediately place in a small beaker or similar container filled with water. Cover one twig in its container with a glass jar. Place a ripe apple alongside the second twig and cover both with a glass jar. Observe the twigs daily for one week. What effect does the apple have on the twig?

3. Compare the effects of different types/brands of rooting hormones on root development.

4. Obtain several potted plants of various species. Plants should have at least three to four mature leaves on each stem. Pinch (remove) the tips of each stem (and the flowers, if present). Maintain good growing conditions and observe the changes in growth pattern in the plants after several weeks. In a related experiment, use young bean seedlings, bedding plants, or indoor plants. Pinch the tip of the dominant stem. Immediately apply a capsule containing a lanolin/IAA paste to the exposed stem. On another pinched stem wait five minutes before applying the hormone paste. Compare the results.

5. Compare the effects of various growth stimulants and growth retardants on several different species of plants. Include young seedlings, larger plants, horticultural plants, and potted agronomic crop species.

Chapter 13

TISSUE CULTURE

Big Litters

AGRICULTURAL APPLICATIONS

Tissue culture is the practice of growing plant cells on artificial media. Since its development in the 1970s and 1980s, tissue culture has had tremendous effects on research and production in the agricultural industry. Based upon molecular biology fundamentals, tissue culture offers significant potential for crop improvement. Tissue culture techniques allow desirable

Figure 13-1. With tissue culture techniques, an infinite number of new plants can theoretically be derived from a single segment of plant tissue.

traits to be selected in large numbers of cells in a laboratory, rather than in large numbers of whole plants in the field. Cells can be exposed to various conditions or treatments, and the surviving ones can be isolated and grown out into mature plants. For example, cells can be extracted from a plant, treated with a herbicide, and the most resistant (surviving) cells can be saved. Plants generated from these cell cultures can subsequently be grown out in field trials and used in conventional plant breeding programs to develop new crop varieties that are resistant to that particular herbicide. Without tissue culture techniques, many discoveries in plant genetic engineering would not be possible.

In general, tissue culture, also known as micropropagation, is used to mass produce plants and to establish virus-free stock plants. Plants have been cloned for many years using various vegetative propagation methods (e.g., root cuttings, grafting, and layering); however, cloning through tissue culture is much faster and, in some cases, more cost effective. A much smaller number of stock plants is needed for reproduction, thus reducing growing space, labor, and plant maintenance requirements. Also, tissue culture allows for the propagation of plants in laboratory conditions throughout the year.

The time required to develop new plant varieties can be greatly reduced with the use of tissue culture. For example, the normal ten-year period required for some trees to produce seed can be significantly shortened using tissue culture techniques. Theoretically, an infinite number of new plants can be generated from one piece of plant tissue using tissue culture.

Tissue culture has been used commercially to eliminate viruses in lilies, carnations, potatoes, citrus, and berries. Diseases normally transmitted from parent plants to offspring are eliminated when tissue culture is used. Tissue

TERMS

agar	explant	sterile
anther culture	in vitro	sterile technique
callus	meristem cells	suspension culture
cloning	meristem culture	tissue culture
differentiation	micropropagation	tissue culture medium
disinfestation	plant hormones	
embryo culture	plantlet	

culture was first used on herbaceous plants, such as ferns, orchids, carnations, tobacco, chrysanthemums, tomatoes, and strawberries. Later, scientists discovered that woody plants could also be micropropagated. Woody species successfully micropropagated include rhododendron, azalea, rose, plum, apple, pear, poplar, blueberry, and almond. Tissue culture has been used for over 25 years to grow orchids. Orchid seeds, the smallest known to exist, must encounter a specific fungus before they will germinate. Without tissue culture the usual time required to go from seed to a flowering plant is about seven years.

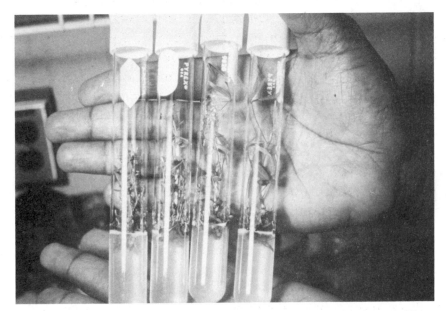

Figure 13-2. Tissue culture can be used to cut years off the time required for natural plant regeneration for some species.

Several types of tissue culture are used, including embryo culture, mericloning, and anther (pollen) culture. Researchers are looking for ways to use tissue culture and other plant biotechnology techniques to increase crop resistance to diseases and tolerance to cold, salinity, and drought. One goal is to develop grass plants that have nitrogen-fixing abilities like legumes. It also may be possible to increase the photosynthetic efficiency of C_3 plants. Tissue culture holds promise in improving the flavor, nutritional value, and storage life of edible plant products.

Figure 13-3. Several methods of micropropagation have been developed, including embryo culture. (Courtesy, OACE, University of Illinois)

OBJECTIVES—QUESTIONS FOR INVESTIGATION

After performing the experiments contained in this chapter and participating in other activities assigned by your teacher, you should be able to answer the following questions:

1. What is plant tissue culture?

2. How do plants respond to tissue culture techniques?

3. Why are growth regulators used in tissue culture?

4. Why is a sterile environment critical when performing tissue culture?

5. How are the plant's nutritional and other growing requirements met when using tissue culture?

LABORATORY INVESTIGATIONS

EXPERIMENT I.
EMBRYO CULTURE OF APPLES

Purpose

The purpose of this experiment is to examine the response of apple embryos, with and without the seed coat, to micropropagation techniques.

Materials

- ethanol (70% solution)
- six apple seeds from a fresh apple
- cheesecloth (3-inch × 3-inch piece)
- bleach solution (10% chlorine bleach)
- six test tubes (large enough to insert forceps)
- liquid dishwashing detergent
- large, clear plastic bag
- distilled water
- small bottles with caps for water and ethanol
- razor blade
- Parafilm
- lima bean agar
- forceps
- petri dish

Procedures

Sterilize the cheesecloth, test tubes, distilled water (in a bottle), razor blade, bottles, petri dish, and forceps (see the *Science Connections* section for suggested procedures). Prepare the agar according to label directions and pour into the test tubes, filling each about 20%. Prepare the bleach solution and add about five drops of detergent per 100 milliliters of solution.

Wash hands thoroughly with soap and water. Do not dry. Swab hands and working surface with ethanol and let air dry.

Extract six seeds from an apple and wrap them in cheesecloth. Place them in the bleach solution for five minutes. Remove from the bleach solution and place in the sterile, distilled water to rinse away the bleach. Gently agitate for five minutes. Swab your hands with ethanol. Grasp a seed and place your hands inside the large plastic bag. Using a petri dish and razor blade, cut through the seed coat. Try not to injure the embryo inside. Remove the seed coat from three of the seeds. With your hands inside the bag, place one seed in each of the six test tubes containing agar. Cap the tubes and seal with Parafilm. Label each tube (with or without seed coat) and place in a well lighted area at room temperature. Do not place the tubes in direct sunlight, as they may overheat. Provide 16 hours of light per day. Observe and compare the growth of the seed embryos daily for one week.

EXPERIMENT 2.
ANTHER CULTURE

Purpose

The purpose of this experiment is to compare the success of anther culture on different flowering plants.

Materials

- at least two different species of plants with flower buds (tobacco, tomato, or others)
- forceps
- ethanol (70%)
- petri dishes with agar
- beaker
- razor blade
- Parafilm
- large, plastic bag

Procedures

Sterilize lab materials and equipment as in Experiment 1. Place sterilized items inside the plastic bag. Select unopened flower buds. In tobacco, the sepals and petals should be the same length. Remove the buds by hand or with a razor blade. Holding it by the pedicel, dip the entire bud in ethanol for 15 seconds. Remove the bud and hold it until the excess ethanol drips off. With your hands inside the plastic bag, use forceps to carefully remove the sepals and petals. The anthers should be exposed.

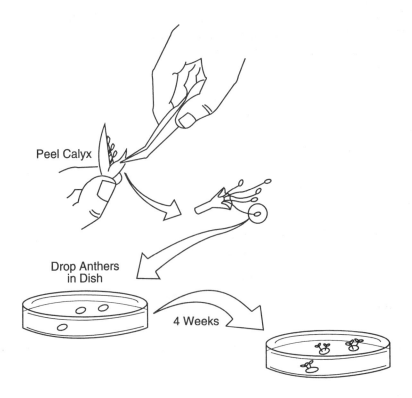

Figure 13-4. Carefully place the anthers from several flowers into a petri dish containing nutrient agar.

Open the petri dish containing the tissue culture medium (agar). One by one, remove the anthers from each bud and drop them onto the medium. Be careful not to damage the anther. Include only the anther; no portion of the filament should be included. Arrange the anthers on the petri plate and repeat the procedure for another bud. Place anthers from three buds of the same plant species in each petri dish. Seal plates with Parafilm and place in an incubator or growing area. Plantlets should develop in four to six weeks. Compare the success of anther culture for each plant species.

SCIENCE CONNECTIONS

Tissue culture is a method of growing pieces of plants, called *explants*, on an artificial medium under sterile conditions. Several other terms are used to describe tissue culture, including *in vitro* culture, *cloning*, and

Figure 13-5. The initial step in micropropagation is establishment of the explant in the culture medium.

micropropagation. However, cloning may also be accomplished by vegetative propagation methods other than tissue culture. A clone is a plant that is produced asexually from a single parent and is, therefore, identical to the parent plant. Explants can regenerate new shoot systems, which can be separated, rooted, and grown as full-sized plants. Some of the original explant can be retained for further regeneration of new plantlets. The steps involved in tissue culture are (1) establishment of the explant (*explantation*), (2) multiplication of cells in the explant (*proliferation*), and (3) readying the plantlet for normal growing conditions (*acclimation*).

BOTANICAL BASIS FOR TISSUE CULTURE

Unlike animals, plants have the unique capability of regenerating complete plants from single cells. Each plant cell has the genetic information it needs to reproduce and develop into an entire plant. Explants should be taken from actively growing (young) tissues found on healthy plants. Shoot tips; sections of leaves, stems and roots; embryos; shoot apical meristems; anthers; and other plant parts have been successfully micropropagated. However, the most responsive plant part varies from species to species.

New tissue growth occurs in *meristematic tissue*, which is found in the most actively growing regions of the plant. These meristematic cells have not yet been programmed to develop into specific plant parts. *Differentiation* into roots, stems, and other plant parts occurs as a result of genetic makeup, environmental conditions, nutrients, hormone levels, and other factors. In some cases, the explant initially forms a *callus*—an undifferentiated mass of cells. The use of certain culture media can cause this callus to then produce roots, shoots, and other differentiated cells. Some cells have the ability to revert to a dedifferentiated state to initiate growth of new, different tissue. These cells also account for the development of *adventitious* roots on stem cuttings.

Plantlets that are grown *in vitro* have unusually small parts. Their tiny leaves, stems, and roots make micropropagation possible. The reason the

Figure 13-6. A callus can be induced to develop roots and shoots by adjusting the culture medium.

plantlets return to a juvenile state when micropropagated is not known. However, after the plantlets have been grown in soil or greenhouse media for a while, they develop normal-sized leaves and become identical to the parent plant. Scientists have found that the younger the parent plant and the explant tissue, the more likely it is that the explant will survive micropropagation.

Apple seed coats contain *growth inhibitors* that prevent seed germination. These inhibitors break down after a sufficient period of cold temperatures. This feature protects seeds over the winter and allows germination when warm weather returns in the spring. Cold storage of apples satisfies this cold requirement. Intact seeds from these apples will germinate as quickly as seeds with the seed coats removed.

Figure 13-7. Micropropagation of corn kernels. (Courtesy, OACE, University of Illinois)

TYPES OF TISSUE CULTURE

A number of tissue culture methods are used in research and commercial settings. These include callus culture, cell suspension culture, embryo culture, meristem culture, and anther culture. Much tissue culture initially results in a callus, which is a mass of undifferentiated cells. A callus can be transformed into differentiated cells with the application of plant hormones. In a *suspension culture*, the undifferentiated cells are gently shaken in a liquid nutrient medium so they become somewhat separated from each other. This technique makes injection of new genetic material possible. *Embryo culture* is performed by excising (removing) an embryo from a plant and placing it on a culture medium.

Anther culture involves the germination of single pollen grains in a sterile medium. The resulting plants have half the number of *chromosomes* as a normal plant in that species. These *haploid* plantlets are also smaller than usual and *sterile*, even though they do produce flowers. Colchicine has been found to double the number of chromosomes, making these plants fertile and completely *homozygous*.

Meristem culture has been extensively used to produce *pathogen-free* stock plants. Plant meristem tissues are found throughout the plant and are the fastest growing plant cells. Since these new, undifferentiated cells grow faster than viruses, meristem culture can be used to grow disease-free plants. Usually the meristem dome and the accompanying pair of *leaf primordia* are used as the explant for meristem culture.

TISSUE CULTURE MEDIA

Excised plant tissues are grown on artificial media that must contain compounds necessary for plant and cell growth. Depending upon the type of culture, some explants are started on an agar medium. *Agar* is a sugar-based gel derived from certain algae. This agar substitutes for sugars that would normally be produced in a plant's leaves via photosynthesis.

Explants may also be initially cultured on a more complete medium that contains mineral salts, sugar, vitamins, and growth regulators. Plantlets started on agar are usually transferred to a specialized medium for further growth and development before being moved to a natural growing environment. Premixed media are available that contain all the plant's nutrient needs. Murashige and Skoog media are widely used, and special formulations have been developed for individual plant species, as well as stages of culture.

Plant growth hormones have a dramatic effect on cell differentiation in tissue cultures. The ratio of *auxin* to *cytokinin* determines whether the explant will develop roots, shoots, or both. A high auxin to cytokinin ratio promotes root formation, while a high cytokinin to auxin ratio promotes shoot formation. (Remember that auxins are used to promote root development in stem cuttings.) A critical mass of tissue is usually required before these hormones will induce such differentiation. A relatively balanced auxin to cytokinin ratio favors undifferentiated cell growth.

Tissue cultures need essentially the same growing conditions that other plants require. Lighting needs are best met with fluorescent lighting 18 to 20 inches above the cultures, with a 16-hour photoperiod recommended.

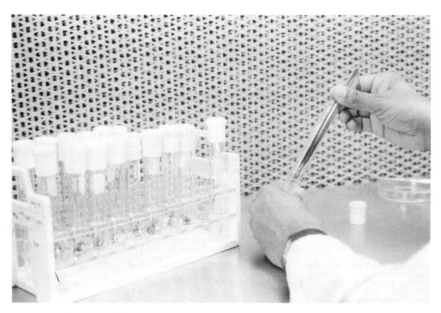

Figure 13-8. Formulations for tissue culture media vary. Premixed media are
available for some plant species and stages of culture.

Cultures should be grown at room temperature. Most test tube caps allow
some air flow, although in most cases the culture container provides enough
oxygen for the explant.

Figure 13-9. The right environmental conditions (light, temperature,
humidity) are crucial to successful culturing. (Courtesy, Beth
Wilson)

STERILE TECHNIQUE

One of the most important aspects of tissue culture is the maintenance of an environment that is free of *bacteria* and *fungi*. Nutrient media used for micropropagation favor the growth of these microbes, so sterilization of the media is essential. In addition, the slightest air movement can stir spores of bacteria and fungi. For this reason, special devices called *Laminar flow workstations* are used where possible. Plastic bags, which are sterile if unused, may be substituted with some success.

Disinfestation of the plant parts prior to removal of the explant is usually accomplished by soaking in a bleach solution. Concentrations and exposure times are critical; too much of either is likely to kill the explant. Plant tissues can survive brief exposure to normally toxic disinfectants because of the waxy *cuticle*. Immediately rinsing plant parts after bleaching prevents injury. One or two drops of detergent is often used to enhance coverage and bleaching action.

The tissue culture medium and other materials used to prepare and place the explant must be sterilized. Placing these items in an *autoclave* for 15 minutes at 245°F is recommended. Other options include a pressure cooker and dry heat sterilization. For the latter wrap items to be sterilized in aluminum foil and place in an oven for 1½ hours at 320 to 350°F. In addition, 70% isopropyl alcohol is used to disinfect tools by submerging them for 10 seconds and then allowing the alcohol to evaporate.

Table 13-1
Keys to Sterile Technique

Disinfestation of the explant

Disinfestation of the workstation, hands, and arms

Sterilization of all tissue culture materials, including media, tools, and accessories

Minimal flow of contaminated air into work area and cultures

TRANSFERRING

Cultures are *transferred* from one container to another at various stages in their development. This transfer must occur under sterile conditions to prevent contamination by microorganisms. Sterilized, long-handled forceps are used to remove the growing material from the container. The callus or mass of plantlets is then dissected into suitable explants. These pieces are placed into the fresh culture medium and pushed slightly into the agar to ensure good contact with the medium. When plants are ready to transplant into potting mixtures, wash off the culture medium to prevent the transfer of microorganisms to the potting medium. Gradual increases in light and gradual decreases in humidity will help prevent transplant loss.

CHAPTER SUMMARY

Tissue culture, or micropropagation, is the growing of plants cells on artificial media. Tissue culture has been used widely in research laboratories and commercial applications in recent years. A large number of plants can be produced from a single stock plant using tissue culture. The time, labor, production, and maintenance costs associated with conventional vegetative propagative methods can be greatly reduced with tissue culture. Micropropagation is an important complement to conventional plant breeding programs and is essential in genetic engineering techniques. Micropropagation holds great potential for crop improvement.

Types of tissue culture include callus, cell suspension, embryo, meristem, and anther culture. Plants have the unique ability to regenerate entire plants from single cells. Many different plant parts can be used to start a plant tissue culture. The plant tissue used is called the explant. A callus, or mass of unorganized cells, usually develops after the explant is placed on a culture medium. Plant roots and shoots can be formed from this cell mass with the use of plant hormones (auxin and cytokinin). The two most important aspects of tissue culture are media selection and sterile technique. An environment free of bacteria and fungi must be maintained to prevent contamination of the highly susceptible culture.

FURTHER LABORATORY INVESTIGATIONS

1. After explants in Experiment 1 have begun to develop shoots and roots, transfer to a growing medium (Murashige Shoot Multiplication Medium C) and examine plantlet establishment and growth. Test the effects of various media on growth.

2. Vary the concentration of growth hormones (auxin and cytokinin) and examine the effects on development of shoots and roots in the explant.

3. Grow plantlets to the stage where they are ready to transplant into pots or other containers. Vary the procedures used for acclimating the plantlets to a natural growing environment. Variables include growing medium, humidity, temperature, light, and exposure to air.

4. Compare the effects of sterile versus nonsterile technique for tissue culture. Obtain four squash seeds and place two in test tubes containing lima bean agar. Cap, seal, and label these two tubes. Follow aseptic techniques for the other two seeds as they are placed into the test tubes. Compare the extent of contamination of the sterile versus nonsterile cultures.

5. Obtain a young, healthy African violet. Remove a leaf with its petiole and wash in water with 1% detergent. Agitate in a 10% bleach solution for about 20 minutes. Rinse three times in sterile, distilled water. Cut the leaf into one centimeter squares and the petiole into two millimeter cross sections. Culture in a Murashige and Skoog (MS) salt base medium. Experiment with other plant species and plant parts from which explant material is taken.

Chapter 14

FOOD PRESERVATION

What's That Fuzzy Stuff?

AGRICULTURAL APPLICATIONS

Maintaining fresh fruits and vegetables from the time they are harvested until they are bought by consumers is a major challenge in the food industry. Consumers have come to expect high-quality produce throughout the year. This means that in some cases the distance from site of production to site of consumption may be halfway around the world. Furthermore, the harvest season for some fruits and vegetables may have been months

Figure 14-1. Modern storage and preservation techniques ensure good quality fruits and vegetables almost any time of the year.

253

ago, yet we are still able to find these high quality plant food products in our grocery stores. How is this possible?

Refrigeration and rapid transportation are essential to maintaining post-harvest quality for fresh products. Microbial invasion of plant tissues can lead to rapid deterioration and spoilage. Softening in fruits and vegetables may cause the loss of up to 50% of all plant products harvested in the United States—a staggering $5 billion in lost income. Physical damage of fresh fruit and vegetables leads to softening, browning, and spoilage. Scientists are constantly looking for ways to extend the shelf-life of fresh plant food products.

Food processors use a multitude of techniques to preserve plant food products so they are available throughout the year. These include cooling, drying, fermenting and pickling, freezing, canning, fumigating, raising the sugar concentration, vacuum packing, salting, and the use of chemical preservatives. In addition, some countries in Europe use irradiation to preserve food quality. These strategies are aimed at retarding or halting deterioration and spoilage caused by microorganisms and natural tissue degradation. Researchers are trying to solve the mysteries of the ripening process so that it may be slowed to preserve fruit quality.

The use of chemical preservatives on plant food products is widespread and yields dramatic results. For example, grapes are protected from the gray mold botrytis by the application of sulfur dioxide. The result is a product that stays fresh under refrigeration for five months, compared to a three-week period before spoilage sets in on untreated grapes. Other examples of chemical preservatives include benzoic acid, propionic acid, and sorbic acid. Chemical preservatives are generally used in connection with natural preservatives to retain food quality.

TERMS

additive	eucaryotic	pH
aerobic	fungi	preservative
anaerobic	melanin	procaryotic
bacteria	microbe	respiration
dehydration	mold	ripening
endospore	mycelium	senescence
enzyme	oxidation	sterilization

The continuing concern over the use of chemical food additives has led to a determined effort by scientists to find effective biological control agents for preventing rot in fruits and vegetables. Gibberellic acid, a natural plant hormone, is used to prevent postharvest mold damage in citrus fruits. The fungus *A. breve* has been found to protect fruit against storage rot (gray mold). Scientists have also discovered a yeast, named US-7, that effectively wards off a fungus that attacks peaches, grapes, citrus, and tomatoes. A bacteria has been isolated that controls blue mold in apples and grows well in cold storage.

Figure 14-2. Close-up of mold growth on sliced fruit.

Because of their unique ability to become incorporated into the genetic structure of many kinds of plants, microbes and their enzymes are being used as molecular tools in genetic engineering. These techniques may lead to significant applications in food preservation. While microorganisms exert many negative effects on food products, they also serve a role in the manufacture of foods such as cheese. The USDA manages one of the world's largest microbial culture collections. Located in Peoria, Illinois, the collection contains more than 80,000 specimens of yeasts, molds, and bacteria of agricultural and industrial importance.

OBJECTIVES—QUESTIONS FOR INVESTIGATION

After completing the laboratory investigations included in this chapter and participating in other activities designed by your teacher, you should be able to answer the following questions:

1. How do microorganisms cause damage to fruits and vegetables?

2. What conditions are most/least favorable for microbial growth on plant food products?

3. How do postharvest techniques help to maintain the quality of fresh fruits and vegetables?

4. How do food preservation methods used in the food processing industry affect microbial populations?

5. What food products are most susceptible to mold growth? Why?

6. What effect does respiration and enzymatic activity have on degradation of fruit and vegetable tissues?

7. What causes browning in some fruits and vegetables when they are peeled or cut? How can this browning be reduced?

LABORATORY INVESTIGATIONS

EXPERIMENT I.
THE RELATIONSHIP OF FOOD PRODUCT AND PRESERVATIVE TO MOLD GROWTH

Purpose

The purpose of this investigation is to compare the extent of mold growth on various food product samples and to examine the effectiveness of different preservatives in controlling mold growth.

Materials

- fresh food samples (four each of bread, apples, cheese)
- microscope and slides

- 12 small containers with tight-fitting lids

- knife or scalpel

- calcium propionate

- sodium benzoate

- potassium sorbate

- three beakers or other containers

Procedures

Prepare a microscope slide for each of the three food samples. Examine their appearance under the microscope and make a rough sketch of each sample. Place a half slice of bread, an apple slice, and a slice of cheese in separate containers (leave about one inch between the top of the sample and the lid). Secure the lids. Keep the samples moist until mold appears (several days). Note the number of days required for mold growth. Using a scalpel, prepare a slide of the mold and examine. Scrape the visible mold from the samples and prepare a slide of each, using tissue about one centimeter below the scraped surface. Again, examine the slide and sketch. Compare the two sketches for each of the food samples.

Obtain an additional set of food samples. Prepare the following food preservative solutions: 0.3% calcium propionate, 0.1% sodium benzoate, and 0.1% potassium sorbate. Spray each preservative on a slice of bread, and place each slice in a separate, labelled container. Dip apple wedges and cheese slices in each of the preservatives and place in a container. Keep the samples moist and maintain for the same number of days required for mold growth in the first set of samples. Remove lids and observe. Examine tissue from each sample under the microscope. Record your results.

EXPERIMENT 2.
ENZYMATIC BROWNING

Purpose

The purpose of this experiment is to investigate the process of browning in fruits and test the effectiveness of various substances in preventing browning.

Materials

- fresh fruits or vegetables (apples, bananas, pears, peaches, avocados)
- organic acids: ascorbic acid (0.1%), citric acid (0.1%), acetic acid (0.1%), acetic acid (1%)
- beakers or wide-mouth jars (five for each fruit tested)
- tongs
- paper towels

Procedures

Prepare a 200 milliliter solution of the four preservatives listed in the materials list. Pour each of the solutions in a separate beaker or jar and put 200 milliliters of water in the fifth beaker. Cut each of the food products into six pieces of about the same size. Ask an assistant to use the tongs to dip one piece of each fruit into each of the beakers as you slice the pieces. After dipping, place each sample on a paper towel in front of the appropriate beaker. The sixth slice will remain untreated (the control). Place it on paper towel. Observe all six samples every ten minutes and record your ratings of the extent of browning.

Enzymatic Browning

Chart for Recording Observations

Time	Level of Browning*					
	Ascorbic Acid	Citric Acid	Acetic Acid .1%	Acetic Acid 1%	Water	Air
0 min.						
10 min.						
20 min.						
30 min.						
40 min.						
50 min.						
60 min.						

*5 = Completely dark brown
4 = Fully covered light brown
3 = Half covered light brown
2 = Slight or scant brown patches
1 = No browning present

Figure 14-3. Data summary chart for Experiment 2—Enzymatic Browning.

SCIENCE CONNECTIONS

Fruits and vegetables are still alive when they are harvested! They are capable of *respiration* and contain substances acted upon by enzymes. This enzymatic activity continues to occur even after harvest. *Ripening* and *senescence* continue to occur after harvest in most fruits. In addition, fruits and vegetables deteriorate after harvest by browning, softening, degreening, starch transformation, increasing sugar content, decreasing acid content, decreasing nutritional content, and through oxidation of lipid material. These biochemical postharvest changes are a function of handling and storage methods. *Degradation* of plant food products is primarily due to respiration and water loss from plant tissues. Respiration uses up sugar reserves in the fruit and leads to losses in flavor.

MICROORGANISMS IMPORTANT IN FOOD PRESERVATION

Microorganisms damage fresh fruits and vegetables by attacking weak or wounded tissues, which leads to rot. Microbial species causing spoilage in fruits and vegetables primarily include *bacteria, molds*, and *yeasts*. Except for a few sterilized foods, these organisms are found in all food products.

Figure 14-4. After harvest, most fruits and vegetables rapidly deteriorate under normal conditions.

Fortunately, most *microbes* are harmless to humans. Food-poisoning microbes grow best at higher temperatures (60 to 90 °F), while the less harmful food-spoilage microbes grow best at much lower temperatures.

Foods vary in their *susceptibility* to microbial damage. The physical and chemical characteristics of the plant food product (both fresh and preserved), along with how it is stored, determine the potential for spoilage. The moisture content of foods greatly affects their susceptibility to spoilage. To prevent spoilage, foods must be stored in such as way as to retard or stop microbial activity.

Bacterial cells have a primitive *nucleus* in which the DNA-containing region lacks a limiting membrane. These cells are known as *procaryotic* cells (as opposed to *eucaryotic* cells—those with a definitive nucleus). Thousands of different kinds of bacteria exist, and they are grouped into spherical-shaped (cocci), rod-shaped (bacilli), and spiral-shaped (spirilli) bacteria. Further, bacteria are classified into two groups, gram-positive and gram-negative, based upon their reaction to a dye. Bacteria of most concern to the food industry are those that must depend on other organisms for their food. These bacteria are called *heterotrophic* bacteria.

About 100,000 species of *fungi* are known today, with about 1,000 new species identified each year. Fungi include mushrooms, rusts, smuts, molds,

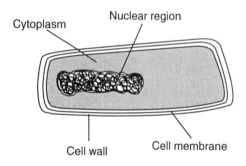

Figure 14-5. Diagram of a procaryotic cell.

Figure 14-6. Diagram of a eucaryotic cell.

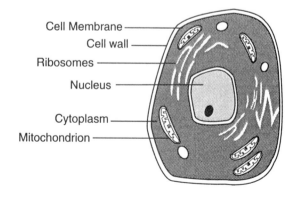

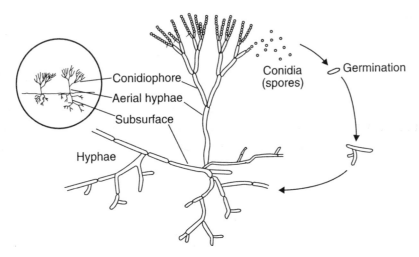

Figure 14-7. Mold life cycle.

mildews, and other organisms. The vegetative body of many fungi consists of a mass of *filaments*, referred to as the *mycelium* or *hyphae*. Fungi reproduce by forming *spores*, which can sometimes be quite resistant to unfavorable environmental conditions. Spores from bread mold have been found just about everywhere, even the North Pole. Yeasts, brown fruit rots, canned fruit fungi, and many other fungi species are classified as cup or *sac* fungi.

Figure 14-8. Close-up of mold on bread.

ENVIRONMENTAL EFFECTS ON MICROORGANISMS

In most environmental conditions there is a minimum level below which no microbial growth occurs, an optimum level at which growth is most rapid, and a maximum level at which growth is halted. Temperature is one of the most important factors in determining microbial growth in plant food products. In general, the lower the storage temperature, the slower the microbial growth and spoilage rate. However, some microbes are able to thrive in refrigerators, so storage for long periods of time is only possible by freezing. But even at temperatures of $-20°C$, some microbes may survive. Thus, freezing prevents microbial growth, but it does not always cause microbial death.

Figure 14-9. This fruit was frozen, thawed, and stored in a refrigerator—even freezing does not kill all microbes.

Sterilization, brought about by heat, chemicals, and radiation, is the complete killing of all organisms. The temperature required for effective heat sterilization depends upon the medium being sterilized. Acid foods, like tomatoes and fruits, are easier to heat sterilize because of their higher pH. In addition, dry cells are more resistant to heat sterilization than moist ones. Bacterial *endospores* are the most heat-resistant organisms known.

As just noted, the *pH* of the food product has a significant effect upon the success of food preservation. Most food spoilage bacteria do not grow at a pH of less than 5.0. This explains why pickling and *fermentation* are effective food preservation methods. (The microorganisms involved in food fermentation are acid tolerant.) Fungi are more acid tolerant than bacteria.

All organisms require water for life. The effect of some food preservation techniques is to reduce the *water content* of the food or make the water less available to microorganisms. Salts and sugars essentially absorb *available water*, thereby decreasing microbial growth. Many fruits are preserved with sugars. However, some yeasts can survive in high salt or sugar concentrations.

Microorganisms vary in their need for oxygen. *Aerobic* bacteria must have oxygen, while *anaerobic* bacteria do not require oxygen. (Even so, some anaerobic bacteria can tolerate oxygen environments.) Some of the most toxic food microbes are anaerobes.

Enzymes play an important role in food deterioration processes. Oxygen is required for enzymatic activity. When certain fruits and vegetables are peeled, the enzyme polyphenol oxidase converts phenol compounds in the fruit tissue to the brown pigment *melanin*. This *oxidation* occurs only in warm temperatures where the pH is between 5 and 7.

THE ACTION OF FOOD PRESERVATION TECHNIQUES

As mentioned earlier, a considerable number of food preservation techniques are successfully used to retard or eliminate microbial growth. *Dehydration*, either naturally or artificially, consists of removing water from the fruit or vegetable tissues. This not only reduces microbial growth, it also stops enzymatic activity, respiration, and natural deterioration. The moisture content of fruits is reduced to 15 to 25%. Due to their lower sugar content, vegetables must be reduced to less than 5% moisture. *Blanching* (heating in boiling water or steam) deactivates enzymes and usually precedes dehydration of vegetables.

Canning destroys food spoilage organisms and inactivates enzymes that naturally deteriorate plant tissues. Some bacteria, like *Clostridium botulinum*, are extremely heat resistant. Storage temperatures above 50°F allow certain bacteria to continue to grow.

A number of chemicals are used to retard or prevent food deterioration. These chemicals alter one or more of the environmental conditions necessary for microbial growth on plant food products. For example, several *chemical food preservatives* are acids which lower the pH of the food product below the minimum level that supports microbial growth. The action of the preservatives used in Experiment 2, Enzymatic Browning, illustrates how

Figure 14-10. Even with a chemical food additive, rapid microbial growth
occurred on this loaf of bread.

chemical food *additives* work. In this experiment ascorbic acid prevents
oxidation by tying up oxygen molecules with ascorbate. Citric acid reduces
enzyme activity. Acetic acid lowers the pH, thus inactivating enzyme activity.
And finally, water restricts the availability of free oxygen, which is needed
in the oxidation reaction.

Table 14-1
Use of Chemical Preservatives in Foods

Compound	Used In	Effective Against
Sodium benzoate	Carbonated beverages, pickles, preserves, fruit juices, margarine	All microbes
Sodium or calcium propionate	Bread	Molds
Sorbic acid	Citrus products, cheese, pickles, salads	Molds and yeasts
Sulfur dioxide	Dried fruits and vegetables	Molds

CHAPTER SUMMARY

Proper storage and preservation of plant food products is crucial to maintaining the postharvest quality of fruits and vegetables. Today's consumers want a variety of fruits and vegetables year round, regardless of the growing season or production site. Losses due to spoilage account for over 25% of potential sales each year. A wide variety of methods are used to preserve plant food products. Researchers continue to seek safer and more efficient techniques for food preservation. While several chemicals are crucial to effective food preservation today, scientists are developing biological controls that may one day find widespread applications.

Ripening and senescence continues in fruits and vegetables even after harvest. This natural degradation is due to water loss, respiration, and enzymatic action. A wide variety of yeasts, molds, and bacteria can attack plant food products and cause spoilage. These microorganisms often enter plant tissues at an injury site.

The susceptibility of food products to microbial invasion depends largely upon the inherent characteristics of the food. However, water content has much to do with susceptibility—drier foods are less susceptible. Under the right conditions, food microbes can spread rapidly. Microbial populations are affected by changes in temperature, pH, water content, and oxygen. Modern food preservation methods alter one or more of these environmental conditions to reduce or eliminate microbial growth.

FURTHER LABORATORY INVESTIGATIONS

1. Test the effects of other substances (salt, cloves, cinnamon, pepper, sugar, etc.) on controlling mold growth on food samples.

2. Compare the rate of mold growth on a variety of food products held under the same storage conditions. What factors might explain the differences in rate of ripening and spoilage?

3. Examine the extent and rate of enzymatic browning in a variety of fruits and vegetables. What effect does preservative concentration or exposure time to the preserv-

ative have on browning? What happens if preservative treatment is delayed for 30 seconds, one minute, five minutes?

4. Design and conduct an experiment for determining the degree of enzymatic browning based upon fruit freshness, fruit quality, moisture content of fruit, temperature, and oxygen availability.

5. Obtain live cultures of non-hazardous bacteria that may be found in spoiled foods (ask your teacher for assistance). Culture multiple samples of each bacteria on nutrient agar. Expose the samples to varying pH, temperature, sugar content, and other conditions. What effect does each condition have on each species of bacteria?

Chapter 15

BIOTECHNOLOGY IN AGRICULTURE

Is That a Cow?

AGRICULTURAL APPLICATIONS

"PHARM" ANIMALS

One of the most exciting biotechnological developments in animal agriculture involves using farm animals to produce medicines (pharmaceuticals) and other useful products in their milk. By transferring selected genes into an animal, large quantities of beneficial milk components may

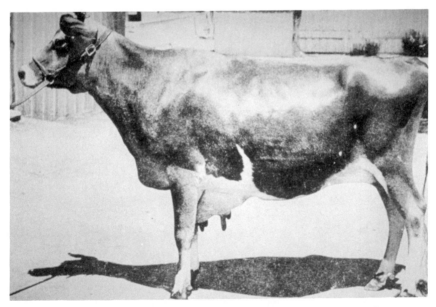

Figure 15-1. Animal biotechnology won't do this, but it has resulted in some valuable products for society.

267

be produced at affordable costs. Scientists have successfully transferred a gene into pigs that results in increased milk protein. The goal is to accomplish the same results with dairy cattle and goats. Many other products are being developed. One company expects to develop high nutritional products by separating protein antibodies from the milk of transgenic animals. Patients with immune deficiencies could benefit from such a product. A genetically engineered goat could produce enough blood-clotting factors in its milk to treat the world's hemophiliacs. Cows could be programmed to produce more milk casein, a protein necessary for cheese making.

By the year 2000 many believe that a number of commercial drugs will be produced from the milk or blood of livestock. By transferring into animals genes that are coded to produce human hormones or proteins, valuable drugs may be produced 100 times faster than in laboratory bacterial cultures. Herman, a transgenic Freisian bull in Holland, possesses a gene that expresses lactoferrin, a human protein found in mother's milk. Lactoferrin improves digestion and prevents disease in infants. Cows sired by Herman are expected to provide a plentiful, inexpensive source of lactoferrin.

The first transgenic animal patent was issued in the late 1980s for transgenic mice. Nearly 200 patents for transgenic animals are pending at the current time. The potential of this technology for improving animal agriculture is limited primarily by progress toward mapping genes. In addition to the production of pharmaceuticals, future applications are likely to involve the transfer of genes both between and within some species to increase selected production factors and resistance to disease.

TERMS

bovine somatotropin (bST)	gender preselection	recombinant DNA
cell	gene mapping	RFLP map
DNA	genome	RNA
DNA probe	nucleus	RNA analysis
electrophoresis	ova	sperm
embryo transfer	ovulation	superovulation
estrous cycle	plasma membrane	transgenic organism
	pronucleus	

GENDER SELECTION

Gender preselection techniques are rapidly becoming available for commercial use. Dairy producers may use gender preselection techniques to produce more female calves, necessary for replacement stock and milk production. On the other hand, beef producers can preselect female calves for replacements or male calves for feedlots. One biotechnology company is ready to market a sperm cell sorting kit for use with dairy, beef, swine, and possibly horses. The kit, used in conjunction with artificial insemination, is claimed to be 95% accurate and will add $20 to $50 to artificial insemination costs. The sex of the embryo after fertilization can now be determined by examining a few cells removed from the embryo, and new ultrasound techniques allow detection of pregnancy as early as the third week after conception.

GENOTYPING

The current emphasis in animal biotechnology is to identify (map) and manipulate genes that affect disease and parasite resistance, growth rate, meat quality, reproduction, metabolism of fat and muscle, and other economically important traits in livestock. A good example is the current work aimed at identifying the genes responsible for the tremendous reproductive prolificacy in Chinese pigs, which often have litters of up to 20 pigs. Scientists are attempting to map the genome of swine and cattle. Over 200 bovine genes have been identified, but scientists estimate that swine

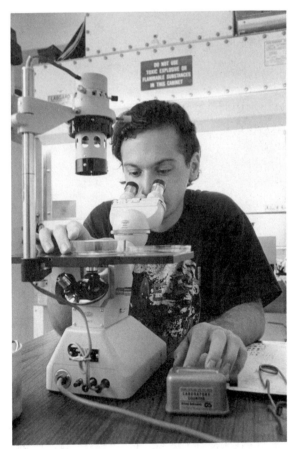

Figure 15-2. Much of today's animal biotechnology is based upon cell and molecular biology. (Courtesy, OACE, University of Illinois)

Figure 15-3. Gene mapping research is aimed at identifying genes that express important production traits.

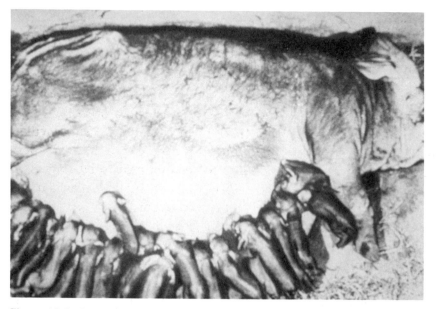

Figure 15-4. Reproductive prolificacy of Chinese pigs is one trait that researchers would like to transfer to other swine breeds.

have from 50,000 to 100,000 genes! Researchers throughout the world are collaborating to develop a genome map database.

As a result of gene mapping work, researchers can now better select for certain traits. USDA scientists have found two genes that are important in determining the amount of fat in market lambs. As a result, a simple blood test at birth might be all that is needed to identify fat-prone lambs. Further, lambs with preferred genes can be selected for breeding. In 1991 a test for detecting the mutant gene responsible for porcine stress syndrome was developed. This was the first use of biotechnology in the pig breeding industry since the use of artificial insemination.

A new technique for determining the cheese-making ability of a cow's milk has been developed. Producers simply collect the milk samples and send them to researchers for quick analysis. The same technique may be used to determine if the animal is carrying genes that express certain diseases. Gene mapping will eventually lead to the selection of genetically superior animals and isolation of superior alleles. This technology will reduce the time needed (often 5 to 10 years) to place superior alleles together in one genome. However, producers may find that selecting for one trait (e.g., increased milk production) may be at the expense of another (e.g., disease resistance).

SUPEROVULATION AND EMBRYO TRANSFER

The discharge of large numbers of female reproductive cells (ova) at one time is a key area of biotechnology research and product development. The ability to control superovulation is crucial to embryo transfer and genetic engineering. These technologies will lead to a breeding program in the near future that consists of the following stages (1) superovulation of the female, (2) *in vitro* fertilization of the ova with X or Y sperm, (3) freezing of the embryos, (4) delivery of the embryos to customers, and (5) nonsurgical implantation of the embryos into recipient females. In addition to the obvious advantages in genetic improvement, risks of diseases are also lowered. However, much research is needed to identify ways of increasing the survival rate of these embryos.

Although embryo transfer is still too costly for widespread application, further research may allow producers or veterinarians to retrieve embryos from superovulated females, freeze them, and then implant them when desired. Researchers have also been able to keep cattle and sheep embryos alive and growing outside the mother's womb for up to six days. This embryo culture technique will ensure that only cells that survive genetic

Figure 15-5. Embryo transfer allows numerous offspring to be simultaneously produced from parents of superior genetic makeup.

manipulation are implanted into surrogate mothers. In addition, embryo splitting is now being used in the cattle and swine industry to produce multiple copies (clones) of an embryo.

OTHER APPLICATIONS

Many other applications of biotechnology in animal agriculture have occurred and are being developed. Current areas of emphasis include estrus synchronization, developing superior forms of vaccines, better disease diagnosis procedures, and products that transfer and stimulate immunity. Some companies currently produce feed-grade enzymes that increase digestion when used as feed additives. Researchers at Michigan State University have developed a technique for separating and removing cholesterol from milk, a discovery that could eventually become a part of the pasteurization process. Biotechnology promises to provide an economical means of detecting carriers of genetic disease.

Perhaps the most notable product of biotechnology at the current time is bovine somatotropin (bST), a genetically engineered hormone supplement that increases milk production in dairy herds by 10 to 15%. bST is a hormone (protein) naturally produced by a cow's pituitary gland. Use of bST in dairy herds was finally approved by the U.S. Food and Drug Administration in November 1993 after nearly 10 years of review. Daily injections or sustained-release formulations are used by producers.

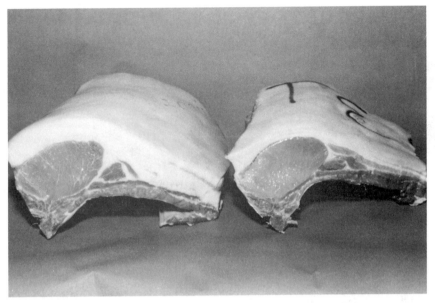

Figure 15-6. Effects of porcine somatotropin (pST) on the fat content of a pork carcass. (Courtesy, OACE, University of Illinois)

OBJECTIVES—QUESTIONS FOR INVESTIGATION

After completing the laboratory activities that follow and participating in other learning activities assigned by your teacher, you should be able to answer the following questions:

1. What is biotechnology?

2. How do biotechnology procedures of today differ from those of 20 or more years ago?

3. What cell features are important in contemporary biotechnology applications?

4. What role does DNA play in developing transgenic animals?

5. How is gene identification and transfer accomplished?

6. How is superovulation induced?

LABORATORY INVESTIGATIONS

EXPERIMENT I.
DNA EXTRACTION

Purpose

The purpose of this investigation is to extract DNA from the bacterium *E. coli* and study some of the physical and chemical properties of DNA.

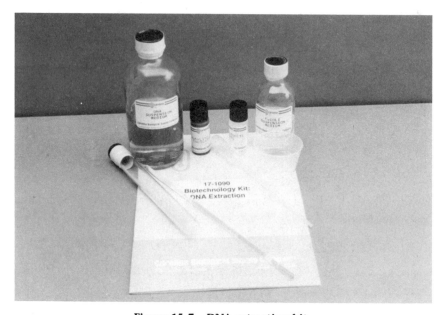

Figure 15-7. DNA extraction kit.

Materials *(most are contained in the Carolina DNA Extraction Kit provided by your teacher)*

- freeze-dried *E. coli*
- *E. coli* suspension medium
- DNA suspension medium
- sodium dodecyl sulfate
- alkaline pH indicator

- medicine cups

- pipets

- spooling rods

- 95% ethanol

- test tube

- beaker

- thermometer (°C)

- hot plate

- water

Procedures

Note: Due to the use of viable bacteria, wash your hands thoroughly before and after performing this investigation.

Detailed procedures for conducting this investigation are included in the DNA Extraction Kit. Follow these procedures carefully. General procedures for DNA extraction are as follows:

1. Place the cells from which DNA will be extracted in suspension in a test tube.

2. Add a detergent to the suspension to break down the cell walls.

3. Heat the suspension to inactivate enzymes which could break down the DNA.

4. Add ethanol to the tube and collect the DNA from the suspension by spooling it onto a glass rod.

EXERCISE I.
ANALYSIS OF ANIMAL BIOTECHNOLOGY PRODUCTS

Purpose

The purpose of this investigation is to examine selected biotechnology products being used in animal agriculture in terms of *how* they are used and *why* they have the effects that they do, from an animal biology standpoint.

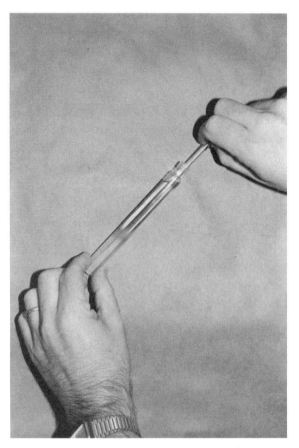

Figure 15-8. Spooling the DNA from *E. coli* bacteria.

Materials

- selected animal biotechnology products (estrus synchronizers, feed-grade hormones used as feed additives, vaccines, superovulating products, etc.)

- product use guidelines and materials

- written references (reports, periodicals, etc.)

Procedures

Obtain one or more of the selected products and any supporting product information provided by the manufacturer. Call or write the manufacturer to obtain additional product information as needed. Identify the set of specific questions that you want to answer as a result of your investigation into the product. Questions might deal with availability, cost, performance, approval procedures, problems, use, mode of action, and so on.

Interview (by phone or in person) two experts for each selected technology. Try to include a user of the technology (producer) and a research perspective (veterinarian, Extension specialist, researcher, or company representative). Supplement these interviews with self-study, using relevant written materials. Be sure to focus your investigation around your original set of questions to answer. Prepare a written report on the product and share your findings with other class members.

SCIENCE CONNECTIONS

SOME CELL BASICS

Cells compose the bodies of all living things (plants and animals) and are the fundamental units of life. The *cell* is both the structural and functional unit for animals and plants. New cells derive from previously existing cells. Animal cells differ in size, shape, and function. A group of similar cells constitutes a tissue, and similar tissues form organs. The delicate, elastic outer surface of animal cells is called the *plasma membrane*.

Inside each cell is the *nucleus*, which contains the chromosomes and controls metabolism, growth, and reproduction. *Chromosomes* are composed of long, thread-like strands of *DNA*. (The average length of the DNA molecule in a human cell is three meters!) Segments of the strand are called *genes*, which are the basic unit of inheritance. Most animals of agricultural importance have from 38 chromosomes (19 pairs) in swine to 80 chromosomes (40 pairs) in turkey in each body cell. The number of genes on each chromosome is not yet known. Each gene occupies a specific location on a specific chromosome. *Genome* is the

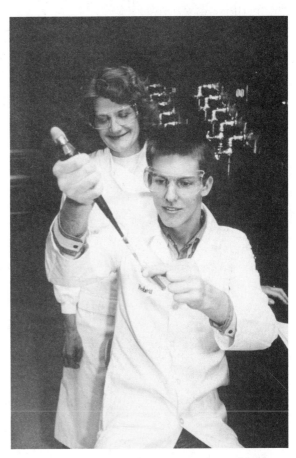

Figure 15-9. Biotechnology companies and job opportunities are rapidly growing. (Courtesy, National FFA Organization)

term used to describe the overall genetic makeup of an animal. Most economically important animal traits are influenced by many different genes.

GENE MAPPING AND TRANSGENESIS

The basics of cell biology described in the previous section are the foundation for current biotechnology techniques, including *gene mapping*. The objective in gene mapping is to identify genes and their locations along the chromosomes that make up the animal species. Once genes have been mapped, they can be isolated and transferred from one organism to another. Current technology (*recombinant DNA*) allows scientists to splice, clone, and insert genes to change the genetic makeup of an animal.

One technique for gene mapping involves the use of *DNA probes*. A probe is a DNA segment that will bind to equivalent genes in the target cell. The chemical components of cattle genes and human genes are similar, allowing researchers to use probes made from human DNA to bind to equivalent bovine genes, and vice versa.

RNA analysis is also used to track genes. Every gene codes for a particular *protein*, and the more times a gene is expressed (or copied) within a cell, the greater the level of that particular protein. *RNA* analysis can reveal the number of times a gene is copied.

Due to environmental circumstances, the physical appearance (*phenotype*) of an animal may not be a true reflection of its *genotype*. Researchers have recently developed a process known as *RFLP maps* to identify genes and more accurately measure genetic composition. In RFLP maps, special *enzymes* are used to cut DNA into smaller pieces. These DNA fragments then undergo *electrophoresis*—separation of DNA proteins with an electrical charge. Because DNA is negatively charged, its fragments migrate to the positive end of the electrical field at a rate relative to their size. This technique allows chromosomal regions to be marked and potentially linked with genes that control important traits.

Enzymes are important in the gene mapping and identification process. By using enzymes to break down the cellular protein surrounding DNA, scientists can genotype milk samples to determine the cheese-making ability of a cow's milk.

A *transgenic organism* carries a foreign gene that was inserted by laboratory techniques in all its cells. A transgenic organism is produced by placing DNA (genes) from another organism into embryos prior to birth. Each transferred gene is expressed in all tissues of the resulting animal.

The objective of this technique is to produce animals which possess the transferred gene in their sperm cells (*sperm* or *ova*). These animals can then produce offspring that carry the desirable genes. The most successful method for producing transgenic animals involves *microinjection* of cloned genes into the *pronucleus* of a fertilized ovum.

SUPEROVULATION AND EMBRYO TRANSFER

Whereas a bull can produce several thousand sperm per day, a cow normally produces one ovum every 17 to 21 days. When given supplemental hormone treatments, a cow can be induced to release 5 to 50 ova at one *estrous cycle*. Since this stepped up *ovulation* occurs over a period of time, the donor cow is artificially inseminated several times. The result is often four to five fertilized eggs that can be transferred to surrogate mothers. *Superovulation* allows rapid production of offspring from superior parents.

Embryo transfer is the placing of an embryo into the uterus of a surrogate mother. Embryo transfer involves (1) synchronizing the heat cycles of the donor and recipient females, (2) administering a hormone treatment to the donor female to cause superovulation, (3) breeding of the donor female, (4) collecting fertilized eggs from donor animal, (5) verifying viability of retrieved eggs, and (6) transferring eggs to surrogate mothers. Offspring

Figure 15-10. This calf was imported from Costa Rica as a frozen embryo and transferred to this Brahman surrogate mother. (Courtesy, Agricultural Research Service, USDA)

Figure 15-11. An ultrasound scanner is used to examine a heifer's ovaries at puberty. (Courtesy, Agricultural Research Service, USDA)

generated through embryo transfer carry the genetic traits of the donor female and the male to which she was bred. The surrogate females serve only as "incubators" and have no influence on the genetic makeup of the offspring.

Gender preselection is a technology that is also dependent upon embryo transfer techniques. Gender preselection is based upon several methods of sperm sorting. One method involves separating sperm cells based upon the amount of DNA they carry. Scientists have found that female-producing X chromosomes carry more DNA, which can be measured with a fluorescent dye and a laser. The X sperm give off more fluorescent light due to their higher DNA content. Other sperm sorting techniques are being rapidly developed.

NEW RECOMBINANT DNA TECHNIQUES

New recombinant DNA techniques have made it possible to efficiently produce an abundant supply of *bovine somatotropin (bST)* for commercial use. bST is produced by isolating the gene responsible for bST production in the pituitary gland of dairy cattle and transferring that gene to bacteria. The bacteria produce bST through standard fermentation techniques. After killing the bacteria, the bST is separated and purified before injection into dairy cows. Milk produced by cows treated with bST is safe to drink because (1) it is a natural component in milk, (2) bST levels in the milk of treated and nontreated cows are the same, (3) bST is inactivated by pasteurization, (4) bST is destroyed in the digestive tract before absorption, and (5) bST is inactive in humans.

CHAPTER SUMMARY

The use of biotechnology in animal agriculture is growing at an astronomical rate. New techniques and products are being continuously developed that have major implications for animal agriculture. Much of the biotechnology work in today's research laboratories is aimed at developing a complete map of an animal's genetic makeup. Although over 200 bovine genes have already been identified, this represents only a small fraction of the total genetic makeup of the species. The objective of this research is to identify the genes responsible for key production traits, including feed efficiency, growth rate, reproductive prolificacy, and disease resistance. Unfortunately, many genes control each of these economically important traits.

Animal biotechnology has already produced desirable results, such as the natural production of medicines. Significant improvements in the composition of meat and dairy products is also a likely result of animal biotechnology. Superovulation and embryo transfer have been successfully performed for several years. New gene transfer techniques are now being tested that will modify the genetic makeup of resulting animals. A number of transgenic animals have already been produced. Gender preselection is another product of biotechnology that has major implications for animal agriculture. Many of these technologies are complementary to each other and are expected to revolutionize animal agriculture in the years ahead.

FURTHER LABORATORY INVESTIGATIONS

1. Using similar procedures as used in Experiment 1, attempt to extract DNA from other plant or animal cells. In addition, test other procedures used in local or university laboratories for DNA extraction.

2. Follow the general procedures in Experiment 1 for DNA

extraction, but examine the effects of suspension temperature, ethanol, and other factors on the solubility of DNA.

3. Obtain a sperm sorting kit and use on frozen semen samples or as directed. Keep track of other new animal biotechnology products as they become available and observe their use and effectiveness.

4. Use commercially available kits or similar procedures to observe the phenotypic effects of adding new DNA sequences to living bacteria. An example is the transfer of an antibiotic-resistant gene into *E. coli*.

5. Separate DNA fragments using electrophoresis techniques. Commercially available kits may be used or assemble the electrophoresis components yourself. Arrange a visit with a researcher to discuss procedures and adaptations for this procedure.

Chapter 16

INHERITANCE OF TRAITS

Just Like Dad

AGRICULTURAL APPLICATIONS

The first U.S. experiment in crossbreeding cattle occurred in the 1800s using the rugged Longhorn and the stylish Shorthorn from Scotland. This combination was the first step in a continuing effort to customize cattle. There are over 50 cattle breeds in the United States today, and the merits of these individual breeds, or various breed combinations, is still a topic of hot debate among producers and researchers. An ongoing USDA research

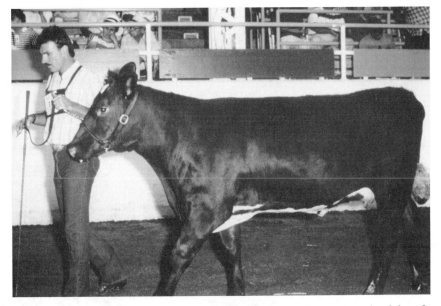

Figure 16-1. The merit of individual livestock breeds continues to be debated. (Courtesy, Illinois Dept. of Agriculture)

program has evaluated more than two dozen different breeds from other countries, using either Hereford or Angus females. Researchers are looking for patterns in growth rate, mature size, lean-to-fat ratio, age at puberty, milk production, and other traits. Matching cattle to production systems and climatic conditions is still a major concern.

A long-term goal of livestock producers is to continue to improve the quality of animals in their herds or flocks. Despite the wide generation intervals that exist in animal breeding when compared to crops, much improvement has been made in all animals species in the last 40 years. For example, the time required to produce a broiler has been cut by 50%, using 40% less feed. Today's steers reach slaughter weight in 14 to 20 months, nearly three times as fast as the old-style Longhorns. For most producers quality encompasses overall appearance and performance of the herd/flock in measures of economical importance. Producers use their working knowledge of genetics to drive their herd improvement plans. Breeding animals, both sires and dams, are selected based upon their potential to bring about rapid improvement in herd quality. Traits of economical importance include prolificacy, longevity, growth rate, feed efficiency, overall health, product (meat, wool, eggs, milk) quality, birth weight, conformation, and muscling.

Producers with the "best" livestock not only select high-quality animals, they also successfully manage the growth environment. Environmental factors that can significantly affect animal performance include housing, feed ration, climate, and herd health. USDA, state agencies, and universities have developed test stations in which similar environmental conditions are maintained for groups of animals so that genetic differences (as evidenced by performance) may be more accurately determined.

Producers use a variety of breeding programs to bring about herd/flock

TERMS

breeding program	heredity	outcrossing
dominant	heritability	progeny testing
environmental factors	heterosis	recessive
genetic potential	hybrid vigor	selection differential
genetic variation	inheritance	traits

Figure 16-2. Improvement in herd/flock quality is slow compared to plants due to much lower prolificacy and longer generation intervals.

Figure 16-3. Environmental factors have a major impact on performance.

improvement. Livestock breeders raise purebred lines and sell breeding stock to commercial producers. Crossbreeding is common in sheep, swine, cattle, and poultry operations. Crossbreeding programs have been used to decrease death loss and increase muscling, conception rates, growth rate, and frame size. Crossbreeding allows producers to introduce new traits into their herds or flocks in a fairly rapid and significant way.

New breeds have been developed through crossbreeding. As an example, the Brangus breed of beef cattle was developed by crossing Angus and Brahman cattle. The resulting offspring have high carcass quality characteristic of the Angus breed and heat tolerance characteristic of the Brahman breed. Two and three rotational crossbreeding programs are used in some sectors of the livestock industry, particularly swine. Inbreeding is used to a limited extent in some herds to increase the frequency of desirable genes. However, inbreeding also increases the frequency of less desirable genes. Recent USDA research has shown that inbreeding reduces reproduction rates, weaning weights, and wool production in sheep, resulting in significant economic losses.

Producers cull animals from their herds on at least an annual basis in order to continue progress toward herd improvement. Replacement animals are added each year to keep herd numbers up and to introduce new traits into the herd. Producers raise some replacement animals, and purchase others from commercial producers or livestock breeders.

Producers use several methods to select the animals for breeding programs. Greater emphasis is placed upon selecting sires for use in the breeding program, since they have a greater multiplier effect when compared to dams. Artificial insemination is now widely used in the cattle and swine industries, making semen from top sires accessible and affordable to many producers. This technology has greatly contributed to the dramatic improvements in the livestock industry during the last 40 years. Artificial insemination has also been useful because many producers cannot afford to own sires of high genetic potential. The selection of sires to use in artificial insemination programs is one of the most important management decisions in the animal breeding program.

Producers often select sires based upon performance tests and progeny tests. When using performance tests, producers select sires based upon their performance in several key areas, including birth weight and rate of gain. Progeny tests, on the other hand, provide evidence of the performance of the sire's offspring. When available, producers use information from both tests to guide their selection process. Private companies that market semen provide performance and progeny test data for potential buyers to consider.

Figure 16-4. Evaluating performance and selecting replacement females are crucial to herd improvement. (Courtesy, Agricultural Research Service, USDA)

Figure 16-5. Artificial insemination has greatly contributed to the rate of improvement in the cattle and swine industries.

OBJECTIVES—QUESTIONS FOR INVESTIGATION

After completing the exercises contained in this chapter you should be able to answer the following questions:

1. How are animal traits passed on from parent to offspring?

2. What animal traits are best transferred to offspring? Why?

3. What effects do environment and genetic potential have on animal performance?

4. Why do producers use crossbreeding to improve herd quality?

5. Why do crossbred animals usually outperform their parents?

6. Why is genetic variability desirable?

7. Why is the rate of improvement slower in animals than in plants?

8. Why do many producers use artificial insemination?

LABORATORY INVESTIGATIONS

EXERCISE I.
PROBABILITY OF TRAIT INHERITANCE

Purpose

The purpose of this exercise is to determine the probability of selected traits being passed on to offspring. In addition, this exercise is intended to help you better understand animal genotypes and phenotypes.

Materials

- 14-inch square piece of cardboard
- spinner
- marker
- pencil eraser

Procedures

Draw a 10-inch circle in the center of the cardboard. Mark the circle into four equal sections and attach the spinner in the center. (You can use a spinner already available from a board game, such as Twister.) Write the possible genotypes for a monohybrid cross beside each of the four sections of the circle (use a pencil). Use the sample crosses that follow, and add additional crosses as desired.

For example, spider syndrome in sheep is a genetic defect that causes structural deformities and eventual death. Spider syndrome is a homozygous recessive trait (*nn*). If a ram with this trait is mated to a known carrier (*Nn*) of the syndrome, but not showing the physical characteristics, determine the possible genotypes of the offspring and pencil in at each of the four sections of the circle on the spinner board. (The following genotypes should be penciled in: *Nn, Nn, nn, nn.*) Thus, the probability of an offspring displaying the defective gene is 50%. Spin the spinner 20 or more times to observe the number of offspring that will show the spider syndrome trait. (Note: The more spins the more accurate the prediction.) Will the phenotypes of the offspring generally match the probability that carrier and defective lambs will be born?

Use the spinner to verify the probability of dominant and recessive traits in each of the following breeding scenarios:

1. In guinea pigs short hair (*L*) is dominant over long hair (*l*). Two heterozygous short-haired guinea pigs are mated. What are the genotypic and phenotypic ratios for this cross? Using the spinner, what is the probability of a short-haired guinea pig?

2. A roan-colored cow has red and white hair (this is considered a codominant color). A red bull (*RR*) is mated to five roan (*Rr*) females and three white (*rr*) females. What are the genotypic and phenotypic ratios for each mating. Using the spinner, determine the probability of obtaining roan calves.

EXERCISE 2.
GENOTYPIC AND PHENOTYPIC RATIOS

Purpose

The purpose of this exercise is to apply the principles of Mendelian genetics in predicting the genotypes and phenotypes of offspring. In addition, you will attempt to determine the genotypes of parents and offspring, based upon the physical characteristics of the parents and offspring.

Materials

- copies of a blank Punnett square
- pencil
- spinner from Exercise 1

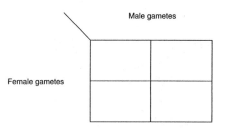

Procedures

A black Angus cow is mated with a Hereford bull. Black is the dominant color and is represented by *BB*. The recessive red color is represented by *bb*. Use the Punnett square above to determine the genotypic and phenotypic ratios for this cross. What would be the genotypic and phenotypic ratio for a heterozygous offspring mated to a red bull?

SCIENCE CONNECTIONS

HERITABILITY

Many animal characteristics or *traits* differ widely. This variation is due to the genetic differences between the animals, as well as the environmental conditions in which they live and grow. The *heredity* of an animal is the sum of all the characteristics inherited from its parents. Offspring acquire (inherit) these traits by way of the genes that are transferred from the parents. In general, *inheritance* accounts for only 30 to 45% of the observed variations in animal traits. *Heritability* is the proportion of variance in animal traits that is due to the transmission of traits from parent to offspring. Thus, heritability gives an estimate of the potential improvement that can occur by selecting animals in the breeding program. Heritability also refers to the relationship between *genotype* and *phenotype*. For example, if the mature weight of beef cattle is a trait with a high heritability, then a bull's mature weight should be a general reflection of his genotype for this trait.

Animals are *selected* for breeding programs based upon the traits that they exhibit. Thus, producers are hoping that these physical traits will be

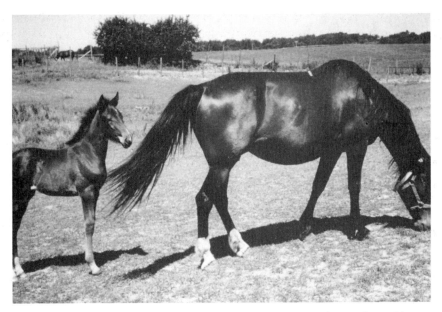

Figure 16-6. An animal's appearance and performance is the product of its genetic makeup and its environment. (Courtesy, Illinois Dept. of Agriculture)

genetically transferred to future offspring. However, the likelihood of trait transfer through the generations depends upon the trait and the animal species, as shown in Table 16-1. Heritability is usually expressed as a percentage, with 20% or less considered low and above 40% considered high. In general, performance traits have lower heritability estimates than carcass traits, which suggests that environment plays a substantial role in performance.

Table 16-1.
Selected Heritability Estimates for Beef and Swine

Trait	Beef Cattle	Swine
	%	%
Conformation score	25	30
Number born	5	10
Birth weight	40	5
Weight at weaning	25	10
Feed efficiency	40	30
Loin eye area	55	50
Fat thickness	40	50
Percent lean	40	35

GENETIC VARIATION AND SELECTION DIFFERENTIAL

Variation in the genetic makeup of a herd or flock is necessary for improvement in overall herd quality. Nevertheless, producers often strive to develop a herd that has a very uniform appearance. However, such uniformity also indicates little variation in animal genotypes in the herd, which reduces the potential for improvement. In a herd with wider *genetic variation*, the producer can more easily select the top females for breeding because these animals will be markedly better than the poorer ones. Thus, the potential for herd improvement is greater. Producers also increase genetic variation in the herd by selecting males that have significantly different (better) traits than the herd average.

Selection differential is the difference between a trait reflected by animals selected for breeding and the overall herd average on that particular trait. When genetic variation is higher, the selection differential will be higher. For example, assume the flock average for days to market for lambs is 180 days (110 pounds). From the total group of lambs the producer selects a group of ewe lambs for the breeding flock. The average days to market for this selected group is 160 days. Thus, the selection differential for days to market weight is 20.

Figure 16-7.   Greater genetic variation offers higher potential for improvement. (Courtesy, Illinois Dept. of Agriculture)

ENVIRONMENTAL EFFECTS

The physical characteristics and performance of a given animal are the product of its genetic makeup and its environment (although environment has little effect on traits like hair color, etc.). *Environmental factors* can include housing, nutrition, disease control, and overall management practices. An animal can have an excellent genetic makeup but still not perform well. Thus, environmental conditions can mask *genetic potential*, making it difficult for the producer to separate the effects of genetics and environment when evaluating performance. Test stations are used to minimize the effects of environment on animal performance. By maintaining identical environments for all animals being evaluated, prospective buyers can be confident that any observed desirable traits are primarily due to genetic makeup and are likely to be passed on to offspring to some degree.

Animal performance-reflecting traits that have low heritability estimates can be primarily due to environmental factors. For example, the number of pigs per litter (prolificacy) has a low heritability estimate. Even so, producers often select pigs from large litters to use in the breeding herd. However, environmental conditions, such as nutritional status of the female, boar fertility, and timing of breeding during estrus, are more important in determining litter size.

Figure 16-8. Poor environmental conditions can mask genetic potential.

SELECTION AND RATE OF IMPROVEMENT

If the heritability of a certain trait is relatively high, then producers can effectively improve their herds for that trait by selecting animals for the *breeding program*. In this case, animals exhibiting the desired trait will tend to transfer that trait to their offspring. *Selection* is the primary means by which producers bring about herd improvement. When heritability of a desired trait is low, selection is less effective and improvement is much slower. On the other hand, when heritability is high, selection is more effective and the rate of improvement is much greater.

In hogs and poultry, where the reproductive rate is higher, the rate of improvement is potentially greater. Producers place more emphasis on the selection of males, since a relatively few number of sires is needed in the breeding program. Thus, the selection differential for the sire is usually greater than for the dam. Producers can, therefore, justify higher investment costs in superior sires that have highly heritable, economically important traits. Purebred sires undergo *progeny testing*, whereby performance records are kept on the sire's offspring. Many believe that the performance of offspring is the best indication of the genetic potential and breeding merit of a sire.

Selection has the greatest potential for herd improvement when (1) genetic variation is high, (2) highly heritable traits are selected, (3) traits

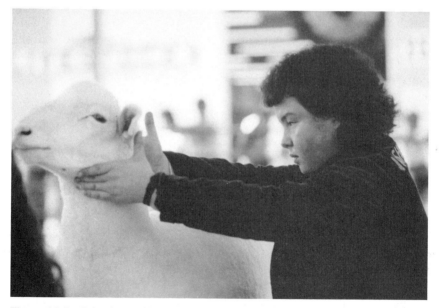

Figure 16-9. Selection is the primary means for improving the herd/flock. (Courtesy, National FFA Organization)

Figure 16-10. Prolificacy and generation interval greatly affect the rate of improvement. (Courtesy, Agricultural Research Service, USDA)

are accurately observed or measured, and (4) animals selected for improvement are effectively used in the breeding program. In addition, the rate of improvement also depends upon prolificacy, generation interval, and the rate of replacing females in the herd/flock. The degree of herd improvement for a particular trait can be predicted by multiplying the selection differential by the heritability estimate. For example, if a 10 pound selection differential in birth weight is achieved in a dairy herd, a 6 pound gain in birth weight would be expected in the offspring of selected females (heritability = 60%).

HETEROSIS

Researchers and producers have discovered that when different breeds are crossed in a breeding program, the resulting offspring show greater growth and vigor. This phenomenon is known as *heterosis* or *hybrid vigor*, and is defined as the extent to which performance of the offspring exceeds the parental average. In general, crossbred animals tend to perform better than the average performance of their parents. Traits high in heritability generally have low heterosis, and vice versa. In addition, the greater the genetic differential between two breeds, the greater the heterosis. Scientists have determined that using three-breed rotational crosses maintains het-

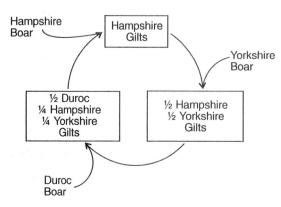

Figure 16-11. A three-breed rotational cross in swine maximizes heterosis.

erosis at about 85% of maximum, significantly higher than with two breed crosses.

BREEDING PROGRAMS

Fortunately, good *genes* tend to be *dominant*, while bad genes are usually *recessive*. A number of major types of breeding programs are used by producers, but the breeding program should take full advantage of the traits introduced to bring about herd improvement. The three primary types of breeding programs are inbreeding, outcrossing, and crossbreeding.

Inbreeding is the mating of closely related animals. Since inbreeding tends to concentrate both good and bad traits, it is seldom used except to develop inbred lines that breed true for certain traits. Highly inbred animals are less vigorous and often smaller in size than other animals.

Outcrossing and crossbreeding are two types of outbreeding. *Outcross-*

Figure 16-12. Crossbred animals are more vigorous in their growth and performance.

ing is the mating of animals within the same breed that are distant relatives. This strategy allows for the introduction of traits from another line within the same breed. *Crossbreeding* is the mating of animals from two different breeds. Crossbreeding is commonly used by producers to (1) increase growth and vigor due to heterosis and (2) introduce new traits into the herd from another breed. The combination of complementary traits through crossbreeding is a goal of producers. The way breeds are mixed greatly affects offspring performance. For example, researchers have discovered that calves from Angus sires and Brahman dams are as much as 25 pounds smaller at birth than calves from Brahman sires and Angus dams.

CHAPTER SUMMARY

Inheritance of traits determines to a large degree the rate of improvement in herds and flocks. Many animal traits are transferred from parents to offspring. Producers use their knowledge of trait inheritance to carefully select breeding animals for incorporation into the breeding program, hoping that any positive traits observed will be transferred to offspring. An animal's physical appearance may be a good indication of its genetic makeup; however, environmental conditions can have a dramatic effect on an animal's performance and may, in fact, mask an animal's true genetic potential. Thus, good management of all aspects of growing conditions is just as important as selecting animals that have outstanding genetic potential.

Producers improve their herds/flocks by culling animals that are performing poorly (in relation to the rest of the herd/flock) and introducing replacement animals that offer greater genetic potential than the herd average. Producers are usually more careful in selecting males, since males have a multiplier effect in bringing about herd/flock improvement. Males are usually selected based upon visual appearance, performance records, and progeny records, depending upon the species. Wider genetic variation in a herd offers greater potential for improving the herd on selected traits. Greater genetic variation can also provide a greater selection differential when choosing animals for the breeding program. Heritability estimates can be useful in predicting potential improvement in a herd. Crossbreeding is one type of breeding program that is popular in most animal agriculture settings, due to performance gains in offspring that occur as a result of heterosis, or hybrid vigor.

FURTHER LABORATORY INVESTIGATIONS

1. Use the Punnett square method to predict the genotypic and phenotypic ratios for a number of additional crosses, such as a polled cow (*PP*) crossed with a horned bull (*pp*). Compare the effects of a homozygous versus heterozygous cow crossed with a horned bull.

2. Interview purebred and commercial producers and discuss their strategies for herd improvement. Present a report to your class that compares the strategies used by the producers.

3. Using heritability estimates and selection differential, estimate the rate of improvement for a herd on the given traits. Case 1—birth weight in cattle: selection differential, 10 pounds; heritability, 40%. Case 2—fleece weight in sheep: selection differential, .6 pounds; heritability, 50%.

4. Obtain a listing of sires available through an artificial breeding service. Using your knowledge of trait inheritance and the performance and progeny data provided for each sire, select a sire that would help reach the following goals: increased weaning weight (herd average is now 520 pounds), decreased birth weight (herd average is 84 pounds), increased milk production (herd average is now 18,000 pounds), and increased litter size (herd average is now 8.8).

5. Interview several producers in your community to determine the nature of breeding programs used. Why do producers use certain breeding programs? What breeding and related performance records do they keep? What are the goals of their breeding programs?

Chapter 17

ANIMAL GROWTH

The Bigger the Better

AGRICULTURAL APPLICATIONS

Animal growth is of utmost concern to the livestock producer, meaning the difference between profit or loss, success or failure. As described in the previous chapter, growth and physical appearance are due to trait inheritance, sex, and environmental conditions under which animals are grown. Environmental conditions are directly under the producer's control,

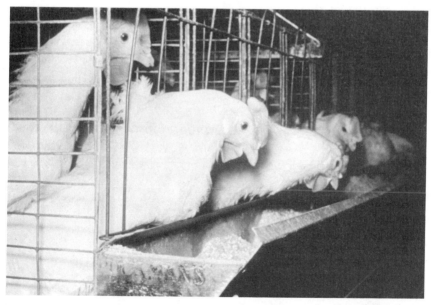

Figure 17-1. Confinement housing protects animals from environmental extremes, requiring less animal energy to regulate body temperature. (Courtesy, OACE, University of Illinois)

and most management efforts are aimed at providing optimal environmental conditions for animal growth. This primarily includes housing, feeding, and health management.

Confinement housing systems are predominant in the swine and poultry industries, offering the advantage of environmental control and more effective feed and health management. These systems allow for better control of feed intake and more constant optimum climatic conditions for growth. Confinement housing removes animals from environmental extremes, which normally cause animals to increase feed intake in order to maintain normal body functions. Ventilation systems are used to remove moisture and lower disease potential. Feedlots used for finishing cattle provide some of the same advantages as confinement housing.

Nutrition is the most important concern in managing animal growth. Feed is the primary expense in animal production. For obvious economic reasons, producers strive to obtain maximum production per unit of feed consumed. Steady growth and development from birth to market or maturity promises the greatest profit and healthiest animals. Animals that have grown under deficient conditions, including nutrition, usually perform poorly in later stages of growth and production.

An animal's nutritional needs vary by stage of growth and use (i.e., growth, maintenance, reproduction, lactation, finishing, work, and wool production). Thus, producers vary the type and amount of feed provided as the animal moves from one stage of growth to another. Feeds, especially forages, differ in quality and nutritional value, thus affecting the rate and quality of animal growth. A major concern of producers is acquiring high-quality feeds at an affordable cost.

Extensive nutrition research has been done to examine the effects of various feed types, rations, systems, and amounts on animal growth. For

TERMS

ad libitum	growth	mitosis
androgen	growth curve	nonruminant
cell cycle	hormone	ration
cell duplication	hyperplasia	ruminant
endocrine glands	hypertrophy	somatotropin

Figure 17-2. Attaching a sensing unit to determine grazing habits and patterns. (Courtesy, Agricultural Research Service, USDA)

Figure 17-3. Nutritional needs vary by stage of growth and development. (Courtesy, Illinois Dept. of Agriculture)

example, one study investigated the effects of feed intake on weight gain, feed efficiency, and cost. Most feedlot managers allow cattle to eat according to their natural appetite, believing that maximum weight gain will result. This study compared a limited feeding program to a free feeding, ad libitum program. Rate of gain for the two groups was the same, but the free feeding group consumed more feed, thus lowering feed efficiency and raising costs. The type of feeding program selected has significant implications for producers in terms of costs, net profit, waste management, feed handling, and marketing.

Producers use a variety of indicators as management tools to measure growth. Rate of gain is the primary growth indicator used for most species. Two commonly used indicators for rate of gain are weight per day of age and average daily gain. In addition, days needed to reach a standard market weight (e.g., poultry—4 pounds; sheep—110 pounds; hogs—230 pounds) is a common growth indicator. In some species weight at a standard age (e.g., cattle—205 days) is an accepted measure of growth. These measures are not only used to evaluate the growth of market animals, they also provide valuable information to producers for selecting breeding animals. Producers also use size, conformation, and visual appraisal to assess the amount and quality of animal growth.

Producers use a number of other techniques to manage animal growth.

Figure 17-4. Good management of environmental factors helps animals reach
             their genetic growth potential. (Courtesy, Illinois Dept. of
             Agriculture)

Since males have higher rates of gain then females, selection of males for cattle feedlots is preferred. Antibiotics and other feed additives are used to reduce the incidence of disease and maintain steady growth by increasing palatability, feed intake, and digestion. In addition, many cattle producers use growth hormone implants to boost rate of gain and feed efficiency. Proper management of all environmental factors allows animals to more fully reach their genetic potential.

OBJECTIVES—QUESTIONS FOR INVESTIGATION

After studying this chapter and completing the laboratory investigations, you should be able to answer the following questions:

1. How does animal growth occur?
2. How does environment affect animal growth?
3. What nutrients are needed for animal growth?
4. How and why do nutritional needs vary during different growth stages?

LABORATORY INVESTIGATIONS

EXPERIMENT I.
EFFECTS OF FEED RATION ON GROWTH OF CHICKS

Purpose

The purpose of this experiment is to compare the growth rate of chicks when different feed types are used.

Materials

- two lots of chicks (at least five per lot, same age, less than a week old)
- commercial starter mix (complete ration)
- alternative ration (commercial mix for older poultry, ground corn/soybean meal mix, or other ration)

- water

- growing area

- scales

Procedures

Obtain newly hatched chicks (or hatch your own!). At least five chicks should be used to test the effects of each feed ration examined. In this experiment you can simultaneously test the effects of several different feed rations on chick growth. A basic design would be to use a commercial starter mix as the control diet, since it will meet the energy, protein, mineral, and vitamin requirements of chicks. Select one or more alternative rations, based upon availability. If a ground corn/soybean meal ration is prepared, use a 60/40 ratio of ground corn to soybean meal.

Tag and weigh each chick at the beginning of the experiment. Provide the same environmental conditions for each treatment group (i.e., water, temperature, light, space). Check feed and water daily. Add feed as needed so that some feed remains in the feeder at all times. Record the weight and visual appearance of each chick every seventh day. Continue the experiment as long as possible or until the chicks are four weeks of age. At the end of the experiment, calculate the overall weight gain and rate of gain for each chick. Then calculate averages for the control and treatment

Table 17-1.
Recommended Ingredients for a Chick Starter Diet

Ingredient	Percentage by Weight	Nutrient Supplied
Corn	53.30	Energy, protein
Soybean Meal	38.00	Protein, energy
Fat (oil)	5.00	Energy
Dicalcium phosphate	1.70	Phosphorus, calcium
Limestone	1.20	Calcium
Salt	0.40	Sodium
Vitamin mix	0.25	Vitamins
Trace mineral mix	0.05	Trace minerals
Methionine	0.10	Amino acid

Note: A chick needs vitamins A, D, E, K, B_6, B_{12}, thiamin, riboflavin, niacin, pantothenic acid, folic acid, and biotin. Trace minerals needed include copper, iron, manganese, selenium, and zinc.

Figure 17-5. A complete diet is essential for steady and vigorous growth.

group(s). In addition, make final observations about the quality of growth by noting visual appearance.

EXPERIMENT 2.
EFFECTS OF FEED FORMULATION AND
FEEDING METHOD ON CHICK GROWTH

Purpose

The purpose of this laboratory is to examine the effects of pelleted versus mashed feed on chick growth. In addition, chick growth will be examined under free feeding conditions and controlled feeding conditions.

Materials

- commercial pelleted feed
- commercial mash feed
- four groups of chicks (at least five birds per group)
- water

- scales

- growing area

Procedures

Obtain a pelleted and mash formulation of commercial starter chick feed. (If a mash is unavailable, grind the pelleted version into a mash.) Provide separate, but environmentally similar, growing areas for each group of chicks. Each group will be fed as follows: (1) pelleted free-feeding, (2) pelleted controlled feeding, (3) mash free-feeding, and (4) mash controlled feeding.

Tag and weigh each chick in the four groups at the beginning of the experiment and record. For the free feeding groups, add enough feed daily so that some feed remains in the feeder at all times. For the controlled feeding groups, the amount of feed provided per day should be 85-90% of the amount consumed on a free feeding (ad libitum) basis. A one week trial feeding period can be used to establish this amount, or records from Experiment 1 can be used. Continue the feeding trial for four to six weeks, weighing each chick on a weekly basis. Record observations of visual appearance as well. Keep accurate records of chick weight and feed consumption. After the experiment, compare the rate of gain and feed consumption/efficiency for each group.

SCIENCE CONNECTIONS

THE CELL CYCLE

Animal *growth* refers to an increase in the size of muscle, bone, organs, or other body parts. Growth is the result of an increase in the number of cells (*hyperplasia*), an increase in the size of cells (*hypertrophy*), or both. Most growth is due to *cell duplication*, known as the *cell cycle*. A new cell is created when the constituents of the parent cell double, followed by division into two daughter cells. *Mitosis* is the cell division phase of the cell cycle. The cell cycle (in both plant and animal cells) requires about 20 hours, of which only about a hour is dedicated to cell division. Scientists have been unable to speed up the cell cycle, although unfavorable environmental conditions may slow it down. Cell division occurs during growth and development of the embryo, in replacing old cells, and in repairing injuries. Body tissues constantly undergo building and destruction through cell growth and cell mortality.

FACTORS AFFECTING GROWTH

As discussed in previous chapters, animal growth is primarily a function of *genetic potential* and environmental conditions. The potential size, growth rate, and appearance (quality of growth) are determined by *inheritance*. The influence of genetics on growth varies by trait and stage of growth. For example, postweaning weight is much more dependent on genetic makeup than is preweaning weight. When climate, health, space, and other environmental conditions are positive, an animal's growth is more likely to match its genetic potential. The influence of heredity on animal growth is largely due to hormonal activity.

Sex also significantly affects animal growth, with males generally showing more rapid growth rates and higher mature weights. This is due to the higher levels of *androgens* in males, which result in greater muscle development. Thus, hormones play a key role in animal growth. A *hormone* is a chemical messenger produced by the *endocrine glands*. Hormones are secreted directly into the bloodstream and exert a specific effect (physiological response) on a distant body part. Growth hormones are species-

Figure 17-6. Males generally have higher rates of gain and mature weights than females due to higher androgen levels.

specific and sex-specific. For example, the newly approved bovine somatotropin (bST) is effective only in cattle. *Somatotropin*, which is secreted by the anterior pituitary, is the primary hormone regulating growth. Other growth hormones include thyroxine, glucocorticoids, androgens, and estrogens.

Females generally grow very little during estrus, and often lose weight. In feedlot operations, an estrus inhibitor is used as a feed additive to maintain growth. Heifers also mature at a lighter weight than steers, and they are usually fatter at the same weight. Feed costs are thus higher, since more feed is required to produce a pound of fat than a pound of lean.

Nutrition is critical in animal growth and development. In general, as nutrition increases, growth increases. Additionally, the composition of feeds influences the type of growth that occurs (fat versus muscle). Nutritional needs of the animal change as different stages of growth are reached.

Temperature is a key environmental factor that affects animal growth. Warm-blooded animals maintain a relatively constant body temperature. Thus, excess heat must be dissipated and heat must be generated in colder temperatures. Animals generate internal heat by muscle movement, digestion, rumen fermentation, and cellular respiration. Animals dissipate heat by radiation, conduction (e.g., lying on cool concrete), or evaporation (respiration and perspiration). In general, when temperatures fall either

Figure 17-7. Much research has been conducted on factors that affect animal growth and performance. (Courtesy, Agricultural Research Service, USDA)

above or below an animal's comfort zone, growth and overall performance decrease. This is due primarily to changes in feed intake and energy required to maintain body temperature. Of course, weather extremes can lead to other complicating factors, such as diseases, which hinder growth.

THE GROWTH CURVE

Growth is basically a function of weight and time. The general rate of growth of all animals from birth to maturity is an S-shaped curve, known as the *growth curve*. The steepness of the curve represents the growth rate at any point in time. The most rapid growth occurs during puberty, when certain growth hormones exert their most dramatic influence on animal growth. Growth during the three basic stages of growth is dependent in part on the rate and type of growth in the preceding stage. The precise shape of the S-curve varies by species, breed, sex, environment, nutrition, and genetic potential.

NUTRITION

A nutrient is commonly defined as a food constituent that is necessary for normal body composition and functioning. The six classes of nutrients include carbohydrates, fats, proteins, minerals, vitamins, and water. An animal's nutritional needs must be met by its feed *ration*. These needs vary, depending upon the animal's stage of growth or production, including maintenance, lactation, reproduction, growth and finishing, and work.

Nutritional requirements for maintenance depend upon species, age, weight, and climate. Nutritional requirements are lowest during the maintenance stage of an ani-

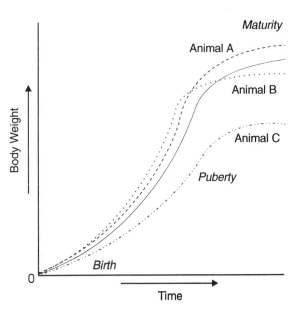

Figure 17-8. The general growth curve (solid line) and specific growth curves for three animals.

Table 17-2.
Nutrients and Their Functions

Nutrient	Description	Function
Carbohydrates	all contain C,H,O	provide energy
Proteins	composed of amino acids, contain C,H,O,N	build and repair tissue
Fats	contain C,H,O, but less than carbohydrates	energy, vitamin absorption
Minerals	solid, inorganic elements that cannot be decomposed or synthesized by the body	body structure, bone strength, regulate body processes
Vitamins	organic compounds, fat-soluble and water-soluble groups	catalytic, regulatory
Water	largest component of the body	medium and ingredient for chemical reactions, transport

mal's life. After partuition, nutritional requirements dramatically increase in order to provide an adequate supply of milk for the offspring. In general, higher levels of milk production should be accompanied by higher levels of protein and energy in the ration. Nutrient needs of the pregnant female steadily increase during gestation, and the last trimester is the most critical period. Differences in nutrient needs for males during breeding seasons are insignificant.

Figure 17-9. Mineral supplements must be provided in an animal's diet.

Figure 17-10. Checking rate of gain in an animal nutrition experiment. (Courtesy, OACE, University of Illinois)

Nutrient requirements, especially protein, are greatest when young animals are growing rapidly. During this stage, protein is being converted into body tissues and organs. Over 20 amino acids are present in animal proteins. When less than adequate amounts of amino acids are present in a *nonruminant* animal's diet, the amino acid present in the least amount becomes the limiting factor. Other amino acids will be used only to the extent that the first-limiting amino acid is present. Fortunately, *ruminants* are able to manufacture their own amino acids (and B vitamins), due to the action of microorganisms in the rumen.

Animals fed under *ad libitum* (free choice) conditions have fluctuations in feed intake, which may result in reduced feed utilization. As feed intake increases, the rate of digestion decreases, because feed is exposed to the digestive tract for a shorter period of time. Thus, while limited or controlled feeding requires more management, it may offer advantages in feed utilization.

Figure 17-11. Ad libitum feeding conditions ensure adequate nutrition but may result in lower feed efficiency.

CHAPTER SUMMARY

Animal growth is of utmost importance to animal agriculture. A faster rate of growth means significantly greater profit potential for the producer. In addition, animals grown primarily for breeding, milk, and other purposes perform better if their own growth rates to maturity were satisfactory. Animal growth is a function of heredity, sex, and numerous environmental factors. Heredity influences growth through hormonal activity. Males generally grow faster and larger due to hormonal differences. Good environmental conditions that keep animals in their comfort zone allow animals to come closer to their genetic growth potential. Animal growth primarily occurs through an increase in the number of cells.

Feeding and nutrition are the most important elements in managing animal growth. Much research has been done to determine the most effective and efficient systems for animal feeding. Producers must provide balanced rations that contain the necessary levels of all essential nutrients. Nutritional requirements depend upon several key factors, including species, breed, sex, environmental conditions, and stage of maturity or production. Producers use a variety of techniques for assessing both the quantity and quality of animal growth.

FURTHER LABORATORY INVESTIGATIONS

(*Note: Any species can be used for animal growth experiments. Chicks are suggested in many of the labs because of their relatively short age to maturity, ease in handling, low cost, and ready availability.*)

1. Compare the growth (quantity and quality) of chicks or other animals when the control group is fed a complete diet and the experimental group is fed a diet with one or more vitamins omitted. In addition, the effects of the amount of vitamin (or other nutrient) fed can be examined. Determine the point at which further amounts of the nutrient in the diet do not lead to increased growth or improved health.

2. Test the effects of environmental conditions on growth and animal health. Environmental factors to examine include temperature, ventilation, light (intensity and duration), sound, space, and others.

3. Compare the differences in growth rate between male and female animals of the same species. Be sure to provide the same growing conditions for all animals in the experiment. Record the weight of each animal at the start of the experiment and at pre-determined stages of growth.

4. Compare the effects of various sources of nutrients in an animal's ration. This can include protein sources (soybean meal, brewer's yeast, etc.), energy sources (peanut oil, cottonseed oil, etc.), high lysine corn, and many others.

5. Perform some basic chemical analysis on selected animal feeds, such as corn, oats, soybean meal, and alfalfa. To test for protein, add several drops of Biuret reagent to small samples of each feed. A color change from pink to purple indicates the presence of protein. Similarly, a drop of Lugol's iodine solution will turn blue-black on samples containing starch. Other simple tests for fat, sugar, and water can be made.

Chapter 18

DIGESTION

My Stomach Hurts

AGRICULTURAL APPLICATIONS

As noted in the previous chapter, animal feed is one of the most

Figure 18-1. Continuing efforts by researchers and producers to improve feeding strategies will cut feed waste and production costs. (Courtesy, OACE, University of Illinois)

Figure 18-2. Animal feed diets have dramatically changed in recent years to reflect consumers' preferences for leaner meat products. (Courtesy, Illinois Dept. of Agriculture)

important and costly inputs in animal production. Animal nutritionists have been working with producers to carefully develop animal diets that fully meet an animal's nutritional needs. Many producers today use computer controlled, automated diets that allow precise rations to be fed to an animal or group of animals. Improving feeding strategies will help to decrease feed costs and feed waste. For example, as animals eat more,

TERMS

abomasum	fat	nutrient metabolism
absorption	forage	polygastric
amylase	gastrointestinal tract	regurgitate
antibiotic feed additive	hydrolysis	rumen
bloat	lignin	stomach
carbohydrate	lipase	tannin
cellulose	mastication	villi
digestion	methane	
enzymatic digestion	monogastric	

digestion decreases because the feed material passes through the gastrointestinal tract quicker.

Animals are fed varying proportions of roughages (high fiber feeds) and concentrates depending upon the species and stage of growth. Some animals, like swine, are unable to digest grasses and other forages, and thus, are fed a grain-based diet. On the other hand, cattle and other ruminants have the ability to digest forages and grains. Corn comprises a large percentage of most feed concentrates. Animal rations have changed greatly over the past 10 years due to research discoveries in feeding and nutrition, as well as changing consumer preferences. For instance, feed formulas have changed, and today cattle are fed grain for a shorter period of time to meet consumers' demands for leaner meat

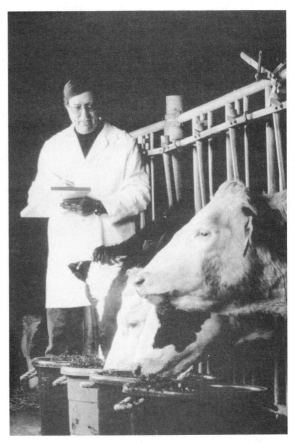

Figure 18-3. Much research has been conducted on the digestibility and palatability of various animal feeds. (Courtesy, Agricultural Research Service, USDA)

products. In addition, feed preparation technologies are undergoing constant change in an effort to improve palatability and digestibility of feeds.

Much research has been conducted on the digestion of animal feeds and the factors that affect digestion. Plant by-products, such as corn stalks, have been tested for their value in animal feeding programs. Treating crop residues with hydrogen peroxide, a common household bleach and antiseptic, has been commercially applied as a way to increase digestibility. Corn gluten feed is a nutritionally rich by-product created when corn is wet milled for alcohol production. Research is underway to find ways to increase the nutritionally important components of corn (protein and oil). In particular, scientists are searching for ways to increase levels of certain

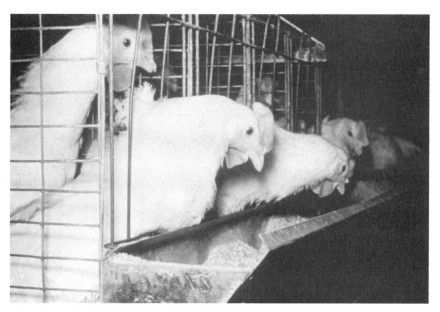

Figure 18-4. Corn and corn by-products are the mainstay ingredients in many animal feeds. (Courtesy, OACE, University of Illinois)

amino acids, such as lysine and tryptophan. Animal species vary in their feed efficiency, with one bushel of corn producing an estimated 5.6 pounds of beef and nearly 20 pounds of chicken.

Forages supply over 80% of all energy consumed by beef cattle. However, the digestibility of some forages still needs improvement. Different plant parts vary in their digestibility, and scientists are using microspectrophotometry to look at individual cells to determine their potential digestibility. Geneticists are using conventional plant breeding programs and genetic engineering to develop new plant varieties that are more digestible. Raw soybean meal contains an anti-nutritional agent, trypsin, which makes it indigestible by monogastric animals (swine, poultry, etc.). However, researchers have discovered two soybean varieties that do not contain trypsin. Commercial soybean processing techniques inactivate trypsin.

Additives and preparation techniques can increase digestibility. Producers use low levels of antibiotics as feed additives for ruminants and swine to increase feed efficiency (digestion and absorption). Flavoring agents are sometimes used to offset the taste of some feed additives. Sprays containing cellulase, a natural enzyme that breaks down cellulose in the rumen, have been found to increase digestion. Most producers grind their feeds in order to increase digestion. Scientists have recently found that microorganisms break down forage faster if it has tiny holes punched in it by a laser beam.

Commercial application of this technique may occur in the near future. Using new RNA sequencing techniques, scientists have recently identified bacteria important in ruminant digestion processes. Researchers are also working to develop an enzyme that releases phosphorus in corn, since most phosphorous in corn is not digestible by non-ruminants.

A number of bloat control products are used in the animal industry. Cattle and other ruminants fed high amounts of leafy forages are susceptible to bloat. Some plant species, like birdsfoot trefoil, contain natural anti-bloating compounds. Again, scientists are using genetic engineering techniques to develop new plant varieties that have high nutritional value yet are less likely to cause bloat. So not only are researchers working with producers to improve palatability and digestibility of animal feeds, they are also searching out new plant varieties that naturally offer these advantages.

Figure 18-5. Plant breeders are working to develop new crop varieties that have higher nutritional values. (Courtesy, OACE, University of Illinois)

OBJECTIVES—QUESTIONS FOR INVESTIGATION

After studying this chapter and completing the following laboratory investigations, you should be able to answer the following questions:

1. How does digestion occur?

2. What factors affect digestion?

3. How are nutrients from animal feeds made available to support body functions?

4. Why are certain animal species susceptible to bloat when placed on certain diets?

5. Why can cattle, sheep, and goats effectively use forages in their diet, while many other animals cannot?

6. Why do antibiotics promote growth and feed efficiency?

7. What role do enzymes and microorganisms play in digestion?

LABORATORY INVESTIGATIONS

EXPERIMENT I.
STARCH DIGESTION BY ENZYME ACTION

Purpose

The purpose of this experiment is to examine the effects of various agents on the digestion of starch, one of three major types of nutrients supplied in animal diets.

Materials

- hot plate
- beakers (2)
- water
- test tubes and rack
- iodine solution
- Benedict's solution
- corn starch

Procedures

Prepare a starch solution by adding 1 gram of corn starch to 100 milliliters of hot water. Bring the solution to a boil to dissolve the corn starch. Set aside to cool. Fill a beaker half full with water and bring to a boil. Add 5 milliliters of the starch solution to each of four test tubes. Label the tubes 1 through 4. Add two drops of iodine solution to test tube 1 and record color. Add 5 milliliters of Benedict's solution to test tube 2 and place the tube in the hot water bath for five minutes. Record the color. Add about 2 milliliters of your saliva to test tubes 3 and 4. Mix and allow to stand for five minutes. Put two drops of iodine in test tube 3 and record color. Put 5 milliliters of Benedict's solution in test tube 4, place in hot water bath for five minutes and record color. What type of carbohydrate is present in each solution?

EXPERIMENT 2.
EFFECTS OF PHYSICAL AND
CHEMICAL TREATMENT OF
FORAGE SAMPLES ON DIGESTIBILITY

Purpose

The purpose of this experiment is to determine the digestibility of grass clippings, leaves, or other forages when exposed to chemical and physical treatments.

Materials

- 50 ml test tubes with stoppers (three for each forage treatment)
- fresh rumen contents
- balance
- pH meter or paper
- filter paper and filter funnel
- oven
- hydrochloric acid
- sodium bicarbonate
- forage samples
- ammonium hydroxide and/or hydrogen peroxide
- aluminum pans
- cheese cloth
- one quart thermos

Procedures

Weigh exactly 0.5 grams of each sample to be tested into a 50 milliliter test tube. At least three test tubes should be used for each forage treatment. Treatments include type of forage, physical treatment (grinding), and chemical treatment (addition of 1 to 5% ammonium hydroxide or hydrogen peroxide).

Determine the dry matter content of each forage type by weighing duplicate 10 gram samples of each forage into aluminum pans. Dry overnight in 215°F oven and reweigh. Calculate percent dry matter as follows:

$$\% \text{ dry matter } = \frac{\text{sample weight after drying}}{\text{sample weight before drying}} \times 100$$

Strain fresh rumen fluid from local slaughter plant or research facility through four layers of cheesecloth into a one quart thermos. Prepare a warm water (100°F) solution of 10 grams sodium bicarbonate per liter of water. Just prior to inoculating test tubes, slowly mix an equal volume of the warm water solution with the rumen fluid. Keep the inoculum warm and do not agitate. Add 30 milliliters of the inoculum to each test tube and place the stopper in loosely so that fermentation gases can escape. Add inoculum to three test tubes without forage samples to be used as the control.

Place tubes in 100°F oven. Gently swirl tubes initially and at six to eight hour intervals to aid in mixing the sample with the inoculum. Gas bubbles in the tube will indicate successful fermentation. Measure the pH of each tube initially and at 12 hour intervals as an estimate of volatile fatty acid production. After 48 hours of incubation, kill the rumen microbes by adding 2 milliliters of a 50% solution of water and hydrochloric acid. Filter samples through previously weighed filter paper, dry filtered samples overnight at 215°F, and weigh. Calculate in vitro dry matter digestion as follows:

$$\frac{(1 - \text{weight of sample after drying} - \text{filter paper weight} - \text{blank})}{\text{weight of original sample} \times \% \text{ dry matter from earlier step}} \times 100$$

("Blank" refers to the weight of a blank piece of filter paper.)

Figure 18-6. The digestion process breaks down large nutrient molecules in feeds into smaller units that are absorbed into the circulatory system.

SCIENCE CONNECTIONS

DIGESTION AND ABSORPTION

Digestion is the physical and chemical breakdown of feeds as they pass through the *gastrointestinal tract*, which includes the mouth, esophagus, stomach, and intestines. Digestion releases nutrients for *absorption* into the circulatory system. In the digestive process large molecules of fats, proteins, and carbohydrates contained in feeds are broken down into smaller constituent units, such as sugar and amino acids. *Hydrolysis*, or the addition of water to the molecule being degraded, is a key part of digestion.

A number of *enzymes* are active in the digestion process. An *enzyme* is an organic (protein) catalyst that promotes change in other organic compounds without undergoing change itself. The presence and action of enzymes depends upon the type of digestive system. In some species (cattle and sheep are exceptions) saliva contains the enzyme *amylase* that begins to degrade starches. *Protease* is an enzyme that breaks down protein in the stomach and small intestine of ruminant animals. Protease, formerly called pepsin, must be activated by hydrochloric acid. Gastric juices secreted by the stomach lining contain water, enzymes, and hydrochloric acid. The acid environment (pH ≤ 2) provided by hydrochloric acid is necessary for protein hydrolysis. *Lipase*, an enzyme secreted by the pancreas, works in the small intestine to break down fats. *Enzymatic digestion* in the rumen is supported by suitable pH, anaerobic conditions, warm temperature, adequate moisture, nutrients from the ingested feed, adequate mixing, and continuous removal of fermentation products.

Absorption occurs after complex nutrients undergo digestion to break them down into simpler compounds. *Absorption* is the process by which smaller compounds are absorbed by cells of the digestive tract by diffusion or active transport. Most absorption occurs in the small intestine. *Villi* are minute, finger-like structures on the lining of the small intestine that increase the surface area for nutrient absorption. Each villus also contains a network of capillaries.

Degraded nutrient molecules are first absorbed through the walls of the small intestine, and then through blood or lymph capillary walls into the circulatory system. Absorbed nutrients are circulated to individual cells where *nutrient metabolism* occurs. *Fats* and *carbohydrates* are further degraded to produce energy, and *amino acids* are recombined to form proteins, and eventually tissues, hormones, or enzymes.

Figure 18-7. Forages account for a large percentage of the feed intake of ruminants.

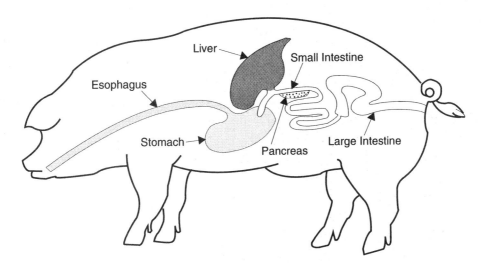

Figure 18-8.   The swine digestive system.

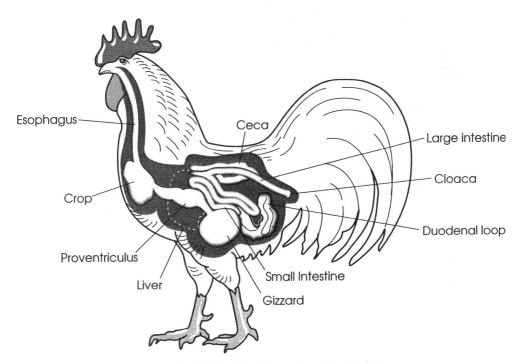

Figure 18-9.   The digestive system of a chicken.

ANIMAL DIGESTIVE SYSTEMS

Animals are classified into those having a single stomach (*monogastric, nonruminant*) and those having four stomach compartments (*polygastric, ruminant*). In nonruminants the stomach functions primarily as a food storage organ, with limited digestion occurring. Monogastrics have relatively small stomachs and must be fed more often than ruminants. Monogastrics are usually fed concentrated diets that are low in fiber and bulk. Most digestion in nonruminants occurs in the *small intestine*. Only protein is digested to some degree in the *stomach*, which usually represents about 30% of the total capacity of the entire digestive system. The absence of certain enzymes and microorganisms means that monogastrics cannot digest *cellulose*. Thus, forages comprise an insignificant part of the diet in nonruminants.

Ruminant animals are unique in that they *regurgitate* their food to chew it further—as much as eight hours per day. Chewing (*mastication*) helps break down feed into smaller particles, increasing the surface area exposed to enzymatic action in the gastrointestinal tract. In birds, the grinding action of the gizzard accomplishes the same result as chewing.

In contrast to monogastrics, the stomach of ruminants represents about two-thirds of the total digestive system capacity. Of the four stomach compartments, the *rumen* is the largest and has a capacity of over 200

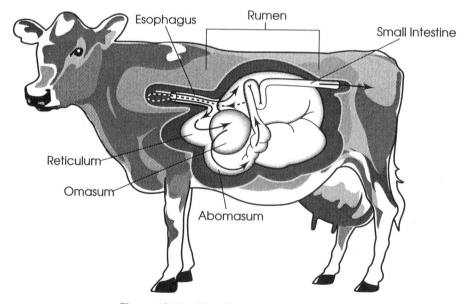

Figure 18-10. The digestive tract of a cow.

liters (over 50 gallons!). As calves grow into mature cows, the relative capacity of their rumens increases from 30% in newborn calves to about 80% in cattle. An interesting note—cows produce as much as 100 pounds of saliva per day! This saliva contains sodium bicarbonate, which maintains the rumen pH at around 7.0. The *abomasum* has an acidic environment and can be thought of as the true stomach in ruminants.

MICROBIAL FERMENTATION

Several *microbes*, including *bacteria, anaerobic fungi*, and *protozoa* are present in the rumen of a polygastric animal and play a key role in the digestion of *forages*. These microorganisms have a *symbiotic relationship* with their host; both the microbe and the animal benefit. These microorganisms produce protease, an enzyme which degrades proteins. They also produce *volatile fatty acids* when converting starch to sugar. Microorganisms synthesize vitamin K, all B vitamins, and all essential amino acids. Without ruminal microbes, ruminants would be unable to digest cellulose, the material that makes up the bulk of plant cell walls.

The rumen is like a giant fermentation vat, containing billions of microorganisms and many different species of bacteria. *Microbial fermentation* produces *carbon dioxide* (CO_2) and *methane*, which must be displaced

Figure 18-11. Birdsfoot trefoil is a legume that contains a natural antibloating compound. (Courtesy, Agricultural Research Service, USDA)

Figure 18-12. Fistulated cows enable researchers to directly examine the rate of digestion of various feed products.

from the rumen to prevent bloat. Ruminants are usually able to accomplish this by belching. *Bloat* is the buildup of gas in the cow's stomach caused by rumen bacteria. Some plant species, such as birdsfoot trefoil, contain a natural anti-bloating compound known as *tannin*. Tannin helps cows digest their food more slowly by binding to plant proteins in the rumen. Protein is then more resistant to degradation by rumen bacteria. But the right balance of tannin is needed—too much tannin allows a significant amount of protein to pass through the rumen without being broken down into smaller compounds for absorption.

Certain ruminal bacteria break down dietary protein into ammonia, a product unusable by the animal and eventually excreted in the urine. *Antibiotic feed additives*, such as *monensin* (trade name Rumensin), increase growth and feed efficiency by destroying certain bacteria, thus increasing protein utilization in the rumen.

Lignin is the substance that together with cellulose forms the woody cell walls of plants and cements them together. Lignin gives plants their structure and rigidity. Since livestock cannot digest lignin, it is the most limiting factor in forage digestibility. Lignin's resistance to digestive degradation is believed to vary somewhat by plant species. In addition, animals differ in their ability to break down forages. A unique bacterium in the rumen of buffalo was recently discovered that may explain why buffalo can digest alfalfa 15% better than other ruminants.

Figure 18-13. The digestibility of various grasses may be genetically linked to compounds that comprise the cell wall of plant tissues. (Courtesy, Agricultural Research Service, USDA)

CHAPTER SUMMARY

Feed is one of the most costly inputs in managing animal growth. Animals differ in their ability to digest various feeds due to differences in their digestive systems. Animals with single compartment stomachs are unable to digest forages. Because of their comparatively simple digestive system, researchers have been able to develop very precise and efficient diets for nonruminants like swine and poultry. On the other hand, digestion in ruminant animals is much more complex. Because of fermentation and the action of microorganisms in the rumen of these animals, high fiber feeds can be broken down into usable components. Researchers continue to investigate ways to increase the nutritional value of feed, especially grains, and the digestibility of forages. Conventional plant breeding and genetic engineering techniques are being used to develop new plant varieties that possess these characteristics.

Digestion is the breaking down of complex nutrients into simpler molecules that can be absorbed and used by the body. Enzymes, such as protease, lipase, and amylase play an important role in digestion. Products of ruminant digestion include sugars, amino acids, and volatile fatty acids.

In addition, microbial fermentation produces CO_2 and methane gas, which must be eliminated from the rumen to prevent bloat. Most absorption of degraded nutrients occurs in the small intestine, where nutrients move through the intestinal lining and eventually into the circulatory system.

FURTHER LABORATORY INVESTIGATIONS

1. Compare the digestibility of various cellulose materials, such as cotton, cardboard, wood, alfalfa leaves, grass, tree leaves, and so on. Use test tubes or flasks as in Experiment 2.

2. Examine different species of rumen bacteria and protozoa under a microscope. Obtain rumen fluid from a fistulated cow or slaughter house.

3. Construct a three-dimensional model of the four-compartment ruminant stomach system. Compare with the nonruminant digestive system.

4. Vary the environmental conditions under which in vitro digestion experiments are conducted. Include temperature, oxygen, and pH as independent variables. Test the effects of various alkaline agents on digestibility.

5. Examine the ingredients in bulk and bagged feeds to determine the feed additives that are used. What feed additives are included? What is their function? How do they work? Interview a veterinarian or animal nutrition specialist to help in answering these questions.

Chapter 19

GROWTH PROMOTERS

Body Building

AGRICULTURAL APPLICATIONS

A major focus in today's animal industry is providing a leaner meat product that is more economical to produce. USDA researchers are working to reduce external carcass fat to a minimum, while keeping 3 to 7% fat in the muscle tissues to ensure good flavor. A combination of strategies is being used by producers and researchers to reach these goals. They include

Figure 19-1. Producers use selection, feeding, and growth promoters to produce desirable meat products for consumers. (Courtesy, National FFA Organization)

selection of breeding animals that offer genetically superior traits with regard to carcass quality. A carefully designed feeding program also helps to reduce the amount of internal and external carcass fat. A third emphasis is on the use of growth promoters, which tend to increase the building of lean tissue (muscle) and reduce fat deposits.

A variety of growth promoters are used by producers today, with many more products being tested and reviewed for commercial use. These may be generally classified as implants (both hormonal and non-hormonal substances) and feed additives. The Food and Drug Administration has approved over 1,000 drugs for use in livestock and poultry production. In general, these compounds, many of which are naturally occurring, increase milk, meat, and egg production by approximately 15%.

Agricultural researchers have found that genetics and feeding system are the two most important factors in determining the cutability (lean to fat ratio) of a carcass. Sex also plays a significant role. After weaning, cattle are either placed on pasture or sent to a feedlot for finishing. Feeding a grain diet boosts weight gain, but fat deposit is also promoted by such high-energy diets. However, growth-promoting compounds have been shown to increase protein deposits (muscle growth) regardless of whether animals are on a high or low nutrition diet. Some compounds simultaneously reduce fat deposits. Animal scientists are attempting to better understand how muscle is built and degraded so they can better control this process, resulting in leaner meat products for consumers. Computer modeling may allow future producers to predict the yield and quality grade of young animals.

The use of growth-promoting implants has become a common practice among beef producers. Few cattle management practices can equal the

TERMS

anabolic agent	implant	steroid implant
androgenic implant	lasalocid	testosterone
dietary energy	monensin	thyroxines
estrogenic implant	muscle	trenbolone acetate
feed additive	repartitioning agents	
glucocortoids	somatotropins	

Figure 19-2. Growth-promoting implants are commonly used in some aspects of the animal industry to improve weight gain and feed efficiency.

economic returns that these compounds offer. In general, growth-promoting implants boost the rate of gain and feed efficiency of cattle at any age, thus reducing production costs. Specifically, implants can be expected to increase the weaning weight of steers by 20 to 50 pounds, boost weight gain 5 to 25%, increase feed conversion by 3 to 12%, and significantly increase muscle growth.

Implants are very economical, ranging from $1.00 to $2.50 per animal. Implants are safe, effective, and reduce production costs about $30 per animal for beef producers. For maximum returns, cattle intended for slaughter are implanted as suckling calves and periodically reimplanted to maintain an effective implant until slaughter. Growth-promoting implants are subcutaneously deposited in the back of the animal's ear. Cattle to be used for breeding purposes are not implanted. Some implants, such as Ralgro, are also approved for use in sheep.

A number of non-implant growth hormones are commercially used or under further review. Melengestrol acetate (MGA) is a synthetic progesterone hormone used as a feed additive for nonpregnant heifers. MGA suppresses estrus and ovulation, which normally slow growth. Somatotropin, the primary growth hormone naturally occurring in animals, continues to receive

Table 19-1
Selected Beef Cattle Implants

Product	Active Ingredient	Use
Compudose	Estradiol	All cattle
Implus-H & Synovex H	Estradiol benzoate & testosterone propionate	Heifers >400 lbs.
Implus-S & Synovex S	Estradiol benzoate & progesterone	Steers >400 lbs.
Synovex C & Calf-oid	Estradiol benzoate & progesterone	Calves <400 lbs.
Finaplix-S	Trenbolone acetate	Steers >600 lbs.
Finaplix-H	Trenbolone acetate	Heifers >600 lbs.
Revalor-S	Trenbolone acetate & estradiol	Feedlot steers
Ralgro	Zeranol	All cattle

heavy attention. Bovine somatotropin (bST) was recently approved for use in dairy cattle to increase milk production, but it is still being tested as a growth promoter in cattle. However, most of the research in this area has focused on the use of porcine somatotropin (pST) to increase growth and reduce fat content in market hogs. Scientists are also investigating the effects of somatotropin on growth rates in sheep and poultry.

Feed additives represent another type of growth-promoting compound that is commonly used today. The benefits of feed additives on animal growth are in addition to those that producers may realize through the use of growth-promoting implants. The 1994 Feed Additive Compendium lists 24 companies that market feed additives containing 63 different active ingredients. This translates to many more actual feed additive products approved for commercial use.

Feed additives are mixed with feed or water and are generally grouped by nutritional or medicinal effect. Many feed additives are antibiotics, and others affect digestive processes in ruminants. For example, six different chemicals used in feed additives are viewed as growth and feed efficiency promoters in cattle (11 for chickens and 14 for swine). Many more are considered to have medicinal effects. Commonly used antibiotics in poultry include bacitracin, bambermycin, and virginiamycin. When used as feed additives, these substances have been found to increase egg production, hatchability, shell quality, and animal growth. Rumensin is an example of a feed additive for cattle that increases feed efficiency.

Figure 19-3. Feed additives are widely used in the poultry industry to improve several key production factors. (Courtesy, Illinois Dept. of Agriculture)

OBJECTIVES—QUESTIONS FOR INVESTIGATION

After completing the laboratory investigations contained in this chapter, as well as other activities provided by your teacher, you should be able to answer the following questions:

1. How do hormone supplements promote animal growth?

2. Why are implants placed under the skin on the back of the animal's ear?

3. How do implants exert a growth response in animals?

4. Why do antibiotic feed additives increase growth?

5. How do feed additives work within the animal's body to increase feed efficiency?

6. From a biological perspective, how safe are animal growth promoters?

LABORATORY INVESTIGATIONS

EXERCISE I.
bST DEBATE OR RESEARCH REPORT

Purpose

The purpose of this exercise is to investigate the pros and cons regarding the use of bovine somatotropin in the dairy industry. (bST was approved by FDA in November of 1993 for use in the dairy industry.)

Materials

- recent bST articles in magazines and newspapers
- bST product materials from manufacturers
- university, government, and manufacturer research reports
- interviews with local producers (bST users and non-users), extension agents, state department of agriculture representatives, or others

Procedures

Check with your teacher to see if your class will organize a debate on the use of bST in dairy herds. If so, identify your student partner(s) and determine which side of the issue you will support (use or non-use). Clarify with your teacher the format for the debate. Obtain and review printed materials that support your side of the bST use issue. Take notes on key points that will support your argument. As you collect ideas to support your position, also pay attention to opposing ideas that may be provided. Obtain addresses or phone numbers for key agencies or businesses and contact them for information. Attempt to incorporate information about the scientific evidence that supports or refutes the use of bST. Organize your ideas on note cards as allowed in the debate procedures. Work with your student partner(s) to sift out your arguments and determine when they can be used most persuasively. Mentally and/or verbally rehearse your arguments in preparation for the debate. Have fun!

If you are preparing a research report instead of participating in a class debate, your objective is to be factual, rather than persuasive. Thus, your report should focus on the scientific evidence regarding the use of bST.

Opinions from producers and local experts can be incorporated. Develop a tentative outline of your report and have it checked by your teacher before proceeding with your investigation and writing.

EXPERIMENT 1.
EFFECTS OF FEED ADDITIVES ON ANIMAL GROWTH

Purpose

The purpose of this experiment is to test the effects of one or more feed additives on the growth rate and feed intake of a selected species.

Materials

- feed additive(s)
- adequate feed and water for normal growth
- two groups of selected animals (at least four per group)
- scales

Procedures

Determine the animal species that will be used in the experiment, based upon availability. If no animals are available at the school or your home, check with relatives or other local producers to gain their consent to assist with your experiment. Cattle, swine, sheep, or poultry will work fine. Younger animals will be easier to handle. (Poultry can be used with minimal space requirements.) Select four animals of about equal size for each group. A simple experiment will involve one group that receives the selected feed additive (the treatment) and one group that receives no feed additive (the control). Identify each individual animal in the experiment and record its initial weight.

A number of feed additives can be used in your experiment. Select one that is easy to administer. For example, Terramycin is an inexpensive soluble powder that can be added to the drinking water of cattle, sheep, and swine. If you select an antibiotic, be sure to use the dosage recommended by the manufacturer for control of diseases. If you use a commercially prepared feed, check the label to see what feed additives are already contained in the feed. Remember, the control group must not receive the selected feed additive. Thus, you should select a feed additive for this experiment that is not already contained in the animal's feed.

Follow the manufacturer's directions for providing the feed additive in the diet of the treatment group. Monitor feed and water intake daily. All conditions of the experiment (feed intake, housing, temperature, species, breed, etc.) should be the same for both the treatment and control groups. Continue providing the feed additive for four to six weeks, if possible. Weigh each animal and record. Compare initial and ending weights for the animals in each group.

SCIENCE CONNECTIONS

MUSCLE FORMATION

Muscle in growing animals is continuously formed and broken down. Scientists believe that *enzymatic activity* is responsible for the degradation of muscle tissue. Researchers can determine the rate of muscle degradation by measuring levels of creatinine and histidine in the urine of animals. As an animal grows, it converts *dietary energy* into either *protein* or *fat*. The amount of protein deposited in animal tissues is a direct indication of the amount of lean meat generated through growth. Protein deposition can be estimated by measuring the amount of nitrogen the animal's body retains from its diet.

GROWTH HORMONES

Hormones are organic catalysts secreted by body glands which function to regulate growth. The primary growth hormones, with their gland source in parentheses, include *somatotropins* (anterior pituitary), *thyroxines* (thyroid), *glucocortoids* (adrenal), *androgens* (testes), and *estrogens* (ovaries). All of these hormones regulate growth, but bone and muscle growth is most affected by somatotropin.

Thyroxine regulates body metabolism, which influences body weight and lean tissue growth. Androgens are responsible for the development of secondary sex characteristics in males. In addition, they have a significant effect on bone and muscle growth in both males and females. *Testosterone*, the primary androgen, is secreted by the male's testes and the female's adrenal gland. The typically greater bone and muscle growth in males is due in part to the higher levels of testosterone secreted by the testes. Estrogens are primarily responsible for development of the reproductive tract in females. Glucocortoids stimulate the mobilization of stored nutrients, resulting in weight loss.

Hormones are chemical messengers that are secreted by the *endocrine glands*. These chemicals are absorbed into blood passing through the glands and are then transported to other parts of the animal's body where they exert their specific influence. Even minute amounts of hormones will exert an effect upon body functioning. The appropriate balance of hormone levels is maintained through a *feedback mechanism*. For example, as levels of a particular hormone increase, factors associated with its release act to limit its secretion.

Figure 19-4. General action of the hormone feedback mechanism, which maintains an appropriate level of hormones in the animal's body.

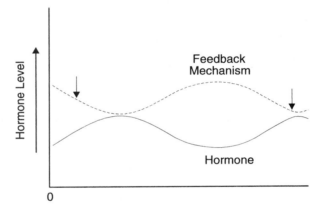

Scientists continue to investigate the effects of increased hormone levels in animals. One method of estimating the effects of hormones is to measure the amount of energy retained by the animal from its diet. Since researchers can determine the amount of energy fed and the amount of energy secreted in waste products, they can also determine the total energy retained. Total energy retained equals energy retained as protein plus energy retained as fat. In one USDA study, steers with increased hormone levels retained the same amount of total energy, but energy deposited as protein doubled. Thus, fat deposits were cut in half.

Energy fed = energy retained + energy excreted

Total retained energy = energy retained + energy retained
as protein   as fat

Figure 19-5. Researchers can estimate total energy retained by comparing energy intake with energy excreted in body wastes. (Courtesy, Agricultural Research Service, USDA)

SOMATOTROPINS

Somatotropins are species-specific hormones that stimulate protein synthesis and reduce the fat content of meat animals. As such, somatotropins are referred to as *repartitioning agents*. These naturally occurring proteins have been found to increase nutrient deposits from fat to lean tissue in meat animals by as much as 25%. The exact mechanism by which somatotropins enhance lean growth are not fully understood. Naturally occurring hormones, like somatotropin, are quickly degraded after they are absorbed into the bloodstream. (For more about the safety of bST, see Chapter 15.)

IMPLANTS

Growth-promoting *implants* can be grouped into natural steroids, synthetic steroids, and nonsteroids. Implants are deposited under the skin in the back of the animal's ear. This allows for steady, gradual absorption of the implant into the animal's bloodstream. If the implant is deposited in a vein, absorption will be too rapid and the growth response poor. If the implant is placed in the cartilage or muscle tissue, absorption will be minimal. The design of the implant pellet also affects the rate of absorption

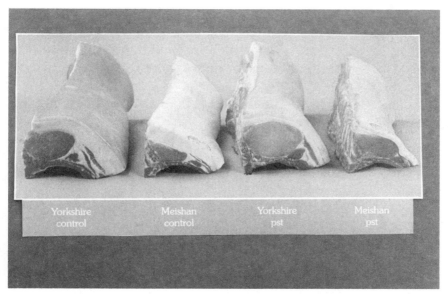

Figure 19-6.   Effects of pST on carcass outside fat.

Figure 19-7.   Implant location within body tissues and formulation of the implant control the rate of absorption.

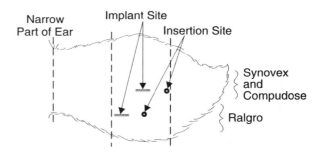

into the bloodstream. Breeding animals are not implanted because of possible retarded development of testicles in bulls and delayed estrus in heifers.

Natural and synthetic *steroid implants* contain estrogens, androgens, or both. Implants containing only natural steroids generally can be used up to slaughter date, since these compounds break down rapidly. Currently, two implant products are approved for use that contain *anabolic (protein building) agents* and are not hormones. These include zeranol (Ralgro) and trenbolone acetate (Finaplix).

Estrogenic implants promote growth by stimulating the release of growth hormones from the anterior pituitary. *Androgenic implants* enhance growth by inhibiting the release of hormones (glucocortoids) which cause degradation of muscle tissue. *Zeranol*, the active ingredient in Ralgro, appears to promote growth by stimulating the release of certain hormones. Zeranol is derived from the mold *Gibberella zeae*, which grows on corn. *Trenbolone acetate* is a synthetic androgen that has more potency than testosterone. It is believed to increase growth by making protein deposition more efficient. Scientists believe that trenbolone acetate increases nitrogen retention in muscle tissues.

Consumers continue to be concerned about the safety of implants. Scientific evidence on steroid implants suggests that they are safe. Estrogen levels in fat tissues of implanted animals are 100 times less than those in a pregnant heifer and 400,000 times less than in soybean oil. Only about 10% of consumed steroids are absorbed into the body. A man eating one pound of beef from an implanted steer would absorb only $\frac{1}{400,000}$ of his natural daily production of estrogen. This figure would be even less for women, since their bodies naturally produce much more estrogen.

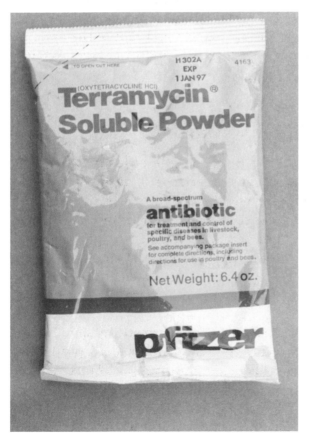

Figure 19-8. A wide variety of antibiotics are used as feed additives in animal production systems.

FEED ADDITIVES

Feed additives include compounds that increase an animal's resistance to disease and substances that alter *microorganism* activity in ruminant animals. *Antibiotics* are chemical substances that are produced synthetically or by microorganisms and act to inhibit the growth of other microorganisms. Antibiotics increase growth by maintaining health (suppressing disease-producing organisms) and decreasing certain microbe populations in the rumen. As a result, the level of nutrients available for absorption is increased. Scientists believe that antibiotics cause the membranes of the gastrointestinal tract to become thinner, allowing for greater nutrient absorption into the bloodstream. Antibiotics also increase feed and/or water intake. Interestingly, antibiotics have been shown to have little effect on growth when animals are kept in a germ-free environment.

Monensin and *lasalocid* are two widely used feed additives that increase feed efficiency by altering rumen metabolism. *Microbial fermentation* in the rumen produces *volatile fatty acids* which are absorbed as energy sources. These include acetic acid, butyric acid, and propionate. *Inophores* such as rumensin increase the proportion of propionic acid and reduce the amount of acetic acid in the rumen. Propionic acid is a more efficient energy source.

CHAPTER SUMMARY

Livestock and poultry producers are responding to industry economics and consumer preferences as they strive to produce a different type of meat animal today, as compared to even 10 years ago. Consumers want leaner meat products, and producers continue to search for ways to increase their returns. Selection of breeding animals and carefully designed feeding programs have been the traditional cornerstones of the meat animal industry. Growth-promoting compounds now represent a third element in the producer's management arsenal and add significant advantages in rate of gain and feed efficiency.

Growth promoters can be expected to increase growth by about 15%, with implants alone adding $30 return per animal for beef producers. Growth promoters include implants and feed additives. Implants include natural and synthetic hormones (steroids), as well as non-hormone products. Other (non-implant) hormones, such as pST, show promising results on growth rate and reduced carcass fat, but these substances are still under review. Feed additives include antibiotics and other compounds that maintain animal health and alter rumen digestion.

Muscle is continually formed and broken down as an animal grows. Animals convert energy from their feed into protein (lean meat) or fat. Growth promoters alter the balance of fat and protein deposition, usually by increasing protein deposition and reducing fat deposition. Growth hormones are chemical messengers that are naturally secreted by the endocrine glands. In essence, growth hormone implants introduce additional levels of selected hormones into the animal's bloodstream.

FURTHER LABORATORY INVESTIGATIONS

1. Compare the product labels of commercially prepared feeds to determine the feed additives present. What are the expected effects on animal growth and/or feed efficiency for each additive?

2. Interview an animal products specialist or other agribusiness representative to determine growth promoters marketed, projected effects, and mode of action.

3. Cooperate with a local beef or sheep producer to test the effects of implants on growth rate and feed efficiency. Compare animal performance with and without implants. The effectiveness of various implant products can also be investigated.

4. Interview local producers (cattle, swine, poultry, or sheep) to determine what growth promoters they use, results, and cost-effectiveness. If you were a producer, which growth-promoting products would you use in your herd or flock?

5. Interview an extension specialist or researcher in an agribusiness or university to obtain research findings on feeding and growth trials of various approved and experimental animal growth promoters.

Chapter 20

VITAL SIGNS

Body Checks

AGRICULTURAL APPLICATIONS

Maintaining animal health is of utmost concern to livestock producers and animal owners. Injury, disease, or illness can quickly slow down or stop weight gain, and at the worst, cause rapid weight loss and even death. Good producers develop a keen sense of animal well-being by consciously observing animal behavior and key vital signs of good health. Producers

Figure 20-1. Knowing your animals and their normal behavior is important in maintaining animal health. (Courtesy, Illinois Dept. of Agriculture)

need to know what is normal behavior for non-stressed, healthy animals. They then check these indicators of animal health and well-being on a regular and frequent basis, preferably daily.

An animal's vital signs include body temperature, pulse rate, and respiration rate. Carefully monitoring these vital signs can lead to early detection and diagnosis of health problems. This may allow the producer to ward off serious diseases or conditions before significant production losses occur. Early detection can also prevent the spread of infectious diseases to other animals in the herd or flock. Thus, being able to recognize changes in an animal's behavior and vital signs can prevent loss of life and save producers thousands of dollars.

In addition to these three vital signs of animal health, the following animal behaviors and symptoms must be carefully monitored by producers: eating behavior, movement, stance and posture, proximity to other animals, animal sounds, special conditions (heat, parturition, etc.), and fecal pattern and consistency. Environment can play a key role in creating stress or animal health problems. Extremely hot or cold air temperatures can affect appetite, strength, activity, and many basic body functions. In addition, nutrition, space, water, and other environmental conditions must be carefully managed by animal owners and producers. Environmental conditions and health status can have a dramatic influence on key vital signs. When problems arise, multiple symptoms are often present, making diagnosis much more difficult.

Producers work with a team of other animal science professionals to check vital signs and diagnose animal health problems. However, animal owners and producers can themselves monitor temperature, pulse rate,

TERMS

animal health	capillary refill time	respiration
arteries	(CRT)	shock
blood circulation	comfort zone	stethoscope
blood pressure	electrolytes	sweat glands
body temperature	heart rate	toxemias
capillaries	hypothalamus	trauma
	pulse	vital signs

Figure 20-2. Extreme environmental conditions affect an animal's basic body
processes and condition.

respiration rate, and general behavior to detect health or stress problems.
Veterinarians are a crucial member of the animal health team, providing
many diagnostic and treatment services. Many large-scale producers hire
veterinarians on a contract basis to manage the health of their herds or
flocks. These services not only include monitoring and diagnosis, but also
the development and implementation of a herd health management program.
Diagnostic laboratories also play an important role in maintaining animal
health by offering specialized services that allow animal health problems
to be accurately diagnosed. In addition, most states have a veterinary college
that not only trains veterinarians, but also provides animal care services
to the community.

OBJECTIVES—QUESTIONS
FOR INVESTIGATION

After studying this chapter and completing the laboratory investigations
that follow, you should be able to answer the following questions:

1. What vital signs are indicators of an animal's general status or
   condition?

Figure 20-3. Colleges of veterinary medicine and diagnostic laboratories play a key role in helping producers and animal owners manage animal health.

2. How does an animal regulate its body temperature?

3. How do environmental factors affect vital signs?

4. How are heart rate and pulse rate related?

LABORATORY INVESTIGATIONS

EXERCISE 1.
SMALL BODY CHECKS

Purpose

The purpose of this lab exercise is to observe the temperature, pulse rate, and respiration rate of a healthy, small animal and give a basic physical exam.

Materials

- rectal thermometer
- petroleum jelly

- stethoscope
- dog
- paper towels or tissues

Procedures

Begin the exam by calming the dog so that it will be easier to handle during the exam. For this first exam use your own dog or one that you know will be cooperative! Assess the overall condition of the animal. Use an examination chart to record your observations on the following items: alertness, activity, posture, hair coat, head position, and eyes. For small animals like dogs, check the capillary refill time (CRT) by raising the dog's upper lip and pressing on the gum. The tissue should turn white, but regain its pink color within 1 to 3 seconds.

Before taking the dog's temperature, shake the thermometer down to 96°F. Apply a small amount of petroleum jelly to the thermometer and then insert it into the dog's rectum about 1.5 to 2 inches. After one minute remove the thermometer, wipe it with a tissue, and read it. To take the pulse rate, use your fingertips to feel the heartbeat on the inside of the dog's thigh about level with its knee. Count the number of beats per minute (or multiply by three the number of beats in 20 seconds). You can also

Figure 20-4. An animal's general appearance can tell much about its overall condition.

Figure 20-5. Checking the pulse rate on a dog.

use a stethoscope to check the pulse rate and listen to the heart. Place the stethoscope in various locations on the left and right side of the dog's chest. Determine the respiration rate by counting the number of breaths per minute. Record your data for each vital sign.

EXERCISE 2.
BIG BODY CHECKS

Purpose

The purpose of this lab exercise is to determine the vital signs of an animal used for agricultural purposes.

Materials

- rectal thermometer
- petroleum jelly
- stethoscope
- young or mature animal (calf, sheep, pig, horse)
- paper towels or tissues

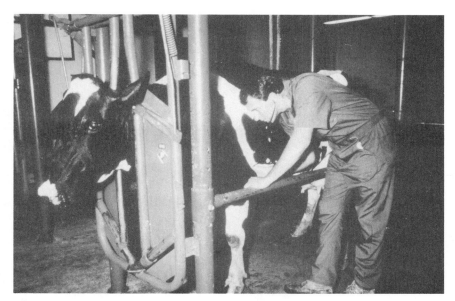

Figure 20-6. Checking heartbeat with a stethoscope. (Courtesy, Agricultural Research Service, USDA)

Procedures

Use the same procedures as in Exercise 1 to note and record the vital signs of the agricultural animal(s) selected. Two unique points apply to this exercise: use a thermometer designed for the animal selected and be sure to safely restrain the animal when taking its temperature. Younger animals will be safer and easier to restrain. Allow three minutes before removing the thermometer and reading the temperature for larger animals.

SCIENCE CONNECTIONS

Animal health refers to the *physiological well-being* of an animal. Animal health is affected by many factors, including disease, stress, nutrition, environmental conditions, infections, injury, activity, and general attention and care. Normal, healthy animals are alert, active, bright eyed, eating well, and following normal behavior patterns for their species. Normal posture and movement and a shiny hair coat also indicate good health. The *vital signs* of an animal include body temperature, pulse rate, and respiration rate. Vital signs change as infectious and non-infectious problems affect the animal. Capillary refill time (CRT) is also used as a measure of the animal's condition.

Figure 20-7. Normal appetite suggests good health.

The concentration of *electrolytes* in an animal's blood also has an impact on the animal's condition. Electrolytes are acids, bases, and salts, which, when dissolved in water, produce electrically charged ions. Examples of salts contained in body fluids include sodium, potassium, sulfate, and chloride. The ions of these and other salts act with *enzymes* to regulate body functions. When an animal becomes *dehydrated*, it loses both water and electrolytes. If dehydration reaches the critical stage, then cellular death can result.

BODY TEMPERATURE

All species have a fairly narrow temperature range (usually 1° to 2°F) that is considered normal. Even slight variation from this limited range can cause death. An animal's *body temperature* represents the balance between *heat generated* by metabolic processes within its body and the amount of *heat dissipated* from its body. Animals have a thermal control center in the *hypothalamus* which responds to changes in blood temperature. When temperature changes are noted, this control center initiates changes in *respiration, metabolism,* and *heart rate* to compensate for gains or losses in *body heat.*

Infections usually lead to a rise in body temperature. This *defense mechanism* helps to destroy invading *bacteria* with heat. As body metabolism increases, the amount of body heat generated also increases. *Subnormal body temperatures* are more of a concern, because this means that the body is not able to maintain itself. *Shock* or *toxemia* is usually associated with a decrease in body temperature. Animals with thicker hair coats or with wool

Figure 20-8. Animals vary in their ability to dissipate and retain body heat, depending upon their hair/wool coat, size, and other physiological differences.

are able to maintain their normal body temperature better. Hair and wool reduces heat loss or gain by trapping a layer of still air next to the skin.

Each species has a *comfort zone* within which ambient temperatures can vary without causing body stress. When air temperature falls below this comfort zone, oxygen intake (respiration) and metabolic rate increase. Cold temperatures also cause the body to secret greater amounts of *hormones* (thyroxine and corticoid), which increase metabolic rate and production of body heat. In contrast, when *heat stress* occurs, thyroxine and corticoid levels decline. Animals under heat stress generally eat less and become less active. Most farm animals do not dissipate body heat very well, due to absent or inefficient *sweat glands*. Higher fiber (roughage) diets generate greater body heat during digestion. Thus, producers often attempt to increase fiber intake during cold weather to help the animal maintain body temperature. By the same token, lower fiber diets in hot weather help the animal combat heat stress.

RESPIRATION

Respiration (breathing) is controlled by specialized *respiratory centers* in

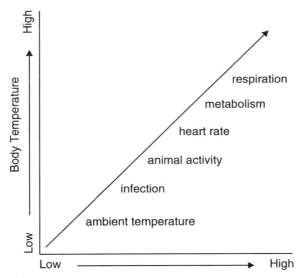

Figure 20-9. Factors associated with an increase in body temperature.

the brain. As body temperature or activity increases, respiration also increases. Inhaling drier air helps to keep body temperature in check. Similarly, as animals become nervous or excited, respiration rate increases. An increase in body temperature can be due to heat stress or infection. Greater body activity causes an increase in metabolism, so the animal will have the energy needed. Greater metabolic activity causes increased concentrations of CO_2 in the blood. This, in turn, increases activity in the respiratory control centers, causing more rapid and deeper breathing. Respiration rate in animals can be checked by observing the expansion and contraction of the rib cage or placing your hand near the animal's nostril.

PULSE RATE

As the animal's heart beats, it forces blood into the *arteries* and stretches them. This alternate stretching and contracting of the elastic tissues comprising the arteries is known as the *pulse*. Thus, except in rare cases, pulse rate is the same as an animal's *heart rate*. Pulse rate is defined as the number of heartbeats per minute. Pulse rate increases with body or ambient temperature and decreases with age and usually with body size. Pulse rate can be checked with the fingertips as follows: cow, ventral side of tail or facial arteries; horse, facial arteries; sheep, inner thigh; and dog, inner thigh. Because of their fat layer and thick skin, it is very difficult to feel a pulse on hogs. Heart beat can usually be felt by placing the fingertips on the left side of the animal, behind the front leg, and between the fourth and fifth rib. A *stethoscope* can be used to check heart rate and functioning of the heart.

Pulse rate increases with an increase in animal activity, as well as body and/or ambient temperature. Shock occurs when an animal undergoes a

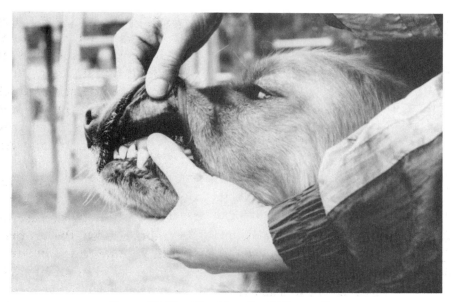

Figure 20-10. Checking the CRT on a dog.

trauma of some sort. Shock is associated with reduced *blood circulation,* lower *blood pressure,* and subnormal body temperature. A quick method of checking blood circulation is the *capillary refill time (CRT).* This is done by pressing on the animal's gum and checking the time required for the tissues to return to their normal pink color (the time required for the blood to return to the *capillaries*). For dogs a CRT of more than three seconds indicates low blood circulation and the likelihood that the animal is in shock.

Table 20-1
Normal Vital Signs in Selected Animals

Animal	Rectal Temperature °F	Respiration Rate	Pulse Rate
Cattle	101.5	30	50
Sheep	102.3	19	75
Swine	102.5	16	60
Horse	100.0	12	45
Goat	102.3	15	80
Chicken	107.1	25	275
Dog.	102.0	22	100

CHAPTER SUMMARY

Animal disease, stress, and injury can lead to significant loss to producers if unchecked. Early detection of problems can prevent loss of life and spread to other animals in the herd or flock. Successful producers develop the ability to note any unusual behaviors in their animals that may be signs of health problems. Knowing what normal animal behavior is and being able to spot animals that are sick or in distress is a key to profit. Producers and animal owners work closely with veterinarians to follow up on early signs of health problems.

An animal's vital signs include its body temperature, pulse rate, and respiration rate. Body temperature can tell much about an animal's well-being and is used as the first and most basic diagnostic tool. An animal's vital signs are affected by activity, stress, infection, nutrition, and injury. Most animals have a fairly narrow range of "normals" for each of the vital signs, especially temperature. In general, infection causes an increase in body temperature. Subnormal body temperatures are of greater concern, because they indicate that the animal is not able to maintain itself for life. Body temperature is the balance between body heat generated by metabolic processes and digestion and heat dissipated from the body. Levels of certain hormones are directly related to increases and decreases in body temperature.

FURTHER LABORATORY INVESTIGATIONS

1. Check the vital signs of an animal under stress and compare to normal readings for that species and age.

2. Determine the vital signs for several animals of the same species. How do respiration and pulse rate vary by age?

3. Visit a small or large animal veterinarian and observe his/her examination procedures, equipment, and method of recording the animal's vital signs.

4. Compare the vital signs of several different animal species and compare. What might account for the differences observed?

5. Visit a farm and observe a herd or flock of animals in their growing environment. What are the general growing conditions? What behavior patterns do you see? Are there animals that do not seem to follow the general behavior patterns characteristic of the herd/flock?

Chapter 21

IMMUNITY SYSTEMS

On Guard!

AGRICULTURAL APPLICATIONS

Animal diseases have been estimated to cost the U.S. agricultural industry $17 billion annually. Pseudorabies, a highly contagious disease caused by a virus, costs the pork industry alone $60 million per year. Over 200 major diseases affect the livestock industry. These diseases cause loss of life, profit, and productivity. The costs of biologicals, labor, facilities, and medical services represent a significant portion of overall expenses for

Figure 21-1. Animal diseases cause huge financial losses in the agricultural industry each year.

producers. Some believe that vaccination against transmissible diseases is just as important as good animal nutrition.

Many agricultural researchers are involved in developing more effective and affordable ways to prevent, diagnose, and treat animal diseases. To date, over a dozen major animal diseases, including hog cholera and Marek's disease in poultry, have been eradicated in the U.S. due to these research efforts. Brucellosis is a serious, highly contagious disease that causes abortions in cattle. Researchers are working to more accurately distinguish between cattle infected with the bacterium *B. abortus* and those receiving the live vaccine. A new technique is being tested that cuts the time required to identify the bacterium from two weeks to one day. Scientists are using biotechnology to develop safer vaccines and to identify the presence of disease-causing organisms in an animal's body. They hope to develop a single, recombinant vaccine that will prevent several diseases with one injection.

The development and testing of new products to help prevent and control disease is a lengthy process. Stages include (1) in vitro (test tube) testing; (2) in vivo (lab animal) testing; (3) pre-clinical trials to determine the appropriate dosage; (4) contact with the FDA by the developing agency; (5) clinical trials, after FDA consent; (6) submission of plans by the developer

TERMS

active immunity	dosage	neoplasm diseases
acute disease	gamma globulin	passive immunity
anomalous disease	immunity	pathogen
antibiotics	infectious disease	phagocytosis
antibody	injection	recombinant vaccine
antigen	intradermal (ID)	sterilized
bacterin	injection	subcutaneous (SC)
broad spectrum	intramuscular (IM)	injection
antibiotic	injection	symptoms
chronic disease	intravenous (IV)	systemic disease
colostrum	injection	toxins
contagious disease	lymphocytes	vaccine
degenerative disease	metabolic disease	white blood cells
disease	monoclonal antibody	
disinfectant	technique	

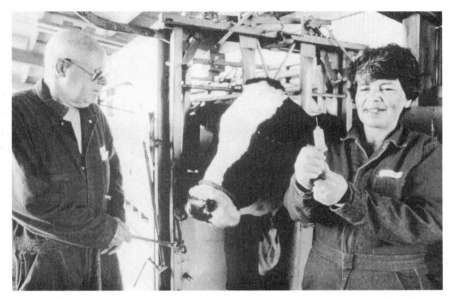

Figure 21-2. New products designed to fight animal diseases are continually developed and tested. (Courtesy, USDA, Agricultural Research Service)

for testing, manufacturing, and labelling the product to the USDA; (7) field trials; (8) application to the FDA to market the new product; and (9) monitoring by the USDA and the manufacturer while the new product is being commercially used.

Producers use many management practices to both prevent and control disease. Providing adequate nutrition and housing can do much to reduce disease. Making sure that newborn animals drink milk from their mothers as soon as possible is extremely important in the young animal's survival. Reducing animal stress when handling is also important. Preconditioning is a practice used by many producers to build the animal's strength and well-being prior to stressful events, such as shipping, weaning, handling, bad weather, and so on. The spread of disease can be slowed by grouping animals into like units (age, sex), isolating new and returning animals from the herd or flock, and avoiding overcrowding. Researchers have found that genetics of the sire has an impact on an animal's resistance to diseases, particularly parasite invasions. Adequate manure disposal also helps to prevent the spread of disease within a herd or flock.

USDA scientists at the Southeast Poultry Research Laboratory in Athens, Georgia have been experimenting with a germ-free housing unit. Air entering the FAPP (filtered air, positive pressure) system is filtered twice to ensure

Figure 21-3. Producers use various management practices to prevent disease.

that no germ-bearing dust particles get into the housing unit. Since filtered air is blown into the unit, internal pressure is built up, and air blows outward when the door is opened. The FAPP system has been widely used by companies that produce eggs for use in growing vaccine viruses.

The use of biologicals, primarily vaccines, is a major phase of any animal care program. In addition, antibiotics are commonly administered through the feed or water of some species, particularly poultry. The timing and administration of injections is crucial to the effectiveness of vaccines in preventing disease. If not administered correctly, some vaccines can have undesirable side effects. Producers can choose from a wide range of biologicals on the market today. Large producers keep an ample supply of refrigerated biologicals on hand at all times.

A vaccination schedule is followed for each species, depending on age and sex. For example, beef calves at weaning should be vaccinated for six or more diseases, depending upon the location and herd health history. They may receive booster injections three weeks later for several of these diseases. In addition, producers must know how and where to inject vaccines to ensure their effectiveness and prevent unwanted side effects.

When producers spot animals that show symptoms of weakness or disease, their first concern is correctly determining the cause of the disease. A general examination of the animal's condition should be performed. Assistance from a veterinarian is often required. Depending upon the diagnosis, sick animals may be separated from healthy animals. Housing may need to be disinfected as well. Field, state and federal veterinarians must report infectious and contagious diseases to prevent their spread. USDA regulatory agencies, as well as state diagnostic laboratories, play a key role in identifying and controlling serious animal diseases.

OBJECTIVES— QUESTIONS FOR INVESTIGATION

After studying this chapter and completing the laboratory investigations that follow, you should be able to answer the following questions:

Figure 21-4. **Many products are available to help combat animal diseases.**

1. What organisms cause disease in animals?

2. How do animals respond to invasions of foreign materials and organisms?

3. How does an animal develop immunity to a disease?

4. Why does vaccination help the animal's body develop resistance to disease?

5. Why are vaccines refrigerated?

6. What determines the type of injection for a vaccine?

7. Why should injection instruments be sterilized? Why should chemical disinfectants not be used to sterilize needles and syringes?

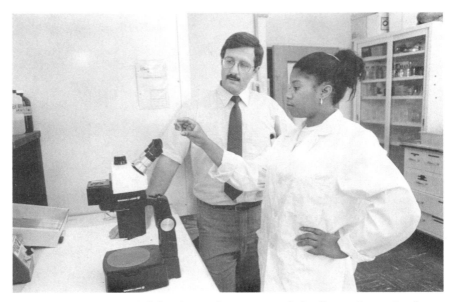

Figure 21-5. Diagnostic labs play an important role in diagnosing animal diseases. (Courtesy, OACE, University of Illinois)

8. Why should animals new to the herd or flock be isolated for a period of time?

9. How are animal diseases transmitted?

10. Why should newborn animals drink milk from their mother during the first several days of life?

LABORATORY INVESTIGATIONS

EXPERIMENT 1.
EFFECTS OF ANTIBIOTICS ON BACTERIA

Purpose

The purpose of this experiment is to determine the effects of antibiotics on different types of bacteria.

Materials

- wax pencil

- ruler
- transfer (inoculating) loop
- Bunsen burner
- luria agar plates (one for each bacterium tested)
- various antibiotic disks with dispenser
- various bacterial cultures (e.g., *E. Coli*, *P. Fluorescens*, *B. Subtilis*, etc.)

Procedures

Transfer the bacterial cultures from the (stock) tubes to the agar plates as follows: (1) disinfect work area and reduce air flow to a minimum; (2) hold the stock tube in the palm of one hand; (3) hold the transfer loop in the other hand and flame for 5-8 seconds; (4) raise the lid on the agar plate and place the hot loop in the agar for several seconds to cool; (5) remove the cap from the stock tube and flame the mouth of the tube; (6) insert the cooled loop into the stock tube and pick up a small amount of the bacterial culture; (7) replace the tube cap and raise the agar plate lid; (8) gently touch the loop to the agar in the top of the dish and streak in a zigzag pattern from side to side to the bottom of the dish; (9) lower the plate lid and flame the loop; and (10) label the dish with the date and type of bacteria.

Repeat the above steps for each type of bacteria to be tested. Select five different antibiotic disks. Record the letters and numbers on each disk and which antibiotic they contain. Raise the lid on one of the agar plates and place one of each type of antibiotic disk on the plate. Cover the plate.

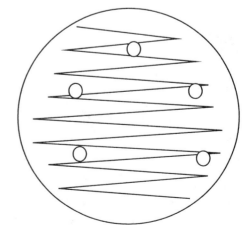

Figure 21-6. Streaked agar plate with five antibiotic disks in place.

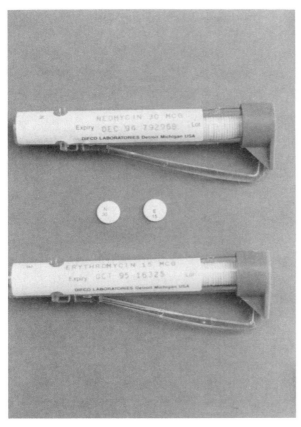

Figure 21-7. Antibiotic disks with dispenser.

Repeat for each agar plate, using the same five types of antibiotic disks. Incubate the plates at room temperature for 48 hours. (Note: If incubated at above 25°C, turn the petri dishes upside down to prevent condensed water from dripping onto the agar.) Observe the clear zones around each antibiotic disk. Measure the width of these zones and record. Compare your findings by bacteria and type of antibiotic.

EXERCISE I. COMPARING MEDICATIONS

Purpose

The purpose of this laboratory exercise is to compare various vaccines and other antibiotics with respect to key characteristics.

Materials

- selected vaccines (antibiotics and viral vaccines)
- selected powdered antibiotics for use in feed and/or water

Procedures

Obtain the desired medications. Try to obtain a variety with respect to active ingredient(s), administration, withdrawal period, species, disease treated, dosage, restrictions, and other characteristics. Develop a matrix for recording information on these characteristics for each product. Read the product labels and record the relevant information. How do the medicines compare? What contradictions, if any, do you see in the product features? How can differences in these products be explained?

SCIENCE CONNECTIONS

TYPES OF ANIMAL DISEASES

Disease can be defined as any departure from a healthy state. This includes changes in function or structure of animal tissues due to *microorganisms* and other causes. Diseases may be grouped into six different types as follows:

Degenerative—Changes in bone, muscle, or organs brought about by age, disuse, or biochemical changes. Often follows other diseases and can lead to infection by microorganisms.

Anomalous—Abnormality at birth (e.g., dwarfism).

Metabolic—Body functions are altered due to nutrition, toxins, or endocrine activity (e.g., milk fever). Losses equal to those from infectious diseases.

Neoplasms—Cancerous (abnormal, rapid) growth.

Infectious—Caused by the invasion of microorganisms. Many are very contagious, and thus, very costly.

Trauma—Violent injury to bone, muscle, or tissue.

By examining the visual condition of an animal, *symptoms* of a disease may be evident. Pneumonia and mastitis are examples of *systemic diseases*, where the entire body or a major body system is affected. An *acute disease* is relatively severe but of short duration, whereas a *chronic disease* is continuous. *Infectious diseases* are always caused by living organisms, and microorganisms always originate from some other organism. *Contagious diseases* are always infectious, but infectious diseases are not always contagious. Disease-producing organisms usually enter the body through the skin and natural orifices, primarily the mouth and nose.

BODY DEFENSES AND REACTIONS

The skin and hair represent the animal's first line of defense against disease. The common response of tissues to disease includes redness, pain, swelling, and heat. Redness is caused by an increased blood supply to the area. An increase in blood pressure causes fluids to enter tissues outside blood vessels in the area, and swelling occurs. Swelling causes pain, and heat is due to increased local cell metabolism.

When a foreign organism or material invades the animal's body, *white blood cells* rush to the site to surround and contain the organism. This process is known as *phagocytosis*. These cells contain antibodies, which act to kill or stop the invading organism, known as an antigen. An *antigen* is any substance which leads to the development of an antibody when it is introduced in blood or tissues. Thus, an *antibody* is a specific substance produced within an animal as a reaction to an invading antigen. *Lymphocytes*, a type of white blood cell, are the key cells in detecting antigens and creating an antibody response to them. Antibodies are specialized *gamma globulin* proteins in the blood that combine with antigens (bacteria, viruses, or parasites) and neutralize them.

Animal scientists have observed that parasite infestations can cut growth in young animals by as much as 50%, and in many cases depressed growth occurs even after parasites are eliminated. White blood cells respond to an

Figure 21-8. Blood tests can reveal much about an animal's ability to fight disease. (Courtesy, USDA, Agricultural Research Service)

infection by producing small proteins called cytokines. *Cytokines* are hormones that have been found to decrease bone and muscle growth, feed intake, and growth hormone secretion. At the same time, parasite infestations have been shown to increase levels of *somatostatin*, another hormone that blocks growth hormone secretion. These changes in hormone levels seem to persist, even after the infection has been cleared up, perhaps accounting for the continued poor performance of infected animals.

Microbiology, parasitology, pathology, and *entomology* all deal with living organisms that cause disease. Scientists are developing several new techniques for diagnosing animal diseases. The *monoclonal antibody technique* involves fusing a cancer cell with one that produces antibodies. The resulting new cell can proliferate indefinitely and has the ability to produce antibodies. *DNA probes* can detect disease-producing microbes by identifying specific genetic sequences of the organism.

IMMUNITY

Immunity is simply an animal's resistance to disease. Some microorganisms form *spores* and are much more *resistant* to the animal's defense systems. *Virulent* microorganisms are able to overcome the animal's natural defenses. Many microorganisms produce *toxins* which can cause cell death.

Figure 21-9. An animal's immune system becomes stronger with each successive exposure to a disease.

Stress makes an animal more susceptible to infection by affecting hormonal balance. Through a series of reactions, the *adrenal gland* is stimulated to produce more *glucocortoids*. These substances attach to receptors on cells and control cell metabolism. An overabundance of glucocortoids is believed to suppress an animal's natural immune system.

Once an animal's body has produced antibodies in response to an antigen invasion, it retains its capacity to produce these antibodies for many years. Due to the cumulative effects of this antibody activity, immunity gradually increases with each successive exposure to a particular antigen. *Active immunity* is due to production of antibodies by the animal itself when antigens are present (either from disease or a vaccine). Thus, active immunity is usually long lasting, often for the animal's lifetime. On the other hand, *passive immunity* is obtained from the introduction of antibodies from an outside source and lasts only a few days or weeks.

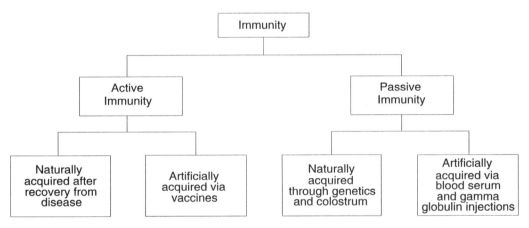

Figure 21-10. Developing immunity to a disease.

New animals in a herd or flock are isolated from other animals until they have been gradually exposed to local conditions. This allows an opportunity for the animal to develop active immunity to certain antigens. This practice also prevents the spread of disease-producing organisms from the new animal to other animals. An animal can appear healthy but still spread a disease-producing organism. Some animals are *carriers* of diseases. That is, their natural defenses were able to contain the organism but were unable to kill it. Thus, the animal carries the disease-producing organism but does not show symptoms of it presence.

Newborn animals have no immunity to diseases. The mother passes

Figure 21-11. Young animals are very susceptible to disease, since they have no immunity to disease at birth.

antibodies to her offspring though her *colostrum*, the first milk produced after giving birth. Studies have shown that about half of the mother's immunity is obtained by the newborn animal when it ingests the antibody-rich colostrum at the first feeding. Within 48 hours the mother has passed much of her immunity to her offspring. It is important to note that mothers can only pass to their offspring the immunity that they have built up in their own bodies. A clean, disease-free environment gives young animals time to strengthen their immunity system before a *pathogen* invades their body. *Disinfectants*, which destroy microbes by breaking down cell proteins, are often used to ensure a disease-free environment for animals. Since stress breaks down immunity systems, producers should treat newborn animals gently.

BIOLOGICALS

Biologicals are a large group of products derived from living organisms that enhance immunity. Vaccines are the primary biological products used by producers, although others play a vital role in maintaining animal health. Vaccines are used as management tools to help animals maintain high immunity to disease. *Vaccines* are suspensions of bacteria or viruses that create an antibody response when injected in the animal. Vaccines cause an animal to develop an acquired immunity to a disease before infection occurs. Several weeks after vaccination are usually required before immunity is developed. Conventional vaccines contain killed or weakened forms of disease-causing microbes. Though slight, these biologicals always carry the chance of actually producing the disease in the vaccinated animal. This is why only healthy animals should be vaccinated. New, *recombinant vaccines* use only a small portion of the microbe and omit the disease-causing genes. The antigen features of the microbe are still retained so that an antibody response is evoked.

Several different types of vaccines are used in animal health programs today. *Live virus vaccines* are prepared from fluids extracted from infected chick embryos. *Modified live vaccines* cannot cause disease, but they stimulate the immune system to go to work. Distilled water is added to *freeze-dried vaccines* before they can be used. A *bacterin* is a vaccine used to stimulate immunity against bacterial disease. Bacterins contain killed bacteria. Some vaccines stimulate immunity against a single organism, while others stimulate immunity to multiple organisms. Viral vaccines tend to cause long lasting immunity, while immunity from bacterial infections is short-lived. However, viruses are harder to control because they inject their nucleic acids into the *cytoplasm* of the host (animal) cell. Thus, it is difficult to kill the virus without also killing the host cell.

Antibiotics are chemical substances produced synthetically or by mi-

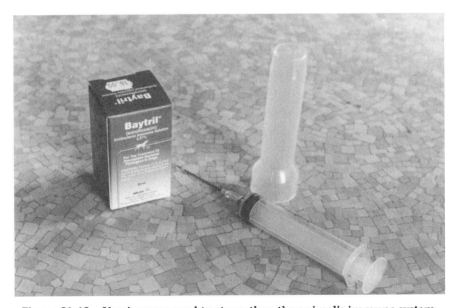

Figure 21-12. Vaccines are used to strengthen the animal's immune system.

croorganisms that inhibit the growth of or kill bacteria and other micro-organisms. Antibiotics are designed to assist, rather than harm, the host's immune system and are thus *selective* in their toxic effects. Bacteria differ in their *cell wall* composition and mode of adhesion for entry into the animal's body. These differences account for the varying *susceptibility* of different bacteria to various antibiotics. A *broad spectrum antibiotic* is effective against several types of bacteria. Examples include penicillin, tetra-cycline, and bacitracin. Microorganisms are killed by direct sunlight (ultraviolet rays) and heat. Thus, biologicals should be kept refrigerated and protected from sunlight.

INJECTIONS

Many biologicals are introduced into the animal's body via *injections.* Injected drugs act faster and last longer than ingested drugs, due to digestive action. Vaccines are usually shaken to uniformly suspend the microorganism in the liquid medium. *Dosage* generally increases with an increase in body size and weight. Vaccines should not be mixed, except as directed, or the microorganisms present in the vaccines might actually kill one another. Vaccines lose their effectiveness after a certain period, due to the gradual dying of microbes in the vaccine. Antibiotics require a definite time period for degradation within body tissues. Thus, *withdrawal periods* are often

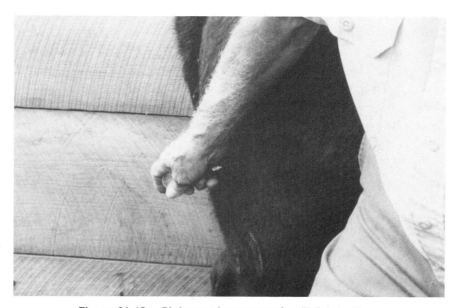

Figure 21-13. Giving an intramuscular (IM) injection.

required before animals are slaughtered or milk is used for human consumption. Instruments should be *sterilized* to prevent the introduction of unwanted microbes into animal tissues. However, chemical sterilization of needles and syringes can kill microorganisms in live vaccines.

Three primary injection types are used for administering vaccines to animals. *Subcutaneous* (SC) injections (usually 2-30 cc) are placed just under the skin but above muscle tissue. SC injections are absorbed more slowly than the other two types of injections, and their effects are longer lasting. *Intramuscular* (IM) injections are placed in muscle tissue. Absorption is relatively rapid, due to good blood supply in the muscle. However, small amounts (12-15 cc) must be injected at a time or muscle tissue damage can occur. *Intravenous* (IV) injections are used when large amounts of a drug are needed and when the drug must be rapidly available to fight disease. *Intradermal* (ID) injections (1-2 cc) are also sometimes used.

CHAPTER SUMMARY

Diseases cost animal producers billions of dollars each year. Loss of life and reduced growth and reproductive performance significantly cut into investment returns. Producers team up with veterinarians and other specialists to diagnose and treat diseases when they occur. Much time is spent preventing, detecting, diagnosing, and treating animal diseases. However, significant progress has been made in these areas, with a number of major animal diseases now eradicated from U.S. herds and flocks.

Producers use a number of management strategies to keep disease losses to a minimum. These include good feeding programs, adequate housing, reduced animal stress, isolation of new and infected animals, and a sound vaccination program. Through the use of biotechnology, researchers have developed new methods of detecting disease-producing microorganisms in animals. In addition, new products aimed at fighting animal disease are continually developed, tested, and released for commercial use.

Many different types of diseases affect animals. Infectious diseases are caused by one or more microorganisms. The animal's body uses several natural defense mechanisms to ward off disease. Most important of these are the antibodies produced by white blood cells when a foreign organism is detected. As an animal is exposed to various microorganisms, it develops an immunity, or resistance to, those organisms. Producers use vaccination programs to strengthen an animal's natural immunity system. A wide variety of biologicals is used to fight animal diseases.

FURTHER LABORATORY INVESTIGATIONS

1. Compare the effects (ability to stimulate immunity) of various biologicals. Make your comparisons as to type, brand name, concentration, active ingredient, and so on.

2. Repeat Experiment 1 in this chapter by using other types of bacteria/antibiotic combinations. Which antibiotics are broad spectrum? Talk to you teacher about obtaining and using various commercial kits to further study bacteria and antibiotics. Suggestions include science kits on bacterial sensitivity to disinfectants and antibiotic production.

3. Develop a vaccination program for a selected species, based upon the age of the animal. What biologicals should be administered, when, and how? Discuss your program with a local producer and veterinarian.

4. Calculate the dosage rates of various medicines. For example, a 400 pound animal requires an injection of 5,000 units/kilogram weight. The antibiotic used contains 100,000 units/milliliter. This animal would weigh 181.8 kilograms and would require 9.1 cubic centimeters (1 ml = 1 cc) of the medication.

5. Practice sterilizing and filling syringes. Obtain several different types of needles and syringes. How should each be sterilized? To fill the syringe, pull back the plunger and fill the syringe with air equal to the volume of medication to be used. Insert the needle through the cleansed rubber stopper in the bottle and slowly inject air into the bottle. Invert the bottle and fill the syringe with the desired amount of vaccine. Holding the syringe upright, tap to remove air bubbles, and push air bubbles and extra medicine back into the bottle. Assist a local producer in giving injections.

Chapter 22

ARTIFICIAL INSEMINATION

Freezing and Thawing

AGRICULTURAL APPLICATIONS

Not widely used until the 1930s, today artificial insemination (AI) is the predominant method of breeding in the dairy and poultry industries and is used to a lesser extent in swine and beef. The use of AI worldwide has enabled breeders to tap into genetic stock anywhere in the world. The potential for genetic improvement using AI is tremendous. Artificial insemination is not yet practical in the sheep industry, due to the difficulty

Figure 22-1. Artificial insemination offers many advantages over natural breeding. (Courtesy, Illinois Dept. of Agriculture)

of inseminating ewes and the low survivability of ram sperm when it is frozen and thawed. Researchers are experimenting with a surgical technique for artificially inseminating ewes, which involves actually injecting the semen into the uterus with a needle.

Artificial insemination offers several major advantages over natural breeding. These include (1) faster genetic improvement due to greater genetic variation, (2) reduced or eliminated costs and labor associated with maintaining males for breeding, (3) decreased risk of spreading certain diseases, (4) greater use of superior males, even after their death, (5) increased availability (theoretically worldwide) of semen from outstanding males, and (6) increased conception rate (poultry industry). The use of artificial insemination greatly multiplies the breeding value of superior males and allows managers to have better control over when animals are bred.

However, the costs of failure when using AI, in terms of poor conception rates, are great. Successful use of AI requires intensified management by producers. Critical areas include accurately detecting heat in females, selecting and handling semen so that quality is maintained, and using proper insemination techniques. Keeping accurate breeding records (e.g., sires used) is also important. Selecting the right males for the artificial breeding

TERMS

accessory glands
acrosome
artificial insemination (AI)
cervix
corpus luteum
epididymis
estrogen
estrus synchronization
fallopian tubes
female reproductive system
follicles

follicle stimulating hormone (FSH)
germ cells
infundibulum
luteinizing hormone (LH)
male reproductive system
morphology
motility
ovaries
polyestrous
progesterone

prostaglandin
puberty
reproductive tract
semen
semen extenders
spermatogenesis
standing heat
suspended animation
testes
uterine horns
uterus
vas deferens
zygote

Figure 22-2. The need for good management is intensified when using AI.

program is a challenging task. In beef, sires account for well over half of the genetic change in a herd.

During breeding periods, producers must check females twice daily to detect heat. Some producers use injections to synchronize estrous cycles,

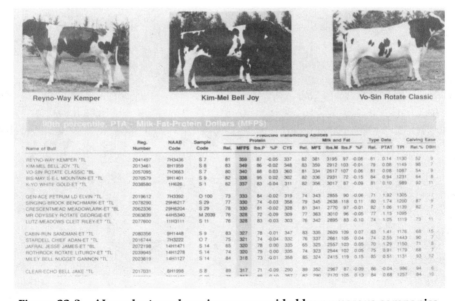

Reyno-Way Kemper   Kim-Mel Bell Joy   Vo-Sin Rotate Classic

90th percentile, PTA - Milk-Fat-Protein Dollars (MFPS)

				Predicted Transmitting Abilities										Type Data			Calving Ease	
				Protein					Milk and Fat									
Name of Bull	Reg. Number	NAAB Code	Sample Code	Rel.	MFPS	lbs.P	%P	CYS	Rel.	MFS	lbs.M	lbs.F	%F	Rel.	PTAT	TPI	Rel.%	DBH
REYNO-WAY KEMPER *TL	2041497	7H3436	S 7	81	359	87	-0.05	337	82	381	3195	97	-0.08	81	0.14	1130	52	9
KIM-MEL BELL JOY *TL	2013461	8H1959	S 8	83	349	86	-0.02	348	83	359	2912	103	-0.01	79	0.06	1149	96	7
VO-SIN ROTATE CLASSIC *BL	2057095	7H3663	S 7	80	340	88	0.03	360	81	334	2617	107	0.06	81	0.08	1067	54	9
BIG-MAY S-E-L MOUNTAIN-ET *TL	2070579	9H1401	S 9	82	338	95	0.02	302	82	336	2931	72	-0.15	84	0.94	1231	64	8
K-YO WHITE GOLD-ET *TL	2038580	1H626	S 1	82	337	83	-0.04	311	82	356	3017	87	-0.09	81	0.10	989	92	11
GEN-ACE PETRUM LD ELVIN *TL	2019612	7H3392	O 100	73	333	84	-0.02	319	74	343	2855	90	-0.06	71	1.92	1305		
SINGING-BROOK BENCHMARK-ET *TL	2078290	29H6217	S 29	77	330	74	-0.03	358	79	345	2638	118	0.11	80	1.74	1200	87	9
CRESCENTMEAD MEADOWLARK-ET *BL	2062336	29H6204	S 29	78	330	81	-0.02	328	81	341	2770	97	-0.01	82	1.06	1139	82	7
MR ODYSSEY ROTATE GEORGIE-ET	2063839	44H5340	M 2039	76	328	72	-0.09	309	77	363	3010	96	-0.05	77	1.15	1095		
LUTZ-MEADOWS CLEIT RILEY-ET *TL	2077600	11H3111	S 11	76	328	83	-0.03	303	76	342	2895	83	-0.10	74	1.05	1119	73	11
CABIN-RUN SANDMAN-ET *TL	2080356	9H1448	S 9	83	327	78	-0.01	347	83	335	2609	109	0.07	63	1.41	1176	68	15
STARDELL CHIEF ADAN-ET *TL	2016744	7H3222	O 7	75	321	74	-0.04	332	76	337	2661	105	0.04	74	2.55	1443	90	7
JAFRAL JESSE JAMES-ET *BL	2072198	14H1471	S 14	65	320	78	0.00	335	65	325	2557	103	0.05	70	1.29	1150	71	8
ROTHROCK ROTATE LITURGY-ET *TL	2039945	14H1278	S 14	74	320	79	0.00	335	74	323	2544	102	0.05	75	0.91	1179	68	7
MILEY BELL NUGGET GANNON *TL	2023819	14H1127	S 14	84	318	73	-0.01	358	85	324	2415	119	0.15	85	0.51	1131	93	12
CLEAR-ECHO BELL JAKE *TL	2017031	8H1998	S 8	89	317	71	-0.09	290	89	352	2967	87	-0.09	86	-0.04	986	94	6

Figure 22-3. AI products and services are provided by numerous companies.

so that groups of animals can be artificially bred at the same time. This offers advantages in feeding, handling, and marketing offspring. Successful artificial insemination requires special training, special equipment, and lots of practice. Using hormonal injections, cows have been stimulated to release multiple eggs (rather than the usual single egg) at ovulation. Several days after fertilization, the eggs are flushed from the uterus and the embryos transferred to recipient cows. Superovulation can allow a superior cow to produce over 40 calves per year, compared to the usual one calf per year.

Collecting, evaluating, and distributing semen is an important element of effective AI programs. A number of U.S. companies specialize in marketing frozen semen to producers. Semen is collected from bulls, horses, and rams with an artificial vagina. Boar semen is usually collected by hand. Fresh semen is used when breeding poultry and swine. In other cases, fresh semen is diluted, placed in a special straw, and then frozen for later use. A new pellet freezing technique is now being used for cattle in some parts of the world.

OBJECTIVES—QUESTIONS FOR INVESTIGATION

After completing the laboratory investigations that follow and partici-

Figure 22-4.   Using an artificial vagina to collect semen from a bull. (Courtesy, Jan Allen)

pating in other activities provided by your teacher, you should be able to answer the following questions:

1. Why are sperm placed in the uterus when using artificial insemination?

2. What is estrus? What causes animals to show estrus?

3. What is ovulation? How are estrus and ovulation related?

4. What determines when an animal should be artificially inseminated?

5. Why is the timing of artificial insemination critical?

6. How do estrous synchronizers work?

7. How do superovulating agents work?

8. Why is sperm diluted before freezing?

9. How is sperm quality evaluated?

10. Why should unused, thawed sperm not be refrozen for later use?

LABORATORY INVESTIGATIONS

EXERCISE I.
COMPARISON OF FEMALE REPRODUCTIVE ORGANS

Purpose

The purpose of this laboratory is to examine the female reproductive systems in two or more livestock species. The focus for this lab is on how the parts of the reproductive system work together in reproduction and how artificial insemination techniques lead to fertilization.

Materials

- scalpel
- female reproductive systems of several species (obtain from local meat packer or butcher)
- latex gloves
- artificial insemination equipment - pipettes, sleeves, gun, straw, and other items (borrow from local technician)

Procedures

Obtain AI equipment and reproductive systems. Spread each reproductive system over a large table having a protective covering. Identify and label the major parts of the reproductive systems for each species. Trace the pathway of the sperm, ovum, and fertilized egg through the organs in each system. Use the AI equipment to practice depositing semen in the uterus.

EXERCISE 2.
EVALUATING SEMEN

Purpose

The purpose of this investigation is to evaluate the quality of a semen sample.

Materials

- microscope with 10X, 40X and 100X oil immersion lens
- microscope slides and cover slips
- 12" × 12" plate glass
- two bricks
- trouble light with 75 watt bulb
- fresh and frozen semen (bull)
- 20 ml normal saline solution (phipiologic saline)
- semen stain (Hancock's or Blom's Eosin-Nigrosin stain)
- water bath (34-37°C)
- two eye droppers
- several test tubes
- thermometer for water bath

Procedures

Place the trouble light under the glass plate supported by two bricks. Preheat microscope slides and cover slips by placing on the clean glass plate for about 10 minutes. Using either a hot plate or thermal container, set up water bath to maintain the temperature of the semen. Place semen sample and saline solution in separate test tubes and maintain at 34-37°C in the water bath.

To evaluate *mass motility*, place a drop of semen on a slide and observe under the microscope. Use the 10X objective and score the semen according to the following scale:

Rapid swirling motion	20
Slow swirling motion	12
Some motion, but not swirling	10
Very slow motion	3
No motion	0

To evaluate *individual motility*, place a drop of semen on a slide and add a drop of saline solution. Gently mix the two and cover with a cover slip. (Note: Do not add saline solution to thawed samples of frozen semen.) Using the 40X objective, focus on a single sperm and observe it as it moves across the field of vision. A strong sperm will move across the field in a straight line in about 5 seconds. Observe several individual sperm cells and calculate an average time for travel across the visual field. Assign an individual motility score as follows:

Rapid, straight line travel in less than 5 seconds	20
Moderate, straight line travel in 5-10 seconds	12
Slow, straight line travel with slightly erratic motion	10
Very slow, erratic motion	3
No movement	0

An average motility score can be determined by adding the mass and individual motility scores and dividing by two.

Evaluate *sperm morphology* by placing a drop of semen on a slide, adding a drop of saline solution, and adding a drop of semen stain. Gently mix and cover with a cover slip. Observe under the microscope using the 100X objective. Locate a section of the slide containing up to 20 sperm. Compare each sperm against the healthy sperm shown in Figure 22-5. Note the number of sperm showing head, mid-piece, or tail defects, as well as the number of healthy sperm in the visual field. Move to other sections of the slide and continue counting and evaluating sperm until 100 sperm cells have been evaluated. In general, no more than 25% of the sperm should show signs of defect in order for the sample to be considered satisfactory.

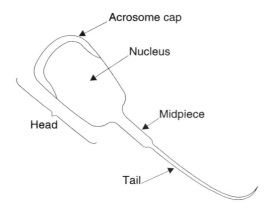

Figure 22-5. Healthy bull sperm.

SCIENCE CONNECTIONS

Artificial insemination is the deposition of semen in the *reproductive tract* of a female by artificial means. Since physical contact by the male is eliminated, the spread of some diseases, like vibriosis, is reduced. Successful AI requires a good understanding of the reproductive cycle and processes in the female.

THE FEMALE REPRODUCTIVE SYSTEM

The *female reproductive system* consists of two ovaries, two Fallopian tubes, the uterus, and the vagina. The *uterus* includes the uterus body, two uterine horns, and cervix. The *ovaries* are surrounded by *follicles*, which contain *germ cells* that develop into the *ova*. *Puberty* is the point at which an animal can produce viable ova and carry out a reproductive function. *Ovulation* is the release of an ovum (or ova in the case of multiple births) from a mature follicle. Estrus is the period of time in which the female is receptive to the male. *Standing heat*, when the female stands still when mounted, is the best indication of estrus. Ovulation corresponds to estrus in most animals, except the cow, where ovulation occurs 12-18 hours after the start of estrus. Insemination should occur as close to ovulation as possible (within 24 hours).

The *estrous cycle* is the reproductive cycle that spans from the beginning of one estrus to the beginning of the next estrus. Ovulation occurs at the end of the estrous cycle in most animals. This estrous cycle ranges from 16 to 23 days for most farm animals. While some are seasonal breeders (sheep), most farm animals cycle year round and are referred to as *polyestrous*.

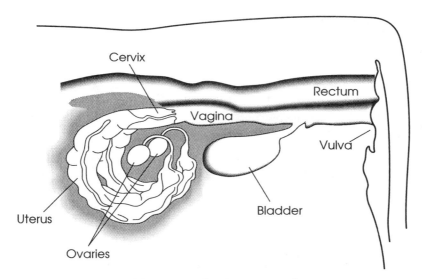

Figure 22-6. Reproductive system of a cow.

The estrous cycle is controlled by hormones secreted by the pituitary gland. *Follicle stimulating hormone (FSH)* stimulates the development of one or more follicles, which in turn are stimulated to produce estrogen. As the follicle increases in size, more estrogen is produced. When estrogen levels reach a certain point, estrus results. A second hormone, *luteinizing hormone (LH)*, causes the follicle to rupture and release the matured ovum. The *corpus luteum* forms where the follicle ruptured, and these tissues begin to produce *progesterone*. If *fertilization* of the ovum occurs, the corpus luteum remains in place and continues to produce progesterone. If pregnancy does not occur, the uterus secretes *prostaglandin*, which causes the corpus luteum to fade, and the estrous cycle begins anew.

Estrus synchronization is a technique which causes a group of animals to show estrus simultaneously. Several estrus synchronization products are commercially available. A popular product contains prostaglandin, which causes the corpus luteum to fade, and the estrous cycle is re-initiated. A related technique is *superovulation*, where outstanding females receive doses of FSH and LH. These increased hormone levels stimulate the development and release of numerous ova. The female is then bred to a superior male, usually via AI. After one week the embryos are removed from the superovulated female and transferred to surrogate females.

When an ovum is released from the ovary, it travels through the *Fallopian tubes* to the uterus. The funnel-shaped portion of the Fallopian tubes located next to the ovary is called the *infundibulum*, which actually

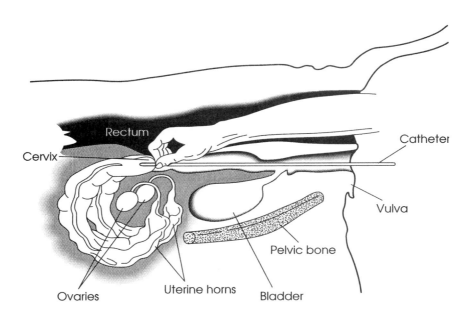

Figure 22-7.   Cow reproductive system showing artificial insemination.

"catches" the released egg. The Fallopian tubes also transport sperm cells from the uterus toward the infundibulum. Fertilization (union of the male and female sex cells) usually occurs in the upper one-third of the Fallopian tubes. After fertilization of the ovum, the *zygote* makes its way to the uterus within several days. Pregnancy usually occurs in the *uterine horns*. The *cervix* serves to protect the uterus from foreign materials during pregnancy.

THE MALE REPRODUCTIVE SYSTEM

The *male reproductive system* consists of the testes, reproductive tract (or duct system), accessory glands, and penis. *Sperm* are produced by tubules in the testicles. *Spermatogenesis* is the production of sperm cells from germ cells in the *testes*. Unlike the female cycle of producing ova, sperm are continuously produced in the male after puberty. FSH also plays an important role in the male reproductive system by regulating the development of sperm. Sperm are stored and matured in the *epididymis*. Greater sperm production is associated with larger testes.

The *vas deferens* transport the sperm from the epididymis to the urethra. Sperm cells combine with fluids produced by several *accessory glands* to form *semen*. The urethra, in turn, carries the semen through the penis to the outside of the body. Sperm can remain viable in the reproductive tracts

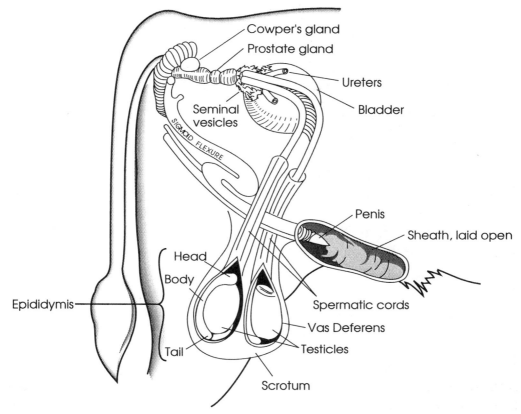

Figure 22-8. Male reproductive system.

of cows and sheep for one to two days. When using artificial insemination, sperm are deposited in the uterus of the female to increase the chances of fertilization. In natural breeding, the male usually deposits semen outside the cervix. Sperm cells are much smaller than ova.

Figure 22-9. Relative size of sperm and egg cells.

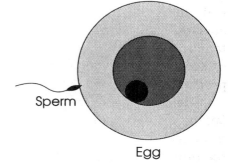

EVALUATING AND STORING SEMEN

The overall volume and sperm concentration in the ejaculate varies from one species to another. One ejaculate from a bull contains enough sperm to inseminate over 125 cows. Thus, semen is usually extended (diluted) before it is frozen for later use. *Semen extenders* provide nutrients, adjust pH, and protect the sperm from damage during freezing. Glycerol dehydrates sperm cells and prevents damage from ice crystals.

The shape of sperm is similar in most species. Major parts of the sperm cell include the *head*, *mid-piece*, and *tail*. The *acrosome* is a membrane cap that covers the head of the sperm cell. Semen quality is decreased by heat, stress, illness (fever), poor nutrition, and extreme or lasting cold temperatures. Heredity also affects semen quality. Fresh semen can live only one to two days and must be maintained at 40°F.

Before freezing, fresh semen is diluted, placed in a plastic straw, slowly chilled to 0°C, then quickly frozen in liquid nitrogen. At -320°F, liquid nitrogen stops sperm cell metabolism and places sperm in a state of *suspended animation*. Liquid nitrogen allows for constant storage temperatures and easy shipping of frozen semen. The *survivability* of sperm cells varies by breed, species, individual animal, and time of year semen was collected. Differences in the nature of sperm cell membranes is believed to play a major role in their ability to survive freezing and thawing. An excellent sample will have 50 to 65% healthy sperm cells after freezing. Frozen semen thaws very quickly. Refreezing will greatly reduce the percentage of healthy sperm cells.

Semen is evaluated based

Figure 22-10. Frozen sperm must be carefully handled to prevent death of sperm cells. (Courtesy, National FFA Organization)

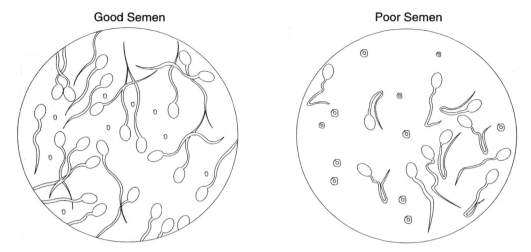

Good Semen   Poor Semen

Figure 22-11. Good and poor semen samples.

upon volume of the ejaculate and sperm motility and morphology. *Motility* is assessed by observing the movement of cells when viewed under the microscope. The tail of the sperm cell is responsible for motility. The motility of sperm cells is a direct indication of their ability to cause fertilization. At least 30% of the sperm cells in a good sample must have high motility scores. *Morphology* refers to the structure of the sperm cells. Morphology is determined by viewing stained sperm under a microscope. *Abnormalities* are classified as to primary, secondary, and tertiary and include defects in the size and shape of parts of the sperm cell. If more than 25% of the sperm in a sample are defective, a negative impact on fertility will result.

CHAPTER SUMMARY

Artificial insemination is the deposition of semen into the uterus of a female by artificial means. Most breeding in the dairy and poultry industries is done using artificial insemination. In addition, AI is used to some degree with beef cattle and swine. Researchers are working to develop practical and effective AI techniques for sheep. AI offers many advantages, foremost of which is the ability to greatly multiply the genetic impact of a single, superior male. The use of artificial insemination requires intensified management on the part of producers. The timing of inseminations is critical to satisfactory conception rates. Some producers use commercially available products to synchronize the estrous cycles of females. This simplifies the breeding program and offers several marketing and management advantages. Superovulation and embryo transfer also require the use of artificial insemination techniques. Collecting, evaluating, and distributing semen are important elements of the animal agriculture industry.

Successful AI requires a good understanding of the male and female reproductive systems and fertilization processes. The ovaries release a female sex cell (ovum) that travels through the fallopian tubes toward the uterus. If it joins with a sperm cell along the way, fertilization occurs, and a zygote is formed. The fertilized egg works its way to the uterus, where pregnancy occurs. Two hormones, follicle stimulating hormone and luteinizing hormone, play a critical role in developing and releasing the ovum. Other hormones also control the reproductive cycle in the female.

Sperm are formed in the testes of the male reproductive system. After storage in the epididymis, they are transported through the duct system and combined with fluids to form semen. Collected semen is used fresh or diluted and frozen for later use. Many factors can affect semen quality. High quality semen contains a high percentage of motile, normal sperm cells. Frozen semen can be stored for many years without a significant decline in its quality.

FURTHER LABORATORY INVESTIGATIONS

1. Examine the effects of temperature on motility and survivability. Use conditions (or observations) for Exercise 2 as the control. Use several variations in the temperature of the water bath, such as 90°F and 105°F. Observe individual and mass motility.

2. Using a microscope, compare the appearance of sperm cells from several different species.

3. Obtain the male reproductive organs from one or more species. Identify the parts of the reproductive system. Trace the path of the sperm through the system.

4. Test the vitality of fresh semen samples at 1, 5, 10, and 24 hours after collection. Evaluation of the sample at collection can serve as the control. The effects of semen extenders can also be examined.

5. Test the effects of thawing techniques and refreezing semen on sperm motility.

Chapter 23

MEAT CURING AND PROCESSING

Tender and Tasty

AGRICULTURAL APPLICATIONS

The meat processing industry in the United States is a huge part of the agricultural industry and the U.S. economy as a whole. Curing and processing allows meat to be stored longer and made available to consumers practically worldwide at any time of the year. Processing techniques also enhance flavor, appearance, color, and tenderness. Due to these techniques, consumers are provided an amazing variety of meat products at a relatively

Figure 23-1. A tremendous variety of cured meat products is available today.

low cost. U.S. consumers spend only about 12% of their income on food, among the lowest of all nations.

Today's consumers demand fresh and preserved meat products that are leaner, healthier, and tastier than ever before. Producers have responded by shipping leaner animals to the market, and processors continue to change their product lines to meet consumer preferences. Palatability, which refers to taste and tenderness, is a high priority among processors and consumers. Water content of meat products is directly related to meat palatability. Processors usually add water during processing to increase product weight and palatability. Salt, nitrite, phosphates, sugar, starch, sodium erythorbate, and other substances are used in the meat processing industry.

A major concern among producers and processors today is the varying degree of tenderness in retail cuts of meat. Many meat processing techniques are designed to improve tenderness of the meat product. Beef carcasses are usually aged under refrigeration for 7 to 14 days to increase tenderness. A new technique under development could reduce this aging time to a single day. Scientists have found that an injection of calcium chloride within 24 hours after slaughter produces the same effects on tenderness as refrigeration, without affecting flavor. If commercially developed, this technique could have a huge impact on the condition of cattle that are sent to market. Marketing much leaner animals could greatly reduce feed costs, growing time, and alter breed selection. Calcium chloride is already approved by the FDA as a food additive.

TERMS

absorbed	food deterioration	phosphate
aged	glycogen metabolism	plasmolysis
bacteriostatic	lactic acid	proteolytic enzymes
calcium	metmyoglobin	salmonella
calpains	microbial spoilage	salt
color stability	myofibrillar protein	sodium nitrite
curing	myoglobin	sugar
electromagnetic scanning	nitric oxide myoglobin	tenderness
erythorbate	nitrosyl hemochrome	ultrasound imaging
fat oxidation	optical probe	video image analysis
fibrils	oxymyoglobin	

Figure 23-2. A major concern of the beef industry is the variation in tenderness of retail cuts.

Figure 23-3. Producers will be using new techniques to help them select leaner market animals.

Considerable effort is being aimed at developing accurate, affordable techniques for measuring the amount of lean and fat tissue in live animals and carcasses. In Europe today, producers are paid based upon the amount of lean meat contained in the carcasses of the animals they send to the market. These newer techniques for measuring carcass composition include (1) fat-lean optical probe, (2) ultrasound image analysis, (3) video image analysis, and (4) electromagnetic scanning. Some of these techniques are used on live animals and may be used in the future to select animals for breeding. Electromagnetic scanning is soon to be used in commercial processing plants in the United States.

Bacterial contamination of meat during processing is an area of concern for processors. Natural organic acids, such as ascorbic acid and lactic acid, are now used to sanitize carcasses. Processors are most concerned about *Salmonella* bacteria. Scientists are working to develop better techniques for detecting and eliminating *Salmonella* bacteria from live animals and carcasses. This is of particular concern in beef products, since they are often not well cooked before consumption. A new, automatic, high-pressure washer has been developed that removes over 90% of the foodborne pathogens on the beef carcass surface. In addition, laboratory techniques have removed 99.9% of the *Salmonella* bacteria on carcasses, and researchers are now working to adapt these techniques for commercial application.

Figure 23-4. Researchers take tissue samples for microbial analysis from a carcass cleaned with a new high-pressure washer. (Courtesy, Agricultural Research Service, USDA)

OBJECTIVES—QUESTIONS
FOR INVESTIGATION

After completing the laboratory investigations and other activities contained in this chapter, you should be able to answer the following questions:

1. What are the effects of curing on fresh meats?

2. Why do cured meats develop a bright pink color when cooked?

3. What role does salt play in the curing process?

4. How do various curing agents work to preserve meats?

5. Why does cured meat have a longer shelf life, even with reduced or no refrigeration?

6. Why does moisture content and temperature affect the shelf life of meat products?

7. Why do meat products spoil?

LABORATORY INVESTIGATIONS

EXPERIMENT I.
THE EFFECTS OF SODIUM NITRITE
AND TEMPERATURE ON PORK CURING

Purpose

The purpose of this experiment is to examine the effects of sodium nitrite and temperature on fresh pork.

Materials

- four fresh pork chops, deboned and cut in half

- sodium nitrite (Note: Pure sodium nitrite is not recommended because very small amounts can be toxic. Obtain a 6.25% sodium nitrite mixture from local research lab, meat packer, or science supplier.)

- 100 grams table salt

- 36 grams brown sugar

- eight plastic containers with lids for the meat pieces
- knife, cutting board
- cooking equipment
- small containers to make curing mixes
- refrigerator thermometer (optional)
- balance
- refrigerator
- plastic gloves

Procedures

Prepare the eight pieces of pork. Each of the four different curing mixtures will be tested on two pieces of pork. Prepare the curing mixtures, each containing a different amount of sodium nitrite. Measure out four 25-gram units of salt and four 9-gram units of brown sugar. Then measure out .025 grams, .05 grams, .10 grams, and .20 grams of sodium nitrite (active ingredient). (Note: If the sodium nitrite mixture contains 6.25% sodium nitrite, then 3.2 grams of the sodium nitrite mixture will be needed to actually obtain .20 grams of sodium nitrite.)

Figure 23-5. The meat sample on the right, which was treated with sodium nitrite, shows color change after cooking.

First, mix the sodium nitrite and salt together for each of the four batches. Add the brown sugar to each batch and mix well. Using plastic gloves, rub each curing mixture over the surface of two pork pieces at the rate of 25 grams per pound of meat. Place each piece of pork in a separate plastic container and label as to the type of curing mixture it received. Place one set of the pork pieces in the refrigerator, and leave the other at room temperature. Measure and record the inside temperature of the refrigerator. After 24 hours remove the pork pieces from their containers and record your observations. Repeat 24 hours later. Cook each of the samples, one treatment set at a time, for about 20 minutes. Raising the temperature of the pork to 150° will stabilize the color development. Compare the appearance of each of the pork samples.

EXPERIMENT 2.
EFFECTS OF CURING INGREDIENTS
ON MEAT PRODUCTS

Purpose

The purpose of this experiment is to investigate the effects of sodium nitrite and salt on fresh ground beef.

Materials

- four pounds of ground beef
- table salt
- 6.25% sodium nitrite
- water
- food mixer
- oven
- scale
- four bread loaf pans
- cooking thermometer
- spatulas
- graduated cylinder
- plastic gloves

Procedures

Prepare four different batches of ground beef as shown below. (Note: 454 grams = 1 pound). Prepare the batches in the following order to prevent cross contamination: 4, 3, 2, 1.

	Batch Number			
Ingredients	1	2	3	4
Ground beef	454 g	454 g	454 g	454 g
Salt	9.1 g	0 g	9.1 g	0 g
Sodium nitrite mixture	1.1 g	1.1 g	0 g	0 g
Water	91 g	91 g	91 g	91 g

Combine the ingredients for each batch in a food mixer or food processor and mix thoroughly. Mix all batches an equal amount of time. Number and weigh each of the four pans. Place each batch in a separate baking pan and pat down firmly. Weigh and record. Allow the batches to equilibrate overnight in a refrigerator.

Bake in a 300-325°F oven until the internal temperature reaches 150°F (about 25 minutes). Record the weight of each pan after cooking. Drain excess fluids from each pan and record their volume. Weigh each pan again. Calculate the product yield of each batch using the following formula:

$$\text{Product yield (\%)} = \frac{\text{(cooked batch less pan weight)}}{\text{(raw batch less pan weight)}} \times 100$$

SCIENCE CONNECTIONS

Food deterioration is a broad term that includes a reduction in nutrition, safety, or aesthetic appeal of food. Heat, cold, light, oxygen, moisture, dryness, natural food enzymes, microorganisms, macroorganisms, industrial contaminants, and time can lead to food deterioration. Meat curing and processing techniques are used to prevent and/or slow down food deterioration.

Microorganisms (bacteria, yeasts, and molds) are frequently the cause of food deterioration. Microorganisms are found in the soil, water, air, and on the exterior surface of practically anything that has not been sterilized. These microorganisms generally prefer moist, warm conditions. *Salmonella*, a bacterium of particular concern in meat and other food products, is killed by heat. Since beef products are sometimes not well cooked, *Salmonella* represents a significant health concern. Organic acids and high-pressure washers are being used to remove microbes from the surface of a carcass before it is processed into wholesale and retail cuts. An increase in acid concentration or temperature is associated with a decrease in microbe survival.

TENDERNESS AND LEANNESS

The presence of certain *muscle proteins* has much to do with meat *tenderness*. Parallel muscle fibers contain small, thread-like tissues called *fibrils*. *Myofibrillar protein* is muscle protein that contains fibrils, which are capable of contracting. This shortened muscle will be tough when cooked. Unfortunately, the myofibrillar protein content of a cut of meat cannot be visually determined. Thus, it is not possible to judge the tenderness or tastiness of fresh meat by appearance.

Animal tissues contain *enzymes*, which largely survive slaughter. *Calpains* are one group of enzymes that cause muscle to deteriorate, and therefore, become more tender. Calpains are calcium-dependent *proteases* (enzymes that break down protein). Injecting a carcass with calcium chloride activates the calpain enzymes, causing the meat to become more tender. Since calpains break down while muscle is degrading, overtenderness in the meat is not

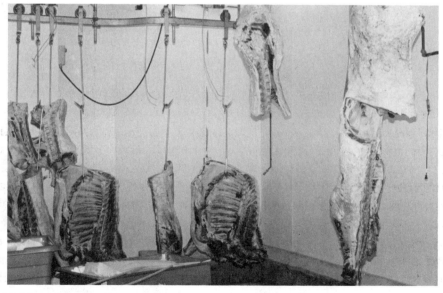

Figure 23-6. Refrigeration is used to reduce food deterioration and increase tenderness.

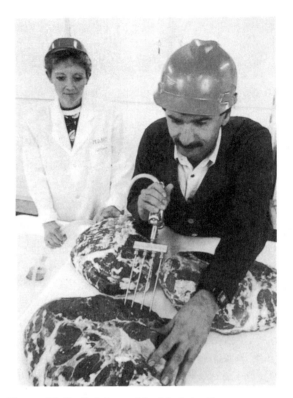

Figure 23-7. Calcium chloride injections can produce a tender product in just one day, compared to the usual refrigerated aging of 7 to 14 days. (Courtesy, Agricultural Research Service, USDA)

a problem. Many fresh meat products are *aged* under refrigeration to make them become more tender. Tenderizing effects occur because refrigeration causes a buildup of *calcium* in the meat, which in turn activates the calpains and tenderizes the meat.

Several techniques are under development which will aid in determining the quality of meat products, even before an animal is slaughtered. *Ultrasound imaging* uses high frequency sound waves to measure fat and lean in live animals and carcasses. This procedure is 80% accurate and does not require that the skin be penetrated. A similar procedure is the *optical probe* technique, which estimates the percent of lean in a carcass. A probe is inserted in the loin of the carcass, and the depth of muscle and backfat is measured as the probe is withdrawn. These technologies are based on the fact that fat and lean tissues reflect light and sound differently.

Video image analysis involves the use of digital television to collect data on live animal or carcass measurements. A computer is then used to calculate lean meat areas. *Electromagnetic scanning* is a fourth technique for estimating the lean and fat tissues. Using this technique, a carcass is passed through an electromagnetic field, and a computer predicts the amount of lean (with 90% accuracy). The readings are based on the different degree to which fat and lean conduct electricity.

The *water content* of meat products has a major effect on taste and tenderness. Water constitutes about 60% of the weight of fresh meat. There

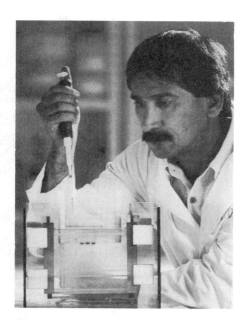

Figure 23-8. Separating meat muscle proteins to study meat tenderness. (Courtesy, Agricultural Research Service, USDA)

is a constant relationship of 3.7 to 1 between the water and protein content of meat. Protein binds with water in animal cells because of a polar attraction between the two molecules. When an animal is slaughtered, the muscle's ability to retain water is reduced, due largely to a drop in pH. The lowered pH is due to the accumulation of *lactic acid* in the muscle tissue. Lactic acid, a product of *glycogen metabolism*, becomes concentrated in the muscle because the circulatory system can no longer remove it. Thus, water loss can be slowed by reducing lactic acid production in the muscle tissues. This is commonly done by lowering temperature. Additives, such as salt and phosphate, are also used to promote water retention. These compounds neutralize *cations* and allow water molecules to more easily attach to protein.

CURING PROCESSES

A traditional red color is associated with cured meat products, such as ham, bacon, bologna, and hot dogs. The color of meat, both before and after curing, depends upon the amount of the muscle pigment *myoglobin* contained in the muscle tissues. The common ingredients used in commercial curing solutions include salt, nitrite, phosphates, sodium erythorbate, sugar, and starch. The *curing* (pickling) solution is pumped into the meat

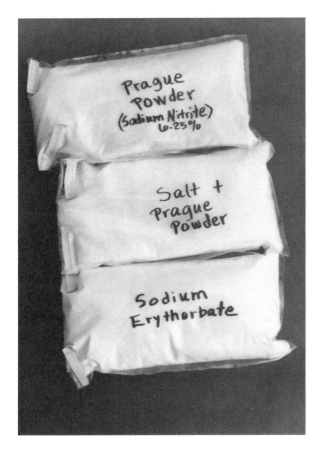

Figure 23-9. Sodium nitrite and sodium erythorbate are primary agents used in curing meat products.

muscle using closely spaced, small diameter needles. This ensures uniform curing throughout with minimal damage to the meat tissue.

Sodium nitrite is the curing agent responsible for the color change in cured meats. Sodium nitrite reacts with the myoglobin pigment in muscle to form *nitric oxide myoglobin*, giving the meat a dark red color. When the meat product is cooked, the nitric oxide myoglobin is denatured to form *nitrosyl hemochrome*, which gives a bright pink color to the meat. If sodium nitrite has not been added to the meat before cooking (e.g., ground beef), the meat turns brown because the myoglobin denatures. Most cured meat products in the grocery store are pre-cooked during processing and will thus show a bright pink color. Celery contains nitrite and thus, will also cause a color change in cooked meats. Sodium nitrite also reduces *microbial spoilage* and enhances flavor by preventing *fat oxidation*.

Salt in the curing mixture provides flavor and preserves the meat. Salt also helps to tenderize meat by extracting myofibrillar protein. As a pre-

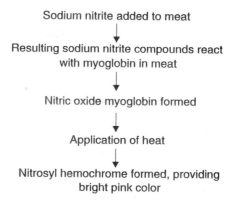

Figure 23-10. How cured meats develop their characteristic pink color.

servative, salt lowers the *availability of water* to the point where microbial activity is minimized or stopped. Salt also causes *plasmolysis* (dehydration) of microbial cells, a reduction in oxygen supplies needed by microbes, and greater sensitivity of microbes to carbon dioxide. Salt helps to preserve meat by interfering with the action of *proteolytic enzymes.*

Some curing mixtures are dry-rubbed onto the meat surface (e.g., sugar cured hams). The dry mix is first *absorbed* into the normal moisture of the meat. The curing agents then permeate throughout the meat by *osmosis.* Wood smoke also has a curing effect on meats by enhancing flavor and creating a pink color. The acidic compounds contained in wood smoke are responsible for these curing effects. Smoke has a *bacteriostatic* effect on meats and reduces microbial growth by its drying action.

Erythorbate stabilizes the color development in cured meats, reduces fat oxidation, and inhibits undesirable nitrite reactions. *Phosphates* improve color development, inhibit fat oxidation, and promote myofibrillar protein extraction. *Sugar* and seasonings are primarily used for flavor, although dissolved sugar reduces water availability and the growth of microorganisms.

The *color stability* of fresh meats is largely dependent upon storage temperature, packaging environment, and oxygen. Higher temperatures accelerate discoloration (from red to brown in beef). When fresh meats are exposed to high concentrations of oxygen, myoglobin is converted to the bright red *oxymyoglobin.* However, when oxygen concentrations are low, myoglobin combines with oxygen to form *metmyoglobin*, which is brown in color. This is why fresh, packaged meat usually turns brown from the center outward. Different meats exhibit different rates of metmyoglobin formation.

Figure 23-11. Sugar and salt are everyday products that have dramatic curing effects on meat.

CHAPTER SUMMARY

Meat curing and processing are a huge part of the process of providing desirable, safe food products to consumers. Meat curing and processing techniques have resulted in a tremendous variety of tasty meat products at comparatively low costs. In addition, these techniques have dramatically increased the storage life and availability of meat products. Today's health-conscious consumers prefer lean, tender, and flavorful meat products. Producers have responded with leaner market animals, and processors have responded with healthier products. A number of new techniques are being tested which will enable producers and processors to identify animals that carry more lean. Tenderness is a major concern in the meat industry. Refrigeration is used to promote tenderness by activating enzymes that break down proteins in the meat muscle. Cheaper, faster processes that simulate this effect are being developed.

Muscle tenderness is largely determined by the presence of certain types of protein. Curing and processing techniques improve meat tenderness by extracting some of these proteins. Water content of the meat also directly affects tenderness. A number of curing agents are commercially used to enhance flavor, color, and storage life of meat products. These agents reduce fat oxidation, decrease water availability, and function in other ways to improve meat quality. The characteristic pink color of cooked, cured meats is caused by sodium nitrite reactions with muscle pigment.

FURTHER LABORATORY INVESTIGATIONS

1. Compare the effects of various curing mixtures on fresh meats. Premixed meat cures sold in stores can be compared against the mixtures used for the two experiments contained in this chapter.

2. Instead of using sodium nitrite, add chopped celery to a batch of fresh ground beef. Allow to equilibrate overnight. Cook and observe the results.

3. Compare the amount of water contained in various brands of hot dogs. Cut one hot dog of each brand to be tested into small pieces. Place each cut hot dog in a preweighed dish and weigh. Place each dish in a 200°F oven for about 24 hours. Remove and weigh each dish. Calculate the difference in weight of each hot dog before and after cooking. What percent water does each contain?

4. Test the effects of salt and phosphate on water retention in meat. Treatments could include salt only, salt and phosphate, and neither. For the control, add 10 milliliters of water to 100 grams of ground beef and cook in a beaker at 65°C until brown. Drain the liquid from the cooked beef. Weigh the cooked beef and calculate product yield. For the salt treatment add 2.5 grams of table salt to the beef/water mixture and stir before cooking. After cooking, drain fluids and record the weight of the cooked beef. For the salt/phosphate treatment, add 2 grams salt and .5 grams sodium tripolyphosphate before cooking. Compare the product yields of each of the three groups.

5. Test the preservative effects of salt by covering some fresh fish samples with salt, placing in a reclosable plastic bag, and storing at room temperature. Compare with fish samples with no salt added.

Chapter 24

BACTERIA IN MILK

What's the Count?

AGRICULTURAL APPLICATIONS

Milk is one of our most important and nutritious foods. The number of dairy cows on U.S. farms has declined by nearly 60% in the last 50 years, while the average pounds of milk produced per cow has more than doubled. Not only have dairy producers greatly increased production in their herds, they have also made major advances in improving milk quality. Grade A herds (those that produce milk used for drinking) are frequently

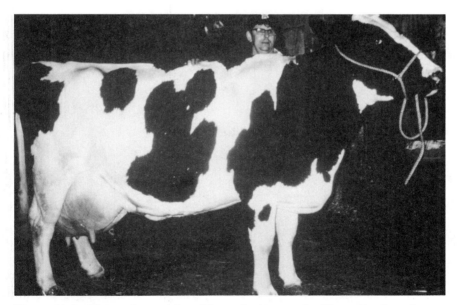

Figure 24-1. Major advances in milk production and milk quality have been made in the dairy industry.

inspected to ensure that proper sanitation practices are being followed. Standards for Grade A herds are enforced by the Food and Drug Administration.

Modern milking operations consist of a milking machine and a pipeline to transport milk to a refrigerated, bulk tank where the milk is cooled and temporarily stored. Immediate and continuous refrigeration of milk at about 40°F is essential to preserving its quality. Within a few days raw (fresh) milk is transported by refrigerated truck to a processing plant, where it is pasteurized. Strict sanitation and health standards apply at both the farm and the processing plant. Pasteurized milk can often be stored up to 14 days at 45°F before spoilage.

Mastitis is a disease of major concern to the dairy industry and the most common udder problem in dairy cows. Mastitis is a highly contagious disease that is estimated to affect 40-50% of all U.S. dairy cows in at least one quarter of their udder. An Ohio study estimated that mastitis infections annually cost producers $40 per cow in the herd ($4,000 for a 100-cow herd). Mastitis decreases milk production by as much as 20% and shortens the productive life of the cow. Infected milk must be discarded until the mastitis infection clears up. Several tests are used to detect mastitis. These include the California Mastitis Test, which is a quick, easy test that provides immediate results on mastitis infection. In addition, a strip cup is used to

TERMS

agar plate method	epithelial cells	raw milk
ammonia products	heritability estimate	refrigeration
bacillus	immune system	repeatability estimate
bactericide	keratin	somatic cell count
bone marrow	lactobacillus	(SCC)
California Mastitis Test	lactose	somatic cells
(CMT)	leukocytes	sour
chemical environment	mammary gland	streptococcus
clinical mastitis	mastitis	subclinical mastitis
coagulates	milk quality	teat canal
coliform bacteria	pasteurization	udder
direct microscopic	perishable	water
count method	putrefaction	
enzymatic action		

Figure 24-2. Improved sanitation and processing techniques have increased the shelf life of many dairy products. (Courtesy, Illinois Dept. of Agriculture)

collect the first milk during a milking and screen for the presence of mastitis.

Laboratory tests are also used to monitor and diagnose mastitis in dairy herds. The Somatic Cell Count (SCC) (also called the Somatic Cell Score) is a standard measure of the microbial quality of milk. Effective in July 1993, the legal SCC standard is 750,000 somatic cells per milliliter. However, producers attempt to keep their SCC around 300,000 or below. Monthly SCC reports are available through DHIA (Dairy Herd Improvement Association), processing plants, and private laboratories. Other lab tests for mastitis include standard plate (bacteria) counts (goal is less than 25,000/ml) and preliminary incubation (PI) counts (goal is less than 20,000/ml).

Since mastitis infections are a heritable trait (25%), some bulls are now ranked on their daughter's susceptibility to mastitis. Producers use this score along with other traits to select bulls for artificial breeding. Scientists have discovered that the genes responsible for high milk production are also responsible for a higher somatic cell count. Thus, as milk production increases, SCC also increases. Researchers are testing the effects of injecting a natural protein on the cow's ability to resist mastitis infections.

The incidence of mastitis increases with improper care and treatment

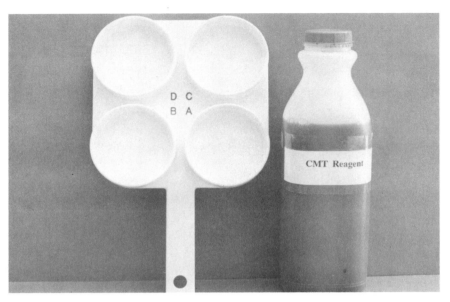

Figure 24-3. The California Mastitis Test.

of cows, over-milking, poor milking procedures, worn or improperly adjusted milking equipment, poor housing, and udder injury. Producers use many management practices to combat mastitis. Still, some mastitis infec-

Figure 24-4. Some bulls are now ranked on their daughters' susceptibility to
           mastitis.

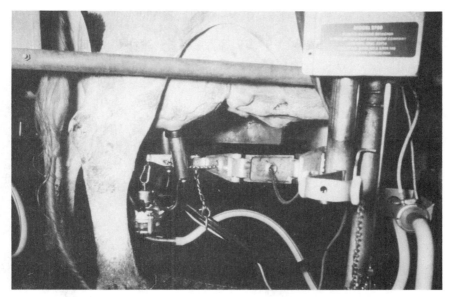

Figure 24-5. Proper milking techniques help to lower microbial populations in milk. (Courtesy, Illinois Dept. of Agriculture)

tions occur, regardless of the preventative strategies in place. Common practices include washing the udder before milking, dipping teats after milking in an antibacterial solution, cleaning milking equipment thoroughly, using correct milking procedures, treating infections promptly, separating infected animals, and culling animals with persistent mastitis. Completely milking out the udder also helps to reduce mastitis.

Providing clean, dry bedding and removing objects that might cause udder injury are important prevention strategies. A new practice involves the use of rubber-filled mats in stall barns. Antibiotic treatments are commonly used to fight more serious mastitis infections. In most cases an antibiotic is administered by inserting a treatment tube into the teat canal. An intramuscular injection may also be given in severe cases. Antibiotic treatment requires a specified withdrawal period during which the milk must be discarded.

OBJECTIVES—QUESTIONS FOR INVESTIGATION

After completing the laboratory activities contained in this chapter, you should be able to answer the following questions:

1. Why do bacteria grow well in milk?

2. How do bacteria get into milk?

3. What effect does pasteurization have on bacteria in milk?

4. Why are antibiotics effective in treating mastitis?

5. What bacteria are responsible for milk spoilage?

6. Why do milking procedures and injury affect the incidence of mastitis?

7. How do field and laboratory tests assess mastitis infections and milk spoilage?

8. Why does a high somatic cell count indicate mastitis?

9. Why is milk held under constant refrigeration?

LABORATORY INVESTIGATIONS

EXPERIMENT I.
EFFECTS OF STORAGE TEMPERATURE
AND MILK FAT ON BACTERIAL GROWTH
IN PASTEURIZED MILK

Purpose

The purpose of this experiment is to determine the effects of temperature and milk fat on milk quality and to illustrate the succession of bacterial growth in milk.

Materials

- 375 ml whole pasteurized milk
- 125 ml each of other milk products (skim milk, chocolate milk, buttermilk, etc.)
- nutrient agar
- pH paper
- compound microscope
- bacterial stain (crystal violet or methylene blue)

- inoculating loop
- graph paper
- petri dishes
- 250 ml beakers
- 25 ml Erlenmeyer flasks
- microscope slides

Procedures

The following levels of the independent variables can be used: whole milk at room temperature (25°C); whole milk at refrigerator temperature (4°C); whole milk boiled and then cooled to room temperature; and skim milk, buttermilk, and chocolate milk at room temperature. Place 125 ml of each milk type in an Erlenmeyer flask. Following the directions provided by the agar manufacturer, prepare one nutrient agar plate for each milk sample to be tested.

Use an inoculating loop to transfer some milk to petri dishes containing agar. Prepare one isolation streak plate for each sample. To do this, flame an inoculating loop and touch the agar to cool. Place the loop into a milk sample and remove. Open the petri dish slightly and touch the loop to the agar. Use a zigzag motion to spread the inoculum across one quadrant of the petri dish. Flame the loop again. Carry the inoculum to an adjacent quadrant but at a right angle to the first. Spread in quadrant two using a zigzag motion (see illustration). Repeat this procedure for quadrants three and four. Be sure to flame the inoculating loop between quadrants to prevent contamination from the air. Use this technique to prepare a streak plate for each milk sample. Place petri dishes for each sample at the same temperature as the milk sample.

Use a simple stain to help identify bacteria shapes. Use the following steps to perform a simple stain: (1) place a drop of distilled water on a clean slide; (2) use a flamed

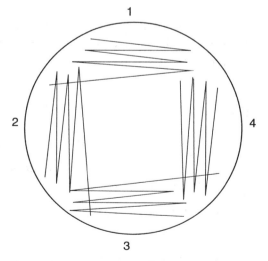

Figure 24-6. Isolation streaking technique for inoculating agar plates.

loop to place a small amount of the sample on the slide; (3) mix the sample with the water and allow to air dry; (4) heat fix the slide (smear side up) by passing it three times over the a flame; (5) let the slide cool; (6) flood the slide with bacterial stain and let stand for two minutes; (7) rinse the slide with tap water and blot dry (be careful not to rinse away the smear); (8) observe under an oil immersion lens microscope.

Record daily observations of temperature, pH, odor, color, and bacterial growth on agar plates. Count the number of colonies growing in the petri dishes. Pay particular attention to physical changes in the milk and record your observations. Continue your observations for 10-14 days. At the end of the experiment graph the pH data.

EXPERIMENT 2.
RELATIONSHIP BETWEEN MILK STORAGE TIME
AND ACIDITY

Purpose

The purpose of this experiment is to investigate factors which cause milk to sour. Specifically, the relationship between storage time and acidity will be investigated.

Materials

- cartons of refrigerated milk with different expiration dates
- refrigerator
- 125 ml flask (one for each sample)
- phenolphthalein color indicator, 1% alcohol solution
- sodium hydroxide, 0.1 N
- 50 ml burette with stand

Procedures

The following procedures for the titratable acidity test are recommended by the American Dairy Science Association: (1) place burette in stand and fill with 0.1 N sodium hydroxide; (2) place exactly 9 milliliters of the milk sample to be tested in a 125 milliliter flask; (3) add three or four drops of the phenolphthalein color indicator; (4) slowly add the sodium hydroxide a drop at a time while swirling the flask. Continue adding NaOH until a pink color remains for 30 seconds after swirling. Read the burette to the closest 0.1 milliliter, and multiply by 0.1 to get the percent lactic acid.

Repeat this procedure for each milk sample to be tested. Calculate and record the percent acidity for each sample.

SCIENCE CONNECTIONS

Milk contains mostly water (87%), along with proteins, fat, lactose, minerals, and microorganisms. The 13% *total solids* includes fat and solids-not-fat. Whole milk contains 3.3% fat, whereas skim milk contains 0.2% fat. *Milk composition* varies by species and breed, feed, stage of lactation, health and age of animal, season, and environmental conditions.

Dairy products are very *perishable* because they provide essentially all the conditions and nutrients necessary for microbial growth. Milk is free of *microorganisms* when it is in the udder. However, microorganisms get in milk as it passes through the *teat canal* and milking equipment. A high number of microorganisms in *raw milk* suggests sanitation or cooling problems. High microbial populations in pasteurized milk suggest *contamination* during processing or inadequate cooling. The keeping quality of milk is largely a function of the sanitation procedures used at the processing plant between pasteurization and the closing of milk containers. *Refrigeration* drastically

Figure 24-7. **Milk is relatively rich in major nutrients.**

reduces microbial growth in milk, but some *bacteria* (psychrophilic) grow well at refrigerator temperatures.

PASTEURIZATION AND QUALITY TESTING

Pasteurization is a heat treatment performed at the processing plant which destroys harmful bacteria without affecting the quality of the milk. Milk may be pasteurized using a low heat method (63°C for 30 minutes) or a high heat method (72°C for 15 seconds). Pasteurization does not kill all bacteria contained in raw milk, but it does kill those *pathogens* that may cause disease. Bacteria that remain after pasteurization eventually cause milk to *sour* (spoil). Pasteurization inactivates enzymes and destroys yeasts, molds, and pathogenic and most other bacteria. *Coliform bacteria* do not survive pasteurization.

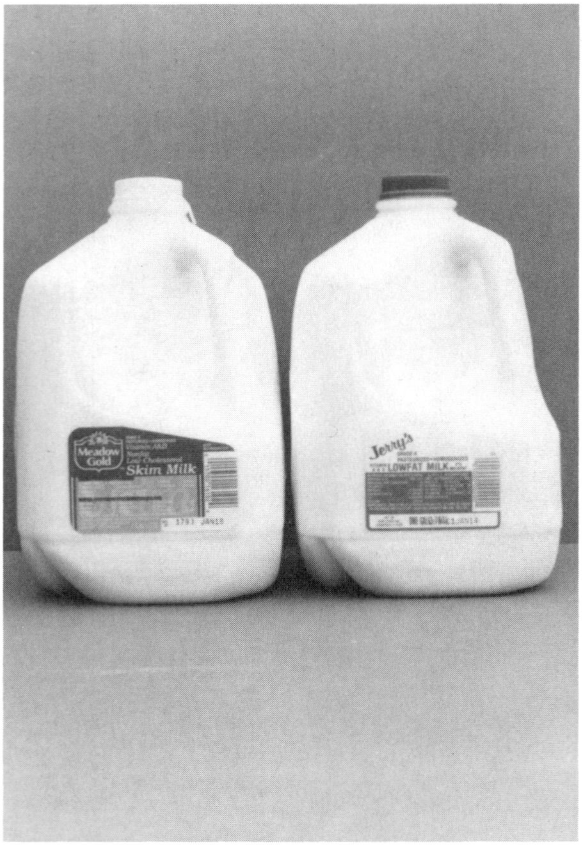

Bacterial populations in milk are a direct indication of *milk quality*. Processing plants and laboratories primarily use two methods to determine milk quality. These techniques are used to estimate the concentration of microorganisms in raw and pasteurized milk. The *agar plate method* requires adding 0.1 ml of a milk sample to a sterile petri dish, mixing the nutrient medium with the sample, and letting solidify. The sample is then incubated for 48 hours at 32°C. Bacterial colonies are then counted and expressed for a 1 milliliter sample. Several variations in the agar plate method are used to determine the keeping quality of milk.

A second technique to assess microbial quality is the *direct microscopic count*

Figure 24-8. Pasteurized milk still contains microorganisms that will eventually lead to spoilage.

method. This procedure detects viable and dead microorganisms. To perform, spread 0.01 milliliter of sample over a 1 square centimeter area of a microscope slide and allow to dry. Stain with methylene blue and view under a microscope. Count the number of cells and clumps of cells in the microscopic field and express as the number of organisms per milliliter of milk sample.

BACTERIAL GROWTH IN MILK

In both pasteurized and raw milk, various microorganisms succeed one another as the *chemical environment* of the milk changes. The microbes themselves bring about these changes. The stages of microbial growth are *Streptococcus*, then *Lactobacillus*, then yeasts and molds, and finally *Bacillus*.

Streptococci convert the milk sugar (*lactose*) to *lactic acid*. The *acidity* of the milk increases to the point where further streptococci growth is inhibited. Lactobacilli then begin to grow and convert the remaining lactose into lactic acid. *Acidity* increases further until lactobacilli growth is suppressed. The lactic acid sours the milk and curdles (*coagulates*) the milk protein. Yeasts and molds grow well in this acid environment, and they

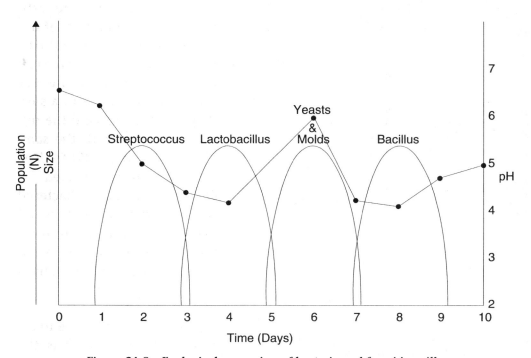

Figure 24-9. Ecological succession of bacteria and fungi in milk.

convert acid into non-acid products. Finally, bacilli multiply in the environment where protein is the only nutrient available.

Bacilli convert protein into *ammonia products*, and the *pH* rises. These bacteria also digest the remaining protein through *enzymatic action*. The odor of spoiled milk becomes apparent once this has happened. Microbial activity causes changes in the pH of the milk. Fluctuations in pH are due to *fermentation* and *putrefaction* (decomposition) processes.

Many factors affect the *titratable (lactic) acid* content of milk. These include percent milk solids, stage of lactation, milk temperature, and age of milk. Milk with 0.2% or less titratable acidity is acceptable. An acid odor and flavor is noticeable when the titratable acidity reaches 0.25% and 0.3%, respectively.

MASTITIS

Mastitis is an inflammation of the *mammary gland* and is usually associated with an *infection*. Mastitis is of most concern in dairy cattle, but it can be a problem in all domesticated animals. Symptoms of mastitis include flakes or clots in the milk, sometimes accompanied by color changes. The affected *quarter(s)* of the *udder* are often swollen and tender. *Subclinical*

Figure 24-10. Mastitis is usually associated with an infection in one or more quarters of the udder.

mastitis may go unnoticed, but the symptoms of *clinical mastitis* are much more obvious.

Streptococcus agalactiae, which lives in milk and mammary tissues, and *staphylococcus aureus*, which lives in the tissues of infected udders, account for 90-95% of subclinical mastitis cases. *S. aureus* bacteria are more difficult to eliminate because they can become walled off in tissues. *S. aureus* infections often become chronic. On the other hand, *S. agalactiae* bacteria respond well to *antibiotic* treatments. Mastitis infections either clear up, become chronic, or in severe cases, cause death.

Since mastitis is usually associated with an infection of the mammary gland, the cow's *immune system* responds by producing more *leukocytes* to fight the infection. Other changes include an increase in *tissue* (epithelial) *cells*, lipase, sodium, chloride, and pathogenic bacteria; and a decrease in casein, lactose, and fat.

As the mastitis infection strengthens, *epithelial cells* from the lining of the teat canal become more numerous in the milk. The most basic standard for monitoring mastitis in a dairy herd is the somatic cell count. *Somatic cells* are any body cell other than germ (reproductive) cells. *Somatic cell count (SCC)* is a laboratory test that indicates the presence and severity of mastitis. The number of somatic cells present in milk is directly proportional to the degree of inflammation and destruction of secretory tissue. An SCC of more than 750,000 is considered abnormal. The *California Mastitis Test*

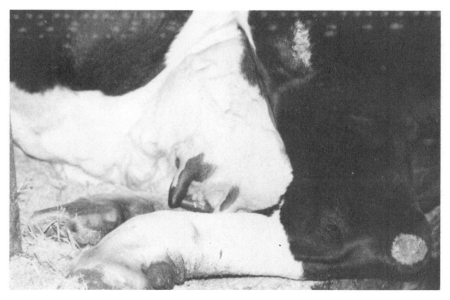

Figure 24-11. Stress and many environmental factors affect the incidence of mastitis.

(CMT) is a field test that estimates the extent of infection. High concentrations of leukocytes and/or epithelial cells in the milk cause the CMT reagent to gel.

The occurrence of mastitis is due in part to *stress*, such as calving. Stress causes the brain to stimulate release of a *pituitary hormone*, which in turn causes the *adrenal gland* to secret *glucocortoids*. Too many glucocortoids in the blood can weaken an animal's immune system. Natural protein injections now being tested have reduced the incidence of mastitis by stimulating the *bone marrow* to produce more *white blood cells*.

Injury is a major cause of mastitis. Physical trauma to the teat and/or udder may result in an infection of the mammary gland. The shape and position of the udder affect its susceptibility to injury. Housing conditions, milking procedures, and other management practices also have a significant impact on mastitis cases. High or low vacuum on the milking equipment can cause teat damage and increase the opportunity for bacteria to enter the udder. The teat canal produces a substance called *keratin*, which acts as a *bactericide* and helps to seal the teat opening. Studies have shown that it takes about one hour for the teat opening to close after milking.

Coliform are bacteria that live in manure and on wood. Keeping housing areas clean reduces the chances of bacteria entering the teat canal. Mastitis has a *heritability estimate* of 25% and a *repeatability estimate* of 35-40%.

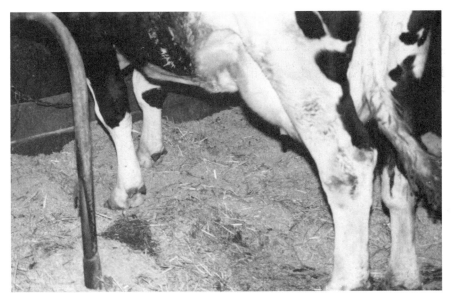

Figure 24-12. Clean housing areas that eliminate causes of potential injury are important in reducing mastitis.

CHAPTER SUMMARY

Over the past several decades, milk production and quality have improved at a remarkable rate. Sanitation, processing, and handling strategies have resulted in a variety of milk products that have wide appeal to consumers. Refrigeration and pasteurization have transformed the dairy production, marketing, and processing industries.

Microbial populations in both raw and pasteurized milk are the major factors affecting milk quality. For the producer, controlling microbial populations in raw milk involves a multitude of management practices. Mastitis is usually an indication of an infection in the mammary gland. This costly, common disease requires producers to continuously monitor, treat, and control mastitis. Several field techniques, including the California Mastitis Test, are used to detect mastitis. Several laboratory techniques are used by the industry to monitor the quality of milk samples. The somatic cell count (SCC) is the standard approach for determining the presence and severity of mastitis in a herd.

The keeping quality of milk varies by composition, storage temperature, age, and other factors. Bacteria are present in both raw and pasteurized milk. Successive growth of various microorganisms occurs as the pH of the milk changes due to microbial action. The development of lactic acid by these microorganisms eventually leads to milk spoilage.

FURTHER LABORATORY INVESTIGATIONS

1. Compare the spoilage rate and bacterial growth in milk samples of varying fat content, such as 2%, whipping cream, and half and half.

2. Compare pasteurized and unpasteurized milk samples with regard to bacterial populations during a 14-day period. Compare refrigerated and non-refrigerated samples.

3. Perform a titratable acidity test on raw milk samples and compare your results with tests run on pasteurized samples. Also compare older milk with fresher milk samples.

4. Use the California Mastitis Test to screen cows for mastitis. Follow this test with bacterial cultures on agar plates. Inoculate plates with milk from cows diagnosed with mastitis.

5. Perform a Gram stain to identify bacteria as Gram-positive or Gram-negative. Repeat the first seven steps as outlined in Experiment 1. Then flood the slide with Gram's iodine solution for one minute. Rinse with tap water. Add 95% ethyl alcohol one drop at a time until the material running off the slide is colorless. Rinse with tap water. Flood the slide with safranin for 60 seconds. Rinse with tap water and blot dry. Observe with an oil immersion lens.

Chapter 25

MAKING YOGURT AND CHEESE

When Bad Guys Do Good Things

AGRICULTURAL APPLICATIONS

Milk produced on U.S. farms today is manufactured into a wide variety of dairy foods. Microbiology, biochemistry, food engineering, and related fields are the backbone of the dairy manufacturing industry. New processing techniques, such as ultrafiltration of milk, have improved the quality and diversity of dairy products.

Cheese making is an effective food preservation method that has been

Figure 25-1. A wide variety of high-quality dairy products is available for today's consumers.

used for centuries. Over 400 types of cheese are manufactured in the United States. Cheese consumption continues to rise annually, with about 12 million tons produced per year. Projected sales of cheese in 1997 are $17.6 billion. Cheeses are classified by the coagulating agent used, texture, and simply as fresh or ripened. Curing is a major cost in cheese production, taking up to one year for certain types of cheese. However, researchers have found that adding microencapsulated enzymes during cheese making can cut the curing time in half.

Processing plants add bacteria or mold to pasteurized milk during the cheese-making process to create a wide variety of cheese products. The specific cheese product manufactured is determined by the emphasis given to each individual step in the cheese-making process. Approximately 30% of all milk produced in the United States is used to make cheese. The protein contained in milk is of very high quality, which makes cheese and other dairy products excellent food products from a nutritional standpoint. About 10 pounds of whole milk and over 6 pounds of skim milk, respectively, are required to make hard cheese and cottage cheese.

Scientists have developed the technology that allows frozen and freeze-dried starter bacteria cultures to be used in cheese making. In addition, new genetic engineering techniques for producing anaerobic bacteria are destined to change the way in which bacteria cultures are made available for use in the dairy processing industry.

Yogurt is the fastest growing segment of the dairy industry. Yogurt is

TERMS

anaerobic respiration	frozen yogurt	rennet
bacteriophage	gel matrix	ripened
casein	hydrolyze	solids-not-fat (SNF)
cheese	isoelectric point	spoilage microorganism
coagulation	lactic acid bacteria	starter culture
culture	microencapsulated	sundae-style yogurt
curd	enzyme	Swiss-style yogurt
curdle	microflora	titratable acidity
digestive tract	mycelia	whey
food-borne pathogen	Penicillium	yogurt
fresh	proteolytic enzyme	

Figure 25-2. Over 400 types of cheeses are manufactured in the United States.

Figure 25-3. Yogurt sales are increasing faster than sales of any other dairy product.

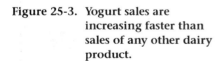

produced by adding bacteria to milk and allowing fermentation processes to take place. Major steps used in manufacturing yogurt include (1) ingredient selection and screening, (2) blending of ingredients, (3) homogenization, (4) heat treatment, (5) culture inoculation, (6) fermentation, (7) packaging, and (8) distribution.

Yogurt can be classified into two major styles: pre-stirred or pre-blended (Swiss style) and fruit on the bottom (sundae style). Quality control in dairy processing plants is critical for the development of high-quality dairy products. Monitoring the major manufacturing steps allows most quality problems to be controlled. Yogurt quality is based upon color and appearance, body and texture, and flavor. Milk used in yogurt and cheese production must be free of antibiotics, sanitizers, and other bactericides.

There is some evidence that yogurt has a therapeutic quality, due to the addition of *L. acidophilus* and other bacteria during the manufacturing process. These bacteria exert beneficial effects in the gastrointestinal tract. Yogurt can also be eaten by those allergic to lactose, since bacteria in yogurt help to improve digestion of this milk-based product.

OBJECTIVES—QUESTIONS FOR INVESTIGATION

After conducting the following experiments and completing other activities provided by your teacher, you should be able to answer the following questions:

1. How are yogurt and cheese made?

2. Why are bacteria and molds added when making yogurt and some cheeses?

3. Why aren't added microorganisms harmful when yogurt and cheese are eaten?

4. What causes milk to curdle?

5. Why does yogurt have a sour taste?

6. What causes yogurt to have a gel-like texture?

7. What effect does temperature have on the yogurt-making process?

8. Why are many cheeses aged before eating?

LABORATORY INVESTIGATIONS

EXPERIMENT I.
MAKING YOGURT

Purpose

The purpose of this experiment is to explore the process of making yogurt and consider the role of bacteria in making yogurt and similar dairy products.

Materials

- two half-pint cartons of whole milk
- 1,000 ml beaker
- ring stand (optional)
- powdered milk
- heat source (hot plate, Bunsen burner, etc.)
- thermometer (0°-100°C)
- starter yogurt culture (any non-flavored yogurt available at grocery stores)
- incubator
- refrigerator

Procedures

Let 2-4 tablespoons (30-60 milliliters) of prepared yogurt stand at room temperature for 2-3 hours. Pour the two half-pint cartons of milk into the beaker. Place the beaker in a ring stand or on a hot plate. Add 22 grams of powdered milk to the beaker and stir. Heat to 96°C (204.8°F), stirring constantly. Do not allow the milk to boil. (A double boiler will prevent rapid fluctuations in the temperature of the milk mixture.)

Remove the milk from the heat and allow to cool to 46°C. Continue to stir as the milk cools. Add 5 milliliters of the starter yogurt culture to one of the empty milk cartons and 10 milliliters of the starter culture to the other. Pour 500 milliliters of the cooled milk into each carton and staple shut. Label each carton. Place the cartons in an incubator at 39°C (102.2°F) for six to eight hours until the milk coagulates. Place the cartons in the refrigerator and cool to 10°C. After the yogurt is cooled, note the texture and odor of the products and compare.

EXPERIMENT 2. MAKING CHEESE

Purpose

The purpose of the experiment is to explore the process of cheese making and examine the action of enzymes on milk samples.

Materials

- A commercially available cheese making kit (Nasco and other suppliers) is a good way to explore cheese making. In general, such kits will contain nearly all that is needed to make cheese. Common kit ingredients include:

    nonfat dry milk

    viable lactobacilli bacteria

    insulated containers (styrofoam cups)

    sodium chloride

    milk clotting enzyme (rennet or similar enzyme)

    stirring rods

    cheesecloth

- thermometer
- incubator or oven
- plastic wrap
- two-quart container for heating milk

Procedures

Mix the nonfat dry milk with water as directed on the package. Use one two-quart container for each batch of nonfat milk. Add lactobacilli bacteria as directed and stir well. Heat the milk to 86°-94°F, and then allow the milk to ferment (4 to 24 hours). This can be done by filling the

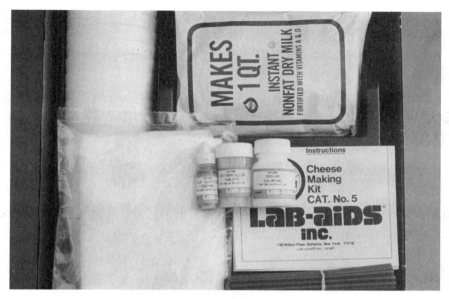

Figure 25-4. Cheese making kit.

insulated containers and placing them in an incubator set at 34°F. Label the containers with students' names and let them sit at the incubated temperature overnight.

After incubation, add ¼ teaspoon of salt (NaCl) to each container. Add a clotting enzyme (rennet) and stir until curds appear. Let the mixture stand for about 15 minutes. Use a stirring rod to break up the curd. Strain the whey from the cheese by filtering the mixture through a double layer of cheesecloth. Place the cheese in aluminum foil and gently squeeze out extra liquid. Wrap the cheese in plastic wrap and allow it to ripen for several weeks (up to three months). Repeat these procedures using whole milk and compare the results.

SCIENCE CONNECTIONS

Yogurt and cheese are examples of dairy products which are produced by the action of bacterial and fungal *cultures*. These microorganisms cause milk to undergo *fermentation* via enzymatic action. *Starter cultures* ferment *lactose* (milk sugar) to *lactic acid* and other products. Lactic cultures are non-spore-forming bacteria. A variety of starter cultures is used in making yogurt and cheese. These lactic acid-producing bacteria include *streptococci*, *lactobacilli*, and others. *Molds* are also used in conjunction with these bacteria to produce special cheeses, such as Swiss cheese and blue cheese.

Figure 25-5. Cultured dairy products are nutritious, and they also make other nutrients more available in the body.

Lactic acid bacteria are harmless, except at very high populations, and offer many beneficial effects. They destroy or inhibit *food-borne pathogens* and *spoilage microorganisms* by lowering the pH of the food products. These bacteria improve the flavor and texture of many dairy products. Lactic acid bacteria have been found to increase the absorption of calcium and the utilization of vitamin D. Researchers believe that lactic acid bacteria may also provide some amino acids and may synthesize B-vitamins.

There is some evidence to suggest that lactobacilli exert a positive influence on the balance of *microflora* in the *digestive tract*. Scientists now know that *L. bulgaricus* does not survive in the gastrointestinal tract of mammals, where *L. acidophilus* normally exists. The microorganisms in cultured dairy products exert a selective action toward food and intestinal microflora, generally enhancing the presence of beneficial bacteria.

A combination of microorganisms is used in making yogurt and similar products. This is because flavor-producing microorganisms are somewhat limited in their fermentive effects, so they are used with highly fermentive microorganisms. A mixture of bacterial strains also protects against *bacteriophage*, which attacks a specific bacterial strain. A bacteriophage is one of a group of viruses that infects and destroys bacteria. Bacterial cultures allow yogurt to be more easily digested by lactose-intolerant people. This is because the bacterial cultures contain an enzyme that breaks down lactose in the lower intestine.

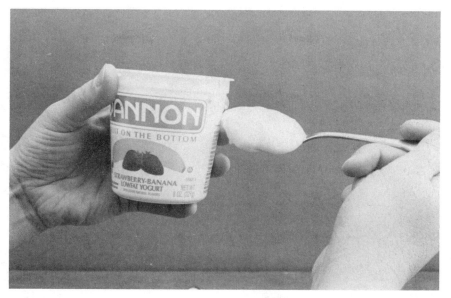

Figure 25-6. Lactic acid bacteria produce the smooth texture and body of
yogurt and its sour, nutty taste.

MAKING YOGURT

Yogurt is a cultured dairy product that has a gel-like, custard consistency.
L. bulgaricus and *S. thermophilus* are used as starter cultures. The fermentive
action of these bacteria is responsible for the texture and flavor of yogurt.
The resulting lactic acid destabilizes the milk protein structure (*casein
micelle*). Increased acidity causes the milk to *coagulate* and form a gel
structure.

During fermentation, enzymes released by the bacteria convert lactose
into lactic acid. Lactic acid is the primary end product of lactic fermentation.
Since acids have a sour taste, yogurt is a sour-tasting dairy product. Fermentation is an example of *anaerobic respiration*. Virtually all metabolic
reactions, such as the production of lactic acid from lactose, are controlled
by enzymes. Some yogurt contains live bacteria, while other yogurt has
been fermented by these bacteria but pasteurized after fermentation.

Milk proteins have the unique ability to *curdle* (form a gel). Curdling
is caused by *proteolytic enzymes*, heat, lactic acid, and other means. Each
milk gel consists of a protein matrix, which is modified by lactic acid to
produce a smooth yogurt product. Heating milk causes the casein micelles
to interconnect to form a *gel matrix*. Heat also destroys undesirable micro-

Figure 25-7. Frozen yogurt has become a very popular cultured dairy
product.

organisms. Lactic acid bacteria produce polysaccarhides that increase viscosity (resistance of a fluid to flow) and water retention. Yogurt has a high
moisture content of 82-86%.

The fat content of yogurt ranges from 0 to 3.5%, but most yogurt
contains 1-1.5% fat. *Solids-not-fat* (SNF) content varies from 9-16% and can
be increased by adding powdered milk. Higher SNF levels are needed to
increase protein content, which helps to improve viscosity. Flavorings,
thickening agents, and sweeteners are added to improve texture and flavor.

When yogurt reaches the desired acidity (pH of 4.25-4.5), bacterial
fermentation is stopped by cooling the yogurt. Cooled yogurt should have
a *titratable acidity* of 0.9-1.2% and a pH of 4.3-4.4. Titratable acidity is
expressed as percent lactic acid, which is determined by the amount of 0.1
N NaOH required to neutralize the lactic acid in 100 milliliters of yogurt.
(Ten ml of 0.1 N NaOH represents a .10% titratable acidity.)

Sundae-style yogurt is incubated in the cup. If fruit flavoring is included,
it is placed in the bottom of the cup and the yogurt mix is poured on
top. *Swiss-style yogurt* is incubated in a vat, with fruit flavorings mixed in
as the yogurt is packaged. *Frozen yogurt* is made by mixing yogurt with ice
milk. Frozen yogurt is usually less acidic than fresh yogurt and has lower
levels of viable bacteria.

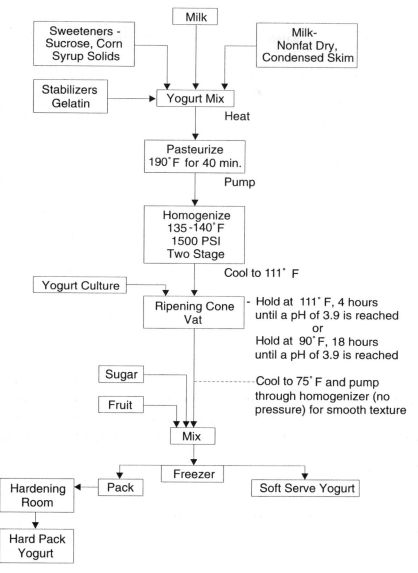

Figure 25-8. The frozen yogurt manufacturing process.

MAKING CHEESE

Milk contains 3.5% protein, of which about 80% is *casein*. *Cheese* is a food product derived from the curd of milk separated from the whey. *Curd* consists mostly of casein and is obtained from milk by *coagulation*. Casein is precipitated (formed into curds) by acid buildup created by bacteria. The

Figure 25-9. Coagulation of milk protein is the basis of the cheese-making
process.

composition and handling of milk, starter culture, heat treatment, flavoring, and salting affect the type of cheese produced. *Whey* is the watery liquid that is separated from the curd after coagulation.

Coagulation of milk is essential for cheese making. Most proteolytic enzymes can cause milk to coagulate. These enzymes *hydrolyze* milk protein and place it in an unstable state where curds then develop at a pH of 4.6. *Rennet* is widely used to coagulate milk when making cheese. Coagulation is also brought about by lactose fermentation, which lowers the pH of the milk to its *isoelectric point* (the pH at which milk is electronically neutral and curds will form). Coagulation occurs because milk proteins link together. An increase in acidity and temperature increases coagulation, whereas higher milk fat decreases coagulation.

Bacterial cultures are used in making both *fresh* and *ripened* cheeses. Cheese is a safe food product because lactic acid and end products in the ripening process inhibit the growth of food-poisoning organisms. Pasteurization or other heat treatment also makes food poisoning unlikely. The type of cheese produced depends upon the emphasis placed on individual steps in the cheese-making process, environmental conditions, and type of microorganism added.

Some cheeses are ripened up to a year to enhance their flavor and texture. During *ripening*, cheese is stored at 5-15°C and 85-95% humidity.

Figure 25-10. The manufacture of dairy products, including yogurt and cheese, is big business in America.

Ripening of cheeses is brought about by enzymes, which are released when starter bacteria break down. Enzymes gradually break down the fats, carbohydrates, and proteins in the cheese. *Microencapsulated enzymes* spread the ripening enzymes more evenly throughout the stored cheese block, thus speeding the ripening process. Temperatures over 13°C also shorten curing time, but increase the likelihood of spoilage.

Mold is added to the starting milk or the drained curds to make certain cheeses. Blue-green mold spores of *Penicillium requeforti* or *P. glaucum* are added to make blue cheese and roquefort cheese, respectively. Several other strains of *Penicillium* are used in cheese making today. Mold *mycelia* interact with enzymes and subsequent surface yeast to produce the flavor and texture of the final cheese product.

CHAPTER SUMMARY

A tremendous variety of cheese products has been developed, and annual sales of cheese continue to climb at a steady pace. Cheese products are generally classified as fresh or ripened. Ripened cheeses are stored up to a year in temperature-controlled environments. This phase of cheese making represents a significant cost of product development. New technologies are being developed that will shorten the ripening period and reduce these storage costs.

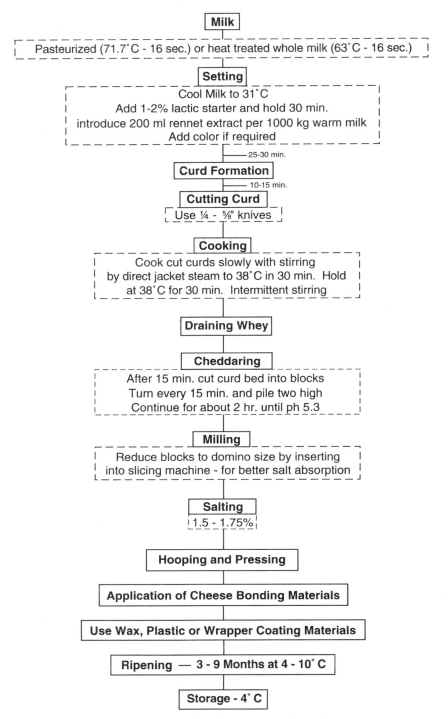

Figure 25-11. The cheddar cheese manufacturing process.

Yogurt is the fastest growing dairy product in the United States. Several major styles of yogurt have been developed, and many variations on these basic styles have led to a wide variety of fresh yogurt products in the grocery store. Frozen yogurt, which is most similar to ice milk, is also growing in popularity. Yogurt has been shown to have beneficial effects on the digestive tract. Yogurt, cheese, and other milk-based food products contain relatively high nutrient levels.

Yogurt and cheese are referred to as cultured dairy products because bacterial cultures are added at some point in the manufacturing process. Lactic acid bacteria and enzymes cause milk protein to curdle (coagulate) and convert lactose to lactic acid via fermentation. These bacteria are responsible for the texture, flavor, and odor of cultured dairy products.

FURTHER LABORATORY INVESTIGATIONS

1. Compare the rate of reaction and characteristics of the yogurt product when skim milk and 2% milk are used.

2. Examine the effects of incubation temperature and duration on yogurt quality. What happens if no powdered milk is added to the mixture? Vary the amount of other ingredients used in making yogurt and observe the results.

3. Add rennet to milk and observe the results.

4. Determine the titratable acidity and pH of various commercially prepared yogurt products. (See Chapter 24 for procedures for measuring titratable acidity.)

5. Perform other experiments in cheese making. Vary the ingredients (whole versus nonfat dry milk), presence of salt, and incubation temperature. Bacteria may be examined by streaking an agar plate, observing the bacteria contained in a small drop of warm milk mixture, or using a simple stain. Also, determine the pH level of the milk and observe pH changes during the cheese-making process.

APPENDIXES

APPENDIX A

GUIDELINES FOR THE USE OF LIVE ANIMALS

1. Develop a plan for obtaining and disposing of live animals *before* animals are secured. Animals should be obtained from reliable suppliers. They should be healthy and free of diseases that can be transmitted to other animals or humans.

2. Animals should be provided sufficient space for normal behavior and posture. Their environment should be free from overcrowding and excessive noise or stress. The housing environment should be clean, dry, and comfortable as required by the species. Ruminants require a resting place. Housing materials should be smooth-surfaced and easy to clean. Easy access to food and water and adequate ventilation should be provided. The biological needs of animals should be met. Animals should be protected from known hazards. An escape-proof enclosure should be provided and well maintained. Exercise areas should be provided.

3. Appropriate care, including well balanced diets, fresh water, clean housing, and adequate temperature, humidity, and lighting, should be provided daily. This includes weekends, holidays, and school vacations. A relative humidity of 40-70% and a temperature of 60-80F is recommended for most animals kept indoors. Animals kept outdoors should be protected from weather extremes. The environment of young animals is especially critical.

4. Report to your teacher any allergies that you might have to specific animals. Scratches, bites, and other injuries should be attended to immediately and reported to the school nurse. Animals should have time to adjust to their environment before handling. Rough handling of any animal should be avoided. The level of restraint applied should be only that needed to safely perform the designated procedure (weighing, vaccinating, etc.).

These recommendations were excerpted from guidelines adopted by

the National Association of Biology Teachers and the publication, *Guide for the Care and Use of Laboratory Animals*, published by the National Research Council (U.S. Department of Health and Human Services). For additional information on animal care guidelines see these and similar documents.

APPENDIX B

INTERNATIONAL SYSTEM OF MEASUREMENT

The International System of Measurement is based on units of 100, which can best be compared to our money system of dollars and cents. Different units are used for measuring length, volume, weight (mass), and temperature. Converting units within SI is extremely simple since in effect, changes are made by moving the decimal point. Initially, it is essential to learn the metric prefixes and which units are used for measuring length, volume, weight, and temperature.

Length

Length is the distance from one point to another. The SI unit of length is the meter. In making measurements, it is often more convenient to report Length in terms which signify a portion or combination of meters. The following prefixes are used with the main unit meter to specify measurements of length.

Prefix	Symbol	Meaning
kilo-	km	1,000 meters
hecto-	hm	100 meters
deca-	dam	10 meters
meter		
deci-	dm	0.1 meter
centi-	cm	0.01 meter
milli-	mm	0.001 meter

Volume

Volume is the amount of space a substance occupies and is based on measurements of length (i.e. length × width × height). The SI unit of volume is the cubic meter, however, this measurement is too large for most scientific work so scientists normally use cubic decimeters (0.1 of a meter)³ to measure volume. One cubic decimeter (1 dm)³ is equal to 1 liter (l). The following prefixes are used with the main unit liter to specify measurements of volume.

Prefix	Symbol	Meaning
kilo-	kl	1,000 liters
hecto-	hl	100 liters
deca-	dal	10 liters
liter		
deci-	dl	0.1 liter
centi-	cl	0.01 liter
milli-	ml	0.001 liter

Weight

Weight is a measure of the pull of gravity on an object. The SI unit of weight is the newton. Since the pull of gravity differs when you leave the earth and experiments are now conducted in space, scientists commonly measure the mass of an object which is how much matter is in something. (For example, the moon's gravity is approximately one-sixth that of the earth.) The SI unit of mass is the gram. The following prefixes are used with the main unit gram to specify measurements of mass.

Prefix	Symbol	Meaning
kilo-	kg	1,000 grams
hecto-	hg	100 grams
deca-	dag	10 grams
gram		
deci-	dg	0.1 gram
centi-	cg	0.01 gram
milli-	mg	0.001 gram

Temperature

Temperature is the amount of heat in something. The SI unit for measuring temperature is degrees Kelvin. One degree Kelvin is equal to one degree Celsius which is the common unit of measurement for the metric system. The metric system of measuring temperature is also based on 100. In this case there are 100 from the temperature at which water freezes to the temperature at which water boils. Common temperature measurements in Celsius are 18°Celsius—room temperature, 37°Celsius—body temperature.

Area

Area is based on measurements of length (i.e. length × width). The SI unit for area is the square meter (m²). However, when measuring plots of land for agricultural purposes, the hectare (ha) is normally used instead of the square meter. 1 hectare = 10,000 square meters.

Conversion Factors for Acceptable Units

To convert Column 1 into Column 2 multiply by	Column 1 Acceptable Unit	Column 2 SI Unit	To convert Column 2 into Column 1 multiply by
		Length	
0.304	foot, ft	meter, m	3.28
2.54	inch, in	centimeter, cm (10^{-2}m)	0.394
25.4	inch, in	millimeter, mm (10^{-3}m)	3.94×10^{-2}
1.609	mile, mi	kilometer, km (10^3m)	0.621
0.914	yard, yd	meter, m	1.094
		Area	
0.405	acre	hectare, ha	2.47
4.05×10^3	acre square	meter, m^2	2.47×10^{-4}
9.29×10^{-2}	square foot, ft^2	square meter, m^2	10.76
2.590	square mile, mi^2	square kilometer, km^2 (10^3 m)²	0.386
		Volume	
35.24	bushel (dry), bu	liter, L	2.84×10^{-2}
28.3	cubic foot, ft^3	liter, L	3.53×10^{-2}
3.83×10^{-2}	cubic foot, ft^3	cubic meter m^3	35.3
1.64×10^5	cubic inch, in^3	cubic meter m^3	6.10×10^4
3.78	gallon, gal	liter, L	0.265
2.96×10^{-2}	ounce (liquid), oz	liter, L	33.78
		Mass	
28.4	ounce	gram, g	3.52×10^{-2}
454	pound, lb	gram, g	2.20×10^{-3}
0.454	pound, lb	kilogram, kg	2.205
907	ton (2000 lb), ton	kilogram, kg	1.10×10^{-3}
		Yield and Rate	
35.84	32-lb bushel per acre	kilogram per hectare	2.79×10^{-2}
53.75	48-lb bushel per acre	kilogram per hectare	1.86×10^{-2}
62.71	56-lb bushel per acre	kilogram per hectare	1.59×10^{-2}
67.19	60-lb bushel per acre	kilogram per hectare	1.49×10^{-2}
9.35	gallons per acre	liter per hectare	0.107
1.12	pound per acre	kilogram per hectare	0.893
		Temperature	
$\frac{5}{9}(F - 32)$	Fahrenheit, F	Celsius, C	$(\frac{9}{5}C) + 32$

GLOSSARY

Abomasum—The chamber that is the true stomach in a ruminant animal.

Abscissic acid (ABA)—The only natural growth inhibitor among plant growth regulators.

Abscission—Shedding of leaves and maturing fruits.

Absorbed—Taken in, sucked up, assimilated, etc.

Absorption—The process by which smaller compounds are absorbed by cells in the digestive tract by diffusion or active transport into the circulatory system.

Absorption spectrum—The pattern of light absorption.

Accessory glands—Glands that secrete fluids which are combined with sperm cells to form semen.

Acrosome—The thin covering or membrane cap over the head of a sperm cell.

Active absorption—The only biological process by which plants draw nutrients from the soil; minerals are actively transported across cell membranes.

Active immunity—Resistance due to production of antibodies by the animal itself when antigens are present, either from disease or a vaccine.

Acute disease—A disease that is relatively severe but of short duration.

Additive—Material added to improve, preserve, or help manufacture another item.

Adhesion—The attraction between unlike molecules involving a mechanical bond or molecular attraction.

Adjuvant—Wetting agent added to herbicides to aid in spray retention.

Ad libitum—Free choice.

Aeration—The process of being supplied or impregnated with air.

Aerobic—Pertaining to bacteria or other organisms which must have oxygen to live and grow.

Aeroponic systems—Plant root systems suspended in air which have a fine mist of oxygen-rich nutrient solution sprayed on them at regular intervals.

Agar—A sugar-based gel derived from certain algae.

Agar plate method—A technique used to determine milk quality using a sterile petri dish, milk sample, and nutrient medium; bacterial colonies are counted after an incubation period.

Aged—Brought to the desired state of aging.

Aleurone layer—The outer layer of the endosperm.

Alkaline—A chemical term where the pH reading is above 7.0 for a substance.

Allele—Matching genes on homologous chromosomes.

Amino acids—Compounds from which proteins are built.

Ammonia products—Any of the liquid or gas chemical compounds composed of nitrogen and hydrogen.

Amylase—An enzyme that breaks down starch reserves to readily useable sugar compounds, glucose and maltose.

Amyloplast—Clusters of starch grains located in statocyte cells, found in the root cap as well as throughout the plant stem.

Anabolic agent—One that is protein building; not a hormone.

Anaerobic—Pertaining to bacteria or other organisms which live or are active without free oxygen.

Anaerobic respiration—The process by which a living organism or cell takes in oxygen where there is no air or free oxygen by getting oxygen from the decomposition of compounds containing it.

Androgen—A growth hormone secreted by the testes that is responsible for the development of secondary sex characteristics in males and has a significant effect on bone and muscle growth in both males and females. *See* testosterone.

Androgenic implant—An implant that enhances growth by inhibiting the release of glucocortoid hormones, which cause degradation of muscle tissue. *See* glucocortoids.

Animal health—Refers to the physiological well being of an animal.

Anion—An ion in solution that carries one or more negative electrical charges depending on its valence or combining power with positively charged cations.

Anomalous disease—Abnormality at birth.

Anther—The knob-like top part of the stamen.

Anther culture—The germination of single pollen grains in a sterile medium.

Antibiotic feed additive—Material added to feed which increases animal growth and feed efficiency.

Antibiotics—Chemical substances produced synthetically or by microorganisms that inhibit the growth of or kill bacteria and other microorganisms.

Antibody—A specific substance produced within the body as a reaction to an invading antigen.

Antigen—Any substance which leads to the development of an antibody when it is introduced into blood or tissues.

Apical dominance—Tip development with suppressed development of lateral buds in plants.

Apical meristems—One of the primary parts of a plant where the hormone auxin is produced.

Arteries—Blood vessels that carry blood from the heart.

Artificial insemination (AI)—The deposition of semen in the reproductive tract of a female by artificial means.

Autotroph—Bacteria in the soil that produce food for plants.

Auxin—A plant hormone that promotes cell elongation.

Bacillus—A genus of bacteria; rod-shaped cells that grow well with or without oxygen (aerobes or facultative anaerobes); usually produce catalase, an enzyme that speeds the decomposition of hydrogen peroxide; organism that causes chemical changes in animal and plant matter.

Backcrossing—The process in which offspring are continuously crossed with one of the parents.

Bacteria—One-celled organisms that have a primitive nucleus; normally classified with fungi.

Bactericide—An agent or substance that destroys bacteria.

Bacterin—A vaccine used to stimulate immunity against bacterial disease.

Bacteriophage—One of a group of viruses that infects and destroys bacteria.

Bacteriostatic—Having an arresting effect on the growth, multiplication, or metabolism of bacteria.

Bag culture—A hydroponic system using plastic bags that are filled with a substrate, such as rockwool, peatlite, or sawdust.

Bare root system—A hydroponic system that does not use a medium or substrate for root development or mechanical support.

Bioassay—A test that predicts potential crop or plant injury due to herbicide carryover in the soil.

Biotechnology—The management of biological systems for the benefit of humanity.

Blanching—Heating in boiling water or steam.

Bloat—The buildup of gas in the stomach; caused by rumen bacteria in ruminant animals.

Blood circulation—The movement of blood out and back from the heart through the arteries and veins of the body.

Blood pressure—The pressure exerted by the blood against the inner walls of a blood vessel.

Body temperature—The balance between heat generated by metabolic processes within the body and the amount of heat dissipated from the body.

Bone marrow—A soft, yellow or red, fatty tissue that fills the cavities of most bones.

Bovine somatotropin (bST)—The primary growth hormone in cattle.

Breeding program—A method of selecting plants or animals for reproduction based on heritability of certain, desirable traits for the purpose of overall improvement.

Broad spectrum antibiotic—A chemical substance, such as penicillin, tetracycline, or bacitracin, that is effective against several types of bacteria.

C_3 plant—A plant that produces a three-carbon acid during the Calvin cycle and has a low net photosynthetic rate; includes cereal grains, soybeans, tomatoes, cotton, tobacco, and peanuts.

C_4 plant—A plant that produces a four-carbon acid during the Calvin cycle and has a high net photosynthetic rate; includes corn, sorghum, sugarcane, millet, and many broadleaf weeds.

Calcium (Ca)—A metallic chemical element essential for plant and animal growth.

California Mastitis Test (CMT)—A field test that estimates the extent of mastitis infection.

Callus—An undifferentiated mass of plant cells which grow from an explant when placed on an artificial medium under sterile conditions.

Calpains—One group of calcium-dependent enzymes that cause muscle to deteriorate and, therefore, become more tender.

Calvin cycle—The dark reactions in photosynthesis where carbon dioxide is combined with five-carbon sugars to produce six-carbon sugars.

Calyx—The outer whorl of protective leaves of a flower.

Canning—Placing food in a container and heating it to kill all microorganisms.

Capillaries—Tiny, microscopic blood vessels that connect arteries and veins.

Capillary refill time (CRT)—The amount of time necessary for capillaries to refill; a quick method of checking blood circulation by pressing on an animal's gums and checking the time required for the tissues to return to their normal pink color.

Carbohydrate—Any of certain organic chemical compounds of carbon, hydrogen, and oxygen, including the sugars, starches, and celluloses.

Carbon dioxide (CO2)—A colorless, odorless gas, normally 0.035% in the atmosphere, absorbed by green plants through their stomata and used as a source of carbon for producing starches, sugars, and proteins.

Carotenoid—Accessory orange pigment that transfers its absorbed light energy to chlorophyll-a, improving the plant's overall ability to absorb and use light energy.

Carpel—*See* pistil.

Carryover—Refers to the persistence of the herbicide in the soil after harvest or at the next scheduled planting date.

Caryopsis—The fruit of a grass.

Casein—A phosphoprotein that is one of the main components of milk and the basis of cheese.

Cation—An ion in solution carrying one or more positive electrical charges depending on its valence.

Cell—The basic structure of life consisting of a mass of protoplasm, including a nucleus, surrounded by a membrane.

Cell culture—A technique that involves growing cells in a specially prepared medium, modifying their genetic makeup, and then regenerating them with the desired traits.

Cell cycle—The process of creating a new cell when the constituents of the parent cell double, followed by division into two daughter cells.

Cell division—The process of cells splitting.

Cell duplication—*See* cell cycle.

Cell membrane—The outer covering of a cell.

Cellulose—The primary substance composing the cell walls or fibers of all plant tissue.

Cervix—The protective seal between the uterus and vagina that serves to protect the uterus from foreign materials during pregnancy.

Cheese—A food product derived from the curd of milk separated from the whey, with the type produced depending upon the emphasis placed on individual steps in the cheese-making process, environmental conditions, and type of microorganism added.

Chemical energy—The ability to do work contained in the chemical bond between atoms.

Chemical environment—The substances obtained by, or used in, a chemical process, along with all of the external conditions that may act upon or affect an organism.

Chemical food preservatives—Chemicals used to retard or prevent food deterioration.

Chlorophyll—A green pigment contained in the chloroplast of plant cells that must be present for photosynthesis to take place.

Chloroplast—A specialized, subcellular structure in green plants that contains chlorophyll pigments.

Chlorosis—A lack of chlorophyll in green plants causing yellowing of leaves.

Chromatography—The process of separating plant pigments into distinct bands on an absorbent material.

Chromosome—That part of a cell which contains information about genetic makeup and transmits that information to offspring; made up of proteins and nucleic acids; consists of DNA.

Chronic disease—A disease lasting a long time or recurring often; continuous.

Clinical mastitis—An inflammation of the mammary gland(s) with obvious symptoms and a relatively high level of infection.

Cloning—A process of asexually reproducing organisms from a single parent.

Closed hydroponic system—A system that recovers and recirculates the nutrient solution.

Coagulate—*See* coagulation.

Coagulation—The curdling (thickening) of milk protein caused by the fermentive action of lactic acid bacteria and certain enzymes.

Cohesion—Attraction between like molecules involving a chemical bond.

Coleoptile—The protective sheath for the epicotyl of a seed embryo during germination.

Coleorhiza—The protective sheath for the radicle of a seed embryo during germination.

***Coliform* bacteria**—A group of bacteria that usually inhabits the intestines of animals, lives in manure and on wood.

Color stability—The ability of a color to resist change, usually dependent upon its environment.

Colostrum—The first fluid secreted by the mammary glands for several days after birth of the young.

Comfort zone—The ambient temperature range that does not cause body stress.

Conclusions—Specific statements about the relationships between variables.

Contact herbicide—A chemical that kills only the portions of the plants that it contacts.

Contagious disease—An infectious disease spread by direct or indirect contact; communicable.

Contamination—The addition of bacteria or other foreign substances, pollution.

Continuous flow hydroponic system—A bare root system made up of shallow pools with floating panels that contain plants.

Control—To hold constant.

Corpus luteum—A mass of tissue that forms at the site where the follicle ruptures after an ovum has been shed.

Cotyledons—Seed leaves attached to a seed embryo.

Crossbreeding—Mating of different genotypes of different species.

Cross-pollination—Transfer of pollen between different flowers on plants of different cultivars.

Cultivar—A plant variety that is cultivated and retains its features when reproduced.

Culture—To cultivate or grow in a specially prepared medium; a microorganism that is grown.

Curd—An acid buildup created by bacteria, consisting mostly of casein and obtained from soured milk through coagulation.

Curdle—Form a gel structure, thicken.

Curing—Adding substances to foods to prevent spoilage; salting, smoking, pickling, etc.

Cuticle—A thin, waxy layer of cutin that covers the epidermis of plants above the ground and helps to reduce water loss from plant tissues.

Cutin—A waxy, fatty substance secreted by epidermal cells in plants.

Cytokinins—Organic compounds that affect plants and plant tissues, including cell enlargement and division, tissue differentiation, dormancy, and retardation of leaf senescence.

Dark reactions—*See* Calvin cycle.

Degenerative disease—A disease that causes changes in bone, muscle, or organs brought about by age, disuse, or biochemical changes.

Dehydration—The process of naturally or artificially removing water from a substance, compound, food, or body tissue.

Dependent variable—The variable that is measured to determine the effects of the independent variable.

Dicot—A plant with two seed leaves.

Dietary energy—Energy contained in an animal's feed/diet.

Differentiation—The development or growth of a cell or mass of cells into a complete organism as a result of genetic makeup, environmental conditions, hormone levels, and other factors.

Diffusion—The movement of molecules from a region of higher concentration to a region of lower concentration.

Digestion—The physical and chemical breakdown of feed as it passes through the gastrointestinal tract.

Digestive tract—The mouth, esophagus, stomach(s), small and large intestines, and anus of an animal through which food passes.

Dihybrid cross—Involving two pairs of alleles, two genes.

Direct microscopic count method—A technique used to determine milk quality by using a microscope to detect viable and dead microorganisms in the microscopic field.

Disease—Any departure from a healthy state.

Disinfectant—A chemical which destroys microbes by breaking down cell proteins.

Disinfestation—The destruction of disease-producing microorganisms and parasites.

DNA—Deoxyribonucleic acid; forms the basic material in the chromosomes of the cell nucleus.

DNA probe—A DNA segment that will bind to equivalent genes in a target cell.

Dominant—Relating to one of a pair of allelic hereditary factors that dominates the other and appears in the organism.

Dominant gene—Causes a certain characteristic to be expressed, present in offspring.

Dormancy—A physiologic state where growth ceases when the metabolic processes are slowed.

Dosage—The system to be followed in taking a medicine.

Drip irrigation—The technique of watering plants through a tube at a low rate of flow so that the plant's immediate root area is moist.

Economic injury level—The point where crop or plant losses due to pests are equal to the cost of control.

Electrolytes—Acids, bases, and salts that produce electrically charged ions when dissolved in water.

Electromagnetic scanning—A technique for estimating the lean and fat tissues of a carcass by passing it through an electromagnetic field.

Electromagnetic spectrum—Radiant energy from 10^{-4} to 10^{12} nm.

Electrophoresis—Separation of DNA proteins with an electrical charge.

Embryo culture—The process of removing an embryo from a plant and growing it on a culture medium.

Embryo transfer—Placing of an embryo into the uterus of a surrogate mother.

Endocrine glands—Those glands that produce hormones.

Endosperm—The major food storage tissue consisting mostly of starch and protein.

Endospore—An asexual spore formed within the cell wall of the parent cell, as in certain bacteria, fungi, and algae.

Environmental factors—Those conditions other than genetic makeup such as housing, nutrition, disease control, and overall management practices that affect physical characteristics and performance of an animal.

Enzymatic action—The promotion of chemical processes by an enzyme or group of enzymes.

Enzymatic digestion—The chemical breakdown of feed in the gastrointestinal tract by enzymes such as amylase, lipase, and protease.

Enzyme inhibitors—Substances that disrupt the normal function of the acetolactate synthase (ALS) enzyme.

Enzyme—A complex protein molecule that stimulates or speeds up various chemical reactions without being used up itself.

Epicotyl—The part of the axis above the cotyledons of a seed embryo where the seeding stem develops; also called the plumule.

Epidermis—The continuous, exterior cellular layer of an organism.

Epididymis—A small, tortuous tube leading from the testicle; where sperm are stored and matured.

Epithelial cells—Those cells making up the tissue covering all the free body surfaces, cutaneous, mucous, and serous, including the glands.

Erythorbate—A substance that stabilizes the color development in cured meats, reduces fat oxidation, and inhibits undesirable nitrite reactions.

Estrogen—A growth hormone secreted by ovaries that is primarily responsible for development of the reproductive tract in females.

Estrogenic implant—Promotes growth by stimulating the release of growth hormones from the anterior pituitary gland. *See* somatotropins.

Estrous cycle—The reproductive cycle in the female that spans from the beginning of one estrus to the beginning of the next estrus.

Estrus synchronization—The injection of hormones to cause a group of animals to show estrus (come into heat) simultaneously.

Ethylene—A natural plant hormone that is a water-soluble gas produced in ripening fruits, senescent flowers, plant meristems, and at sites where plant or fruit injury occurs.

Eucaryotic cells—Those cells with a definitive nucleus.

Evaporation—The process of changing from a liquid to a vapor and passing into the air.

Evapotranspiration—Evaporation of water from the soil surface and diffusion of water through stomata in the leaves of a plant.

Experimental method—A process of scientific inquiry where all factors, except the variable under investigation, are controlled or held constant.

Explants—Pieces of plants used to grow new plants in tissue cultures.

Fallopian tubes—Ducts that connect the ovary to the uterus in the female reproductive system; where the released ovum travels and where fertilization usually occurs.

Fat—Any of various solid or semisolid oily or greasy materials found in animal tissue and in the seeds of plants that are composed of glycerides of fatty acids; what excess energy is changed to in the body.

Fat oxidation—A chemical change in the fat tissues of animal products involving the addition of oxygen or its chemical equivalent.

Feed additive—A material added to feed that increases an animal's resistance to disease; substances that alter microorganism activity.

Female reproductive system—Consists of two ovaries, two fallopian tubes, the uterus, and the vagina.

Fermentation—A food preservation method using yeasts, mold, enzymes, or bacteria; the breakdown of complex molecules into organic compounds, caused by the influence of a ferment.

Fertilization—The union of the pollen cell with the ovule in plants; the union of the sperm with the egg in animals.

Fibrils—Small, thread-like tissues in parallel muscle fibers.

Findings—Actual data generated from an experiment.

Follicle—A small sac which appears on the surface of the ovary and contains the developing ovum.

Follicle stimulating hormone (FSH)—A hormone produced by the pituitary gland which stimulates the development of one or more follicles in females.

Food-borne pathogen—A disease-producing agent such as a bacteria or virus present in food.

Food deterioration—A broad term that includes a reduction in nutrition, safety, or aesthetic appeal.

Forage—The portion of animal feed that is largely from the leaves and stalks of plants, such as hay and grass.

Fresh—Recently produced, obtained, or grown; newly made.

Frozen yogurt—A mixture of yogurt and ice milk, usually less acidic than fresh yogurt with lower levels of viable bacteria.

Fungi—Nucleated, usually filamentous, spore-bearing organisms having no chlorophyll.

Gamete—The formation of egg and sperm cells.

Gamma globulin—Specialized proteins in the plasma portion of blood that contain antibodies which combine with antigens and neutralize them.

Gastrointestinal tract—The part of the digestive system that includes the mouth, esophagus, stomach, and intestines.

Gel matrix—A jelly-like substance formed by the coagulation of milk protein micelles.

Gender preselection—A technology based upon several methods of sperm sorting and embryo transfer techniques.

Gene—The specific determiner of heredity.

Gene mapping—Identifying genes and their locations along the chromosomes that make up a species.

Genetic engineering—An advanced form of biotechnology; techniques involve gene splicing, replication, and transfer of genes to other organisms.

Genetic potential—The physical characteristics and performance possible because of genetic makeup.

Genetic variation—A change in the genetic makeup of a group of plants or animals, providing potential for improvement in overall quality.

Genetics—The study of heredity in plants and animals.

Genome—The term used to describe the overall genetic makeup of a plant or animal.

Genotype—The genetic makeup of an organism; allele composition.

Genotypic ratio—Refers to the proportion of allele types for each genetic trait.

Geotropism—Plant growth in response to gravitational forces.

Germ cells—Cells which are capable of reproduction or of sharing in the reproduction of an organism.

Germination—The resumption of growth by a seed embryo; occurs when the embryonic root emerges from the seed coat.

Gibberella zeae—A mold which grows on corn.

Gibberellin (GA)—A water-soluble chemical produced by the seed embryo which stimulates production of enzymes that break down food reserves in the endosperm.

Glucocortoids—Growth hormones secreted by the adrenal gland that stimulate the mobilization of stored nutrients, resulting in weight loss.

Glucolysis—Occurs when the glucose molecule is transformed and then split, eventually producing pyruvic acid as an end product.

Glucose—A monosaccharide sugar that serves as a building block for many carbohydrates.

Glycogen metabolism—The chemical change of a partially soluble, starch-like substance produced in tissues into a simple sugar as the body needs it.

Gravel culture—A method of growing irrigated plants in gravel which provides mechanical support.

Gravitropism—*See* geotropism.

Growth—An increase in size of a living organism.

Growth curve—The general rate of growth of all animals from birth to maturity, plotted on a graph forming an S-shaped curve.

Growth inhibitors—Plant regulators that promote dormancy or slow down plant growth.

Growth regulators—Naturally occurring and synthetic hormones, as well as nonnutrient, synthetic materials that influence growth and development.

Guard cells—Cells around stomata which open and close due to changes in cell firmness or turgor.

Heart rate—The number of times an artery stretches and contracts per minute.

Herbicides—Chemicals used to kill plants, may be selective or nonselective.

Heredity—The passing of traits to offspring; the sum of all of the characteristics inherited from parents.

Heritability—The proportion of variance in traits that is due to transmission of traits from parents to offspring.

Heritability estimate—An approximation of the degree to which heredity influences a particular trait.

Heterosis—The extent to which performance of offspring exceeds the parental average; hybrid vigor.

Heterozygous—Having different alleles for a single trait and therefore producing two or more different kinds of gametes.

Hill reaction—The light reaction in photosynthesis where light strikes chlorophyll molecules and initiates the energy conversion process.

Homozygous—Having identical alleles at one or more loci and therefore producing identical gametes.

Hormone—A chemical messenger substance produced in one location of an organism and carried to another where it has a specific effect.

Hormone type herbicides—Chemicals that affect growth in the newest leaves and stems by affecting protein synthesis and normal cell division.

Hybrid vigor—*See* heterosis.

Hybridization—The crossing of two plants that have different genotypes.

Hydration—Water uptake by the chemical combination of water and some other substance in a definite molecular ratio.

Hydrolysis—The chemical reaction when water is added to a molecule being degraded to create a weak acid and/or base; a key part of digestion.

Hydrolyze—To undergo or cause to undergo a chemical reaction in which a compound reacts with the ions of water to produce a weak acid, a weak base, or both.

Hydroponics—A method of growing plants in which the nutrients needed by the plant are supplied by a nutrient solution.

Hydrotropism—Plant growth response to water.

Hyperplasia—An increase in the number of cells in a tissue or organ.

Hypertrophy—An increase in the size of cells.

Hypocotyl—The part of the axis below the cotyledons of a seed embryo that contains the embryonic root called the radicle.

Hypothalamus—An animal's thermal control center which responds to changes in blood temperature.

Hypothesis—A tentatively accepted theory that explains the relationship between two variables.

Imbibition—Absorption of moisture by the seed when germination begins.

Immune system—That body system that provides resistance to the action of disease.

Immunity—Resistance to disease.

Implant—Insertion of a solid material under the skin.

in vitro—In glass (usually a test tube).

Inbreeding—The process of crossing two similar parents.

Independent variable—The variable in an experiment that is manipulated.

Infectious disease—A disease always caused by invasion of living organisms and originating from some other organism.

Infundibulum—The funnel-shaped structure located next to the ovary on the end of the fallopian tubes that function in collecting ovum during ovulation.

Inheritance—The acquisition of traits acquired by way of genes that are transferred from parents to offspring.

Injection—Insertion using hypodermic needles and syringes to get a substance into the body system.

Inoculate—To treat seeds with nitrogen-fixing bacteria in order to increase the population of these bacteria in the soil.

Integrated Pest Management (IPM)—A pest-management strategy that uses a combination of measures to control pests with the goal of keeping pest populations below the economic injury level.

Interception—Initial contact of a herbicide on a leaf.

Intradermal (ID) injection—Injections placed in skin tissue.

Intramuscular (IM) injection—Injections placed in muscle tissue.

Intravenous (IV) injection—Injections placed in a vein.

Ion—The charged particle when an atom gains or loses a valence electron.

Isoelectric point—The pH at which milk is electronically neutral and curds will form.

Keratin—A complex protein in animals that is highly insoluble and found in such substances as hair, feathers, horns, etc.; also produced in the teat canal of the mammary gland where it acts as a bactericide and helps to seal the teat opening.

Krebs cycle—That part of plant respiration where pyruvic acid goes through the cycle of producing 6-, 5-, and 4-carbon acids and small amounts of energy at successive stages.

Lactic acid—A yellowish or clear, syrupy organic acid, produced by the fermentation of lactose when milk sours or from sucrose and some other carbohydrates.

Lactic acid bacteria—Microbes that destroy or inhibit food-borne pathogens and spoilage microorganisms by lowering the pH of food products; improves the flavor and texture of many dairy products.

Lactobacillus—Lactic acid bacteria found in dairy products and other foods.

Lactose—A white, crystalline sugar found in milk; milk sugar.

Lasalocid—A widely used feed additive that increases feed efficiency by altering rumen metabolism.

Lateral bud—A bud attached to the side of a branch.

Law of limiting factors—When the supply of all essential elements is sufficient except one, growth and yield are limited to the extent that this essential element is lacking.

Leaching—The downward pulling of materials through the soil by percolating water.

Leghemoglobin—A pink substance synthesized by rhizobia bacteria cells in the center portion of legume root nodules.

Legumes—Plants that have the ability to convert atmospheric nitrogen into a form usable by plant root systems (in the nodules).

Leukocytes—Any of the small, colorless cells in the blood, lymph, and tissue which are important in the body's defense against infection; white blood cells.

Light compensation point—The lowest light intensity where the amount of food produced by photosynthesis equals the energy used up in respiration.

Light energy—The ability to do work contained in radiant energy, consisting of electromagnetic waves of varying wavelengths.

Light intensity—A measure of the brightness of light, expressed in footcandles or luxes.

Light quality—Refers to the color or wavelength of visible light. *See* wavelength.

Light reactions—*See* Hill reactions.

Light saturation point—The point at which increases in light intensity do not result in significant increases in photosynthesis.

Lignin—The substance that, together with cellulose, forms the woody cell walls of plants and cements them together.

Lipase—An enzyme secreted by the pancreas that works in the small intestine to break down fats.

Luteinizing hormone (LH)—A hormone that causes the follicle to rupture and release the matured ovum.

Lymphocytes—Types of white blood cells that are the key in detecting antigens and creating an antibody response to them.

Macronutrients—Those elements required in relatively large supply.

Male reproductive system—Consists of the testes, reproductive tract, accessory glands, and penis.

Mammary gland—Female glands that produce milk for newborn young.

Manipulation—Management of the independent variable in an experiment.

Mastication—Chewing, breaking down feed into smaller particles.

Mastitis—An inflammation of the mammary gland, usually associated with an infection.

Meiosis—A type of cell division that results in a reduction in chromosome number, usually by half; controls the formation of egg and sperm cells (gametes).

Melanin—The brown pigment of phenol compounds in fruit tissue.

Membrane disrupters—Substances that tear down internal cell membranes, preventing these cells from manufacturing energy.

Meristem cells—The fastest reproducing plant cells, responsible for growth and found throughout the plant.

Meristem culture—Used to produce pathogen-free stock plants by using the meristem dome and the accompanying pair of leaf primordia as explants.

Meristematic lipid inhibitors—Substances that prevent formation of lipid cells in the shoots of grass plants.

Metabolic activity—The action of chemical changes in cells and tissues whereby one compound is converted to one or more other compounds.

Metabolic disease—A disease where body functions are altered due to nutrition, toxins, or endocrine activity.

Metabolism—The chemical changes in cells, tissues, and organs that provide energy for living organisms for growth, repair, and maintenance.

Methane—A colorless, odorless, flammable,

gaseous hydrocarbon present in natural gas and formed by the decomposition of plant material.

Metmyoglobin—A compound that results when myoglobin in meat combines with oxygen, turning the meat brown.

Micelle—A submicroscopic structural unit of protoplasm.

Microbe—A microscopic organism.

Microbial spoilage—When food becomes unsafe to eat or unacceptable in flavor due to the action of microorganisms.

Microencapsulated enzyme—An enzyme enclosed in a tiny capsule for controlled release.

Microflora—Microbial life found in a particular region, such as bacteria and protozoa found in the digestive tract of mammals.

Microinjection—The mechanical insertion of genetic material into a single, living cell.

Micronutrients—Those trace elements required in small amounts.

Microorganism—An organism so small that it cannot be seen clearly without the use of a microscope.

Micropropagation—The asexual reproduction of cells or tissues in a closed container.

Micropyle—The tiny pore in a seed coat.

Milk quality—A general assessment of the degree of excellence, based primarily upon the degree of bacterial contamination.

Mitosis—The actual cell division phase of the cell cycle.

Mode of action—The metabolic action or enzyme system through which the herbicide destroys the plant.

Mold—Fungi distinguished by the formation of a network of threads or by spore masses.

Monensin—A widely used feed additive that increases feed efficiency by altering rumen metabolism.

Monoclonal antibody technique—A process of fusing a cancer cell with one that produces antibodies.

Monocot—A plant with one seed leaf.

Monogastric—*See* nonruminant.

Monohybrid cross—Involving only one pair of alleles, one gene.

Morphology—The branch of biology that deals with the form and structure of animals and plants.

Motility—Spontaneous motion or movement.

Mottling—A patchy development of deficiency symptoms in plants.

Muscle—The tissue making up any organ consisting of bundles of cells or fibers that can be contracted or expanded to produce movements.

Mycelia—Filaments that compose the vegetative body of fungi and some bacteria; interacts with enzymes and subsequent surface yeast to produce flavor and texture in cheese.

Mycelium—The vegetative body of many fungi consisting of a mass of filaments, hyphae.

Myofibrillar protein—Muscle protein that contains fibrils, which are capable of contracting.

Myoglobin—An iron-containing protein found in muscle and serving as a reservoir for oxygen and carbon dioxide.

Necrosis—Browning (death) of plant tissue.

Neoplasm disease—A disease with an abnormal growth of tissue, as a tumor.

Nitric oxide myoglobin—The resulting reaction between sodium nitrite and myoglobin in muscle, giving the meat a dark red color.

Nitrogen (N)—A component of chlorophyll, with four nitrogen atoms contained in each chlorophyll molecule; essential to photosynthesis.

Nitrogen fixation—The biochemical process of converting atmospheric nitrogen (N_2) to a form that can be used by plants (Nitrate, NO_3^-).

Nitrosyl hemochrome—The compound formed when a cured meat product is cooked and the nitric oxide myoglobin is denatured, giving a bright pink color to the meat.

Node—The place on a plant stem that normally bears a leaf or a whorl of leaves.

Nodule—A small lump developed on the root surface of a legume where nitrogen is stored.

Noninfectious disease—A disease that cannot be transferred from one organism to another; not caused by a pathogen.

Nonruminant—An animal with a one-chamber stomach that does not further refine what is ingested.

Nonselective herbicide—A chemical used to kill all vegetation without regard to species.

Nucleus—The control center of a cell.

Nutrient film technique (NFT)—A popular bare root hydroponic system that uses a recirculating, shallow stream of nutrient solution that moves through channels in which the plants grow.

Nutrient metabolism—The process by which absorbed nutrients are circulated to individual cells where fats and carbohydrates are further degraded to produce energy, and amino acids are recombined to form proteins, and eventually tissues, hormones, or enzymes.

Nutrient solution—Water with dissolved nutrient salts.

Open hydroponic system—A system which does not recover the nutrient solution.

Optical probe—A technique which estimates the percent of lean in a carcass by inserting a probe in the loin.

Organic matter—Humus; matter found in rotting plants and animals or produced by them.

Osmosis—The flow of a liquid through a semipermeable membrane.

Osmotic flow—The movement of a solvent into a solution of higher concentration.

Osmotic pressure—The force that develops within the cells of seeds as water is absorbed during the germination process; differences in force between cell layers during the uptake of water from the soil.

Outcrossing—Mating of animals within the same breed that are distant relatives.

Ova—Female sex cells.

Ovaries—Glandular organs that produce hormones and give rise to ova in female vertebrates; the enlarged basal portion of a pistil that bears the ovum in angiosperms.

Ovulation—The process of releasing ova; part of the estrous cycle.

Ovule—The developing female sex cell known as the egg.

Ovum—A mature female sex cell, which, generally only after fertilization, develops into a new member of the same species.

Oxidation—Any chemical change which involves the addition of oxygen or its chemical equivalent.

Oxymyoglobin—The compound formed when meat is exposed to high concentrations of oxygen; myoglobin combines with oxygen turning the meat bright red.

Passive immunity—Resistance obtained from the introduction of antibodies from an outside source; lasts only a few days or weeks.

Pasteurization—The process of destroying disease-producing bacteria in substances such as milk, fruit juices, etc. by a low or high heat method.

Pathogen—Any microorganism or virus that can cause disease.

Penicillium—Any of a genus of imperfect fungi growing as green mold on stale bread, ripening cheese, decaying fruit, etc.

Perishable—Any product which is easily or quickly destroyed or made unusable or unsafe.

Permeability—The capacity of soil for transmitting a liquid.

Petal—The leaf of a flower.

pH—An index of the acidity of a substance, with 7.0 being neutral; numbers below 7.0 becoming increasingly acid and those above 7.0 becoming increasingly alkaline (basic).

Phagocytosis—The process of white blood cells rushing to surround and contain a foreign organism or material that invades the body.

Phenotype—The physical appearance of an organism.

Phloem—A vascular tissue that moves food from where it is manufactured to other parts of a plant.

Phosphate—A salt or ester of phosphoric acid, used as a fertilizer; also used to improve color development, inhibit fat oxidation, and promote myofibrillar protein extraction in meat.

Phosphorus (P)—A nonmetallic chemical element found in soils in various mineral forms that affects the flow and retention of substances in and out of plant cells.

Photon—A quantum of electromagnetic energy having both particle and wave behavior.

Photoreceptor—A plant light-sensing mechanism which allows a growth response to light to occur.

Photosynthesis—The conversion of light energy into chemical energy by green plants; chlorophyll and sunlight produce carbohydrates and carbon dioxide while releasing oxygen.

Photosynthetic active radiation (PAR) spectrum—That part of the electromagnetic spectrum to which plants respond; between 300 and 800 nm.

Photosynthetic inhibitors—Substances that block the photosynthetic reaction within cells so that captured light cannot be converted to chemical energy.

Phototropism—The growth response of a plant toward light.

Phytochrome—A photoreceptor in a seed or a plant that acts as a molecular switch to control germination and flowering.

Pigment inhibitors—Substances that prevent the formation of chlorophyll.

Pigments—Molecules that absorb certain colors of light.

Pistil—The female reproductive part of a flower; the stigma, style, and ovary.

Plant breeding—The process of selectively mating plants.

Plant hormone—An organic compound that is produced in minute quantities in one part of a plant and then translocated to another part where growth and development are modified.

Plantlet—A plant which was created from an explant and grown by tissue culture; has tiny leaves, stems, and roots that have not yet developed into normal-sized parts of the parent plant.

Plasma—The yellowish liquid part of blood which contains dissolved nutrients, water products, and disease-fighting proteins called antibodies.

Plasma membrane—The delicate, elastic outer surface of animal cells.

Plasmolysis—Dehydration of microbial cells; shrinkage of the protoplasm from the cell wall.

Platelet—Any of the round or oval, nonnucleated disks in blood which are surrounded by fibers that help to form blood clots.

Plumule—*See* epicotyl.

Pollen—The small reproductive bodies produced by the anthers of a flower.

Polyestrous—Refers to animals that have estrous cycles year round.

Polygastric—*See* ruminant.

Postemergence—After plant emergence.

Potassium (K)—The chemical element, an alkali metal, which occurs widely in minerals and is an essential plant nutrient and enzyme activator.

Preemergence—After planting but before plant emergence.

Procaryotic cells—Cells with a primitive nucleus in which the DNA-containing region lacks a limiting membrane.

Progeny testing—A method of evaluating sires based on the performance records of offspring.

Progesterone—A steroid hormone, secreted by the corpus luteum or prepared synthetically, active in preparing the uterus for the reception and development of the fertilized ovum and the mammary glands for milk secretion.

Pronucleus—The haploid nucleus of either the sperm or the ovum, which unite in fertilization to form the fused, double nucleus of the fertilized ovum.

Prostaglandin—Any of a group of very powerful hormones or hormone-like substances secreted by the uterus if pregnancy does not occur, causing the corpus luteum to fade, and the estrous cycle to begin anew.

Protease—An enzyme that breaks down storage proteins into amino acids.

Protein—Any of a large number of complex organic compounds of amino acids; an essential part of all living organisms.

Proteolytic enzymes—Enzymes which break down proteins to form simpler substances.

Protoplasm—The essential living matter of all plant and animal cells.

Puberty—The age at which an animal is capable of reproduction.

Pulse—The stretching and relaxing of an artery as blood moves through it. *See* heart rate.

Punnett Square—A common method of predicting the genotypes and phenotypes of offspring using a matrix.

Putrefaction—Decomposition of animal or

plant matter by microorganisms in the absence of oxygen.

Radicle—The embryonic root in the hypocotyl part of a seed embryo.

Ration—The total amount of feed an animal gets in a 24-hour period.

Raw milk—Untreated milk as it comes from the cow; fresh milk.

Recessive—An allele that is not expressed phenotypically when present in the heterozygous condition.

Recessive gene—Causes the character to be expressed only if the alleles from both parents are recessive.

Recombinant DNA—A technology that allows isolated genes to be transferred from one organism to another by splicing, cloning, or inserting to change the genetic makeup of the recipient organism, taking a tiny amount of DNA from one chromosome and moving it to another.

Recombinant vaccine—A vaccine that uses only a small portion of the microbe with disease-causing genes omitted; antigen features are retained so that an antibody response is evoked.

Recommendations—Suggestions on how results should be used; suggestions for further experimentation.

Red blood cells—Those cells in blood that contain a special compound called hemoglobin, which gives them their color and is used to transport oxygen from the lungs to the cells of the body; red corpuscles.

Refrigeration—Artificial cooling which drastically reduces microbial growth of certain bacteria.

Regurgitate—To return undigested feed from the stomach to the mouth, as by ruminant animals.

Related studies—Similar, previous research findings from printed or informal sources.

Rennet—A coagulating extract containing the enzyme rennin and used to curdle milk, as when making cheese.

Repartitioning agents—Substances that redirect nutrient deposits from fat to lean tissue.

Repeatability estimate—An approximation of the degree to which an animal or group of animals will repeat certain performance traits in subsequent years.

Replication—Exact duplication of an experiment.

Reproductive tract—The duct system of a male or female animal concerned with producing offspring.

Research problem—Specific question under investigation.

Respiration—A process in which oxygen combines with glucose to produce energy; the process used by plants and animals to exchange gases with their environment.

Retention—Refers to the percentage of intercepted herbicide spray that remains on the leaf surface.

RFLP map—A process to identify genes and more accurately measure genetic composition by using special enzymes to cut DNA into smaller pieces which undergo electrophoresis.

Rhizobium—A rod-shaped species of aerobic, soil-inhabiting bacteria that has the unique capability of converting atmospheric nitrogen into a form that is usable by plants.

Riboflavin—A yellow pigment that is the active photoreceptor in grass plants; located at the tip of the coleoptile.

Ripened—Made mature, fully developed, aged, cured, etc.

Ripening—Growing to maturity, such as fruit.

RNA—Ribonucleic acid; a polymer of nucleotides connected via a phosphate-ribose backbone, involved in protein synthesis.

RNA analysis—A method of tracking genes by revealing the number of times a gene is copied for a particular protein within a cell.

Root cap—The tip of the primary root that protects the root as it grows into the soil.

Root mitotic inhibitors—Substances that prevent normal cell division by affecting cell replication.

Rumen—The largest compartment of the stomach in ruminant animals where a large amount of bacterial fermentation of feed materials occurs.

Ruminant—An animal with a stomach divided into three or four chambers for further refining of what it ingested.

Salmonella—Any of a genus of Gram-negative, rod-shaped bacilli that cause various diseases in humans and animals, including food poisoning.

Salt—An essential compound that does not contain carbon, hydrogen, or oxygen; formed when a strong acid and base are combined; commonly used as a seasoning, preservative, nutritional supplement, etc.

Sand culture—The process of growing plants in sterilized sand with individual drip irrigation.

Sap—Plant fluid which is contained in the plant's vascular system.

Scientific method—A carefully controlled, systematic process for discovering the unknown.

Scutulum—The cotyledon of a grass plant.

Seed—A fertilized ovum that contains an embryo and forms a new plant upon germination.

Seed coat—The hard outer layer of a seed; its protective covering.

Seed embryo—A plant in an arrested state of development inside of the seed coat, consisting of an axis and attached seed leaves called cotyledons.

Seed viability—The growing quality of seeds.

Selection differential—The difference between a trait in animals selected for breeding and the overall herd or flock average on that particular trait.

Selective herbicide—A chemical used to kill only certain plant species.

Self-fertile—Describes plants that produce fruit and seed without the transfer of pollen from another cultivar.

Self-pollination—Occurs when the anther and the stigma are from the same flower, from different flowers on the same plant, or from different flowers on different plants of the same cultivar or variety.

Semen—The thick, whitish fluid produced by the male reproductive system and containing spermatozoa suspended in secretions of the accessory glands.

Semen extenders—Substances used to dilute semen before it is frozen.

Senescence—The process of growing old; biological aging.

Sepal—Any of the usually green, leaf-like parts of the calyx of a flower.

Shock—The condition that occurs when life-sustaining functions have slowed down or stopped.

Shoot—The stem of a plant, including the leaves.

Shoot inhibitors—Substances that affect cell growth and division in plants.

Sodium nitrite—The curing agent responsible for the color change in cured meats.

Soilless culture—*See* hydroponics.

Soil nutrients—Substances present in the soil that provide nourishment for plants.

Soil texture—The proportion of sand, silt, and clay in the soil.

Solids-not-fat (SNF)—The parts of a substance, not including the fat, that help it keep its form.

Somatic cell count (SCC)—A laboratory test that indicates the presence and severity of mastitis, also called the somatic cell score.

Somatic cells—Body cells other than germ (reproductive) cells.

Somatotropin—The hormone regulating growth, secreted by the anterior pituitary gland that has primary effect on bone and muscle growth. *See* bovine somatotropin (bST).

Sour—Spoil; a flavor defect usually associated with dairy products that is characterized by taste and odor changes resulting from the reduction of lactose to lactic acid.

Sperm—The male sex cell, found in semen, produced by tubules in the testicles.

Spermatogenesis—The production of sperm cells from germ cells in the testes.

Spermatozoa—The male germ cell found in semen. *See* sperm.

Spoilage microorganism—A microbe such as bacteria, yeast, or mold which changes the flavor of food or makes it unsafe to eat.

Spongy mesophyll—The area of a leaf beneath the palisade cells which allows for the exchange of gases in photosynthesis and transpiration.

Stamen—The male reproductive parts of a flower; the anthers and their supporting filaments.

Standing heat—When the female stands still to be mounted; estrus.

Starch—A carbohydrate produced by plants and stored in seeds, roots, and fruits as a reserve energy supply.

Starter culture—A growth of living cells or microorganisms in a controlled artificial environment that is added to milk when making yogurt and cheese.

Statocytes—Gravity-sensing cells in plants, located in the root cap and throughout the plant stem.

Sterile—Free from contamination with living bacteria, fungi, and viruses.

Sterile technique—Maintenance of an environment that is free of bacteria and fungi.

Sterilization—The process of making free from contamination with living bacteria, fungi, and viruses; complete killing of all organisms.

Sterilized—Free from living microorganisms.

Steroid implant—Implant that contains estrogen, androgen, or both.

Stethoscope—A hearing instrument used for examining the heart or lungs by listening to the sounds they make.

Stigma—The top part of the pistil.

Stomach—A large saclike organ in the gastrointestinal tract after the esophagus where early stages of digestion occur and may contain one chamber (nonruminant animals) that does not further refine what was ingested or more than one chamber (ruminant animals) where further refining does take place.

Stomata—Pore openings in the epidermal layer of plant tissue where transpiration and respiration occur.

Streptococcus—A genus of bacteria; spherical and Gram-positive; convert milk sugar (lactose) to lactic acid.

Stress—A strain, or straining condition, that may be physical, chemical, or psychological and cannot be adjusted to satisfactorily.

Style—The slender, stalk-like part of a carpel (pistil) between the stigma and the ovary in a flower.

Subclinical mastitis—An inflammation of the mammary gland caused by a persistent, low level of infection.

Subcutaneous (SC) injection—Injection placed just under the skin but above muscle tissue.

Substrate system—The use of substrate materials in a hydroponic system, such as sand culture, gravel culture, rockwool culture, or bag culture.

Sugar—Any of a class of sweet, soluble, crystalline carbohydrates used as a food, flavor, or sweetening agent.

Sundae-style yogurt—Yogurt incubated in the cup; fruit flavoring (if included) is placed in the bottom of the cup and the yogurt mix is poured on top.

Superovulation—The release of a larger-than-normal number of eggs for fertilization; usually the result of hormone injections.

Suspended animation—A temporary cessation of vital functions.

Suspension culture—A tissue culture technique where the undifferentiated cells are gently shaken in a liquid nutrient medium so they become somewhat separated from each other, thereby making injection of new genetic material possible.

Sweat glands—Any of the many glands in the subcutaneous tissue that secrete sweat.

Swiss-style yogurt—Yogurt incubated in a vat, with fruit flavorings mixed in as the yogurt is packaged.

Symbiosis—Occurs when two dissimilar organisms live together in a condition of mutual benefit.

Symptoms—Any conditions accompanying or resulting from a disease or physical disorder and serving as an aid in diagnosis.

Systemic disease—A disease where the entire body or a major body system is affected.

Systemic herbicide—A chemical absorbed into the plant's vascular and root system, destroying the entire plant.

Tannin—A natural antibloating compound found in some plant species.

Teat—The small protuberance on an udder through which milk passes.

Teat canal—A tubular passage or duct through which milk passes. *See* teat.

Tenderness—The degree of being soft, easily chewed, broken, cut, etc.

Tensiometer—An instrument which measures soil moisture tension (SMT), thereby providing an estimate of how hard plant roots are working to extract moisture from the soil.

Terminal bud—The bud which develops at the end of a branch or stem.

Testes—Either of two oval sex glands in the male reproductive system that are suspended in the scrotum and secrete spermatozoa; testicles.

Testosterone—The primary androgen, secreted by the male's testes and the female's adrenal gland. *See* androgens.

Thermotropism—Plant growth response to temperature.

Thigmotropism—Plant growth response to a solid object.

Thyroxines—Growth hormones secreted by the thyroid gland that regulate body metabolism, which influences body weight and lean tissue growth.

Tissue culture—To grow a group of cells or a single cell on an artificial medium under sterile conditions.

Tissue culture medium—An artificial medium containing compounds necessary for growth.

Titratable acidity—The percentage of lactic acid in dairy products, determined by the amount of 0.1 *N* NaOH required to neutralize the lactic acid in a known volume of product.

Toxemia—A condition resulting from distribution of poisonous substances throughout the body by the bloodstreams.

Toxin—Any of the various unstable poisonous compounds produced by microorganisms and causing diseases.

Traits—Observable features or characteristics.

Transgenic organism—An organism that carries a foreign gene in all its cells which was inserted into the embryo prior to birth.

Translocated herbicide—*See* systemic herbicides.

Translocation—The movement a substance throughout a plant.

Transpiration stream—The upward movement of water from the roots to the leaves in plants.

Transpiration—Water loss through the leaves of plants.

Trauma—Violent injury to bone, muscle, or tissue.

Treatment—The manipulation of an independent variable.

Trenbolone acetate—A synthetic androgen that has more potency than testosterone.

Trickle irrigation—*See* drip irrigation.

Tropism—The growth of plants in response to external stimuli.

Turgor—The normal rigidity of living animal and plant cells due to pressure against the cell membrane from within by the cell contents.

TZ test—A test for seed viability where test seed samples are treated with the chemical 2,3,5 triphenyl tetrazolium chloride.

Udder—The encased mammary gland in female animals such as cows, sows, ewes, and mares.

Ultrasound imaging—A technique which uses high frequency sound waves to measure fat and lean in live animals and carcasses.

Uterine horns—The part of the female reproductive system where pregnancy occurs.

Uterus—The part of the female reproductive system that includes the uterus body, two uterine horns, and cervix.

Vaccine—Suspensions of bacteria or viruses

that create an antibody when injected into an animal.

Valence—The chemical combining power of an atom indicating the number of electrons that can be lost, shared, or gained by an atom in a compound.

Variable—A characteristic by which an object or phenomenon may be described.

Vas deferens—Transports the sperm from the epididymis to the urethra.

Video image analysis—A method of collecting data on live animal or carcass measurements using digital television.

Villi—Minute, fingerlike structures on the lining of the small intestine which increase the surface area for nutrient absorption.

Viruses—Infective living agents of microorganisms, some with characteristics of nonliving matter, that can multiply only in connection with living cells and are regarded both as living organisms and as complex proteins sometimes involving nucleic acid, enzymes, etc.

Vital signs—Body temperature, pulse rate, and respiration rate.

Warm germination test—The standard test for seed viability run by seed testing centers and seed producing companies.

Water—H_2O; a colorless, transparent liquid; probably the most important of all the nutrients and natural resources.

Wavelength—The measurement of radiant energy emitted through waves.

Whey—The watery liquid that is separated from the curd after milk coagulation.

White blood cells—Cells in the blood that help to protect the body from infection.

Xanthophyll—Accessory light yellow pigment that transfers its absorbed light energy to chlorophyll-a, improving the plant's overall ability to absorb and use light energy.

Xylem—The woody portion of the stem that conducts water and nutrients throughout a plant.

Yeast—Any of various single-celled fungi in which little or no mycelium develops and that ordinarily reproduce by budding.

Yogurt—A cultured dairy product that has a gel-like, custard consistency; fermented by bacteria.

Zygote—The cell produced by the union of two gametes.

INDEX